LIGHTNING
LAB

GREEN IS NOT A COLOUR

ENVIRONMENTAL ISSUES EVERY GENERATION NEEDS TO KNOW

DEVAN VALENTI & SIMON ATLAS

This beautifully crafted and accessible book offers a highly useful primer on the pitfalls of the fossil fuel paradigm and the challenges that the world faces in moving toward a sustainable future. It is not only informative in a factual sense but also does an excellent job of laying out the debates and controversies within the contemporary sustainability movement. It's a must-read for students, educators, and sustainability practitioners.

—JEREMY CARADONNA, P.H.D, AUTHOR OF "SUSTAINABILITY: A HISTORY"

Modern societies are increasingly aware of the urgency to protect our environment. However, very little has actually been done to address the fundamental problems of climate change, accelerated resource depletion, and widespread pollution. This book takes a refreshingly comprehensive view of these problems, and communicates salient strategies for sustainability in a highly accessible and visually immersive way. In order to engage a broad audience and create change at the necessary scale, we need more books like this one.

— BLAINE BROWNELL, FOUNDER AND DIRECTOR OF TRANSSTUDIO, ASSOCIATE PROFESSOR OF ARCHITECTURE AT THE UNIVERSITY OF MINNESOTA

It is predicted that our current cities will double in size by 2050. This presents a major challenge to all of us. We must ensure that the significant developments that will take place in our cities in the future are designed in a responsible, efficient and sustainable manner. Cities of the future should be desirable, vibrant and productive places whereby people live in harmony with the environment. This very relevant and necessary book will contribute immensely to educating us of the importance of making the right decisions in the development of cities in the future.

— KEZ TAYLOR, CEO, ALEC CONSTRUCTION

This resource comes at a critical stage of our existence on Earth. According to conservative estimates, the population of Africa is set to triple in the next four decades as a result of rapid urbanisation across the continent. With these drastic changes set to come about, our very concept of sustainability will be questioned. Hence, the challenges facing our nations, our cities and our fellow citizens cannot be resolved by one specific group or profession, but rather by the collective contribution of society as a whole. This book presents the unique and much needed opportunity to expand our knowledge and understanding of these issues facing our planet, and ultimately our very future. This is achieved in a fashion that is accessible, legible and visually interesting. It provides an important grounding and base of knowledge for our generation.

—RASHIQ FATAAR, FOUNDER AND DIRECTOR, FUTURE CAPE TOWN

'Green is Not a Colour' smartly presents readers with a simple concept: that the environment is an interconnected part of all life on the planet, humans included. This holistic view shows us that the environment is not just some distant scientific problem. Major world-changing problems do exist, however, and the book doesn't shy away from the root causes of much of the environmental damage inflicted on the planet -- namely the consumption and development habits of human beings. But this book is by no means a surrender to a bleak and unavoidable future. Rather, it poses these issues as challenges to be solved, and in many cases offers the solutions. 'Green is Not a Colour' argues forcefully that by better understanding the environment and our sometimes destructive place in it, the better able we will be to live more harmoniously with the world around us.

— NATE BERG, ARCHITECT MAGAZINE, THE GUARDIAN, WIRED.

'Green is Not a Colour' is crammed with expedient information to assist humanity with the climate crisis. It persistently confronts most of civilisations global ecological pressures. Without more primers like this; society as we know it may silently vanish.

—MITCHELL JOACHIM, CO-FOUNDER, TERREFORM ONE, ASSOCIATE PROFESSOR, NYU.

A vital thought provoking reminder of the many actions that we as the current custodians of planet Earth need to consciously and in many cases vociferously work at in order to create a sustainable planet for our future generations.

— KENTON FINE, GROUP CHAIRMAN, SERVEST

In 'Green is Not a Colour' Simon and Devan offer practical solutions to humanity's urgent problems of resource scarcity and wastage. This book compellingly explores a holistic and long-term framework for maintaining a healthy relationship between humans and their environment. If you're looking for a new outlook on sustainability and the future of our planet then this book needs to join your reading list.

—TRISTRAM STUART, ENVIRONMENTAL ACTIVIST AND AUTHOR OF "WASTE: UNCOVERING THE GLOBAL FOOD SCANDAL"

While 'sustainability' and 'eco-friendly' are fashionable terms, our understanding of their core meaning and application is mostly uninformed and misguided. By diving straight into the heart of these issues and clearing up prevailing misconceptions, this book shows us precisely what we need to change and how we can go about doing it. Written in a very clear and practical manner, 'Green is Not a Colour' will, in particular, hold great value and relevance to the future leaders of our world. An excellent resource to inspire and educate our world!

—BRIAN HOWARTH, MANAGING DIRECTOR, MAGNET GROUP

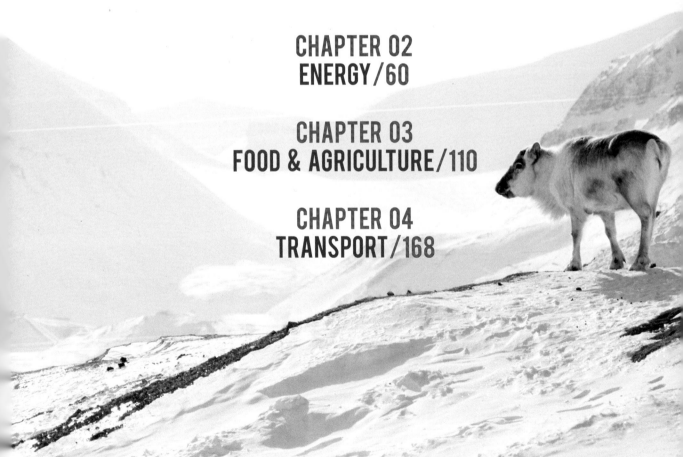

CONTENTS

MICHAEL BRAUNGART

FOUNDER OF THE EPEA, CO-AUTHOR
OF 'CRADLE TO CRADLE' & 'THE UPCYCLE'

Since green is the leading colour in our natural environment, we automatically associate it with something good and positive. Ironically though, in reality the synthetic green pigment that is being used in many consumer products is the most toxic colours of all. Dye fabricants find it normal to put toxic heavy metals like copper and phthalocyanine in it. Both are harming the environment and people's health in a severe way: not really appropriate to associate it with environmental friendly products. This example illustrates the brilliant title of this fantastic book and it stresses also the importance of proper education and the sharing of knowledge. The so needed transition will never become reality, if people aren't aware of the fact that certain products, methods, strategies and decisions will have huge negative consequences, while there are enough alternatives with a positive impact.

The environmental debate of the last 40 years is not a moral discussion; it's about real innovation and product quality. A product which becomes waste and harms people and environment, is only a bad designed product with poor quality. Sustainability is not innovative by definition. Innovations are disruptive and change the status quo instead of preserving it. The good intention of traditional sustainable development will not change anything and is in fact meaningless; to minimize our negative impact on the environment, it would be better not to exist at all. At the very most, this approach extends the moment before this system collapses. Devan Valenti and Simon Atlas understood this completely and cleared many misconceptions concerning sustainability, which touches perfectly the eco-efficiency versus eco-effectivity discussion. Rather than using eco-efficiency to try and minimize material flows, eco-effectiveness transforms products and related material flows to support the relationship between ecological systems and economic growth. Step by step we are realising that humans and nature should be a central element in our economic system.

'Green Is Not A Colour' is beautifully written, contains many interesting facts and creates a perfect extended and multidisciplinary basis to understand the connectedness of economy, technology, society and nature. The broad range of environmental issues are described nuancely, puts them in the necessary historical context and has been made comprehensible for all people with differing backgrounds. The books content makes rather clear that lasting prosperity is not something we can take for granted, but does it without being moralising. Technical developments made our lives easier and created wealth, but the way we have achieved this level of prosperity is flawed. We used any material or chemical that worked for our purpose without thinking or knowing the consequences which we know now are detrimental for our health as well as our planet's health.

Despite all our fantastic inventions and industrial revolutions, real innovation that would transform our linear economy into a 'Cradle to Cradle' economy - the way nature teaches us materials should function - is missing. Despite the many challenges we're facing, the authors are optimistic and full of hope: we are capable to think different and create high-quality alternatives which are beneficial for humans and nature.

Prof. Dr. Michael Braungart
Academic Cradle to Cradle Chair for Innovation and Quality, Rotterdam School of Management - Erasmus University; Founder and Owner, EPEA Internationale Umweltforschung - The cradle of Cradle to Cradle'

FOREWORD:

BRUCE KERSWILL

CHAIR OF THE WORLD
GREEN BUILDING COUNCIL

It was a fresh winter's morning when I first met Simon and Devan in person. I had invited them to my home in Newlands, Cape Town to hear more about an interesting idea they had for a book. As I had used my own house as a testing ground for sustainable design I showed them around the various technologies and design strategies which included sustainable materials, renewable energy and rainwater use. With all three of us being involved in the building industry, there was enthusiastic discussion on the performance of each strategy and how the system could be improved in the future. This evolved into an animated exchange of ideas on the future of the sustainability movement.

It was clear that these two enthusiastic young men were driven by genuine passion and a sense of conviction as to the changes needed in our world and the steps needed to take us there. Their project was ambitious but very worthwhile, as books have great power to influence people, and I was delighted to lend my support.

Looking back on my own story, it was a book (and movie) that first moved me to take action. Al Gore's 'An Inconvenient Truth' brought the public's attention to the 'planetary emergency' of climate change in a simple and compelling way. The evidence was presented in a striking and understandable manner, and it stirred in me a deep conviction of how change was needed. It steered me on the journey of setting up the Green Building Council of South Africa, and later becoming the Chair of the World Green Building Council.

It has been nearly 10 years since Gore's book, and progress has been slow. Our population is growing rapidly and the ecosystems that support our existence are deteriorating. Our economies, ways of life, and indeed our future existence, is under threat. We are pushing beyond the limits, exceeding the capacity of the planet to support us.

So, we have to find a new way of living on the planet – one that reduces our impact, reverses the damage and restores the balance. It can indeed be done as the pages of this book explain. The knowledge and technologies are rapidly evolving, and we know that the costs are manageable. In 2006 the Stern Report estimated that the cost of taking action would be 2% of the annual GDP, while the cost of not taking action would be far greater, at 5%. But we've delayed for too long and the problems are escalating. It is imperative that we act with urgency.

Why aren't we moving more rapidly? Possibly because it is difficult for the man-in-the-street to make sense of it all. There is so much information and misinformation out there; so many divergent views and differing opinions – not to mention a chunk of greenwashing – that it makes it hard to get a proper handle on issues of sustainability. In this book, Devan and Simon have managed to pull this complex array of issues together in a clear and non-judgemental way, to create a resource that clearly identifies the challenges and shows us what needs to be done to address them.

When people are informed and moved to take action, much progress can be made. In the building field, as an example close to my heart, green buildings are making a real impact. Just on the energy side, buildings globally consume 40% of the world's energy and produce 30% of greenhouse gases. Recent green buildings are reducing energy consumption by 70% – and in some areas are targeting 'net zero'! Green Building Councils in 100 countries are rating buildings on detailed sustainability criteria, educating the building industry, and promoting an exchange of knowledge and ideas. These buildings can be built at no extra cost, and are almost invariably better, healthier buildings than conventional ones. When people understand what can be achieved simply through a different approach, their reaction is 'Why would we not build like this??!'

'Green Is Not A Colour' presents information on the most critical issues of our day – information that can enable people to make appropriate choices, hold businesses and governments to account, and ask 'Why would we not do that?'. It packs a powerful punch by clearing up misconceptions, controversies and confusion, and does so with stunning visuals, interesting quotes and very readable text. It's an important book, and I hope that it will inform and inspire people, and move them to take action!

Bruce Kerswill
Chair, World Green Building Council

RICKY TSUI

DIRECTOR OF RESEARCH & DEVELOPMENT, ARUP EAST ASIA

NASA recently announced the discovery of Kepler-452b, claiming the planet to be the closest thing we have to an Earth 2.0 beyond our solar system. Considering the environmental mayhem we are inflicting upon Earth year by year, one has to beg the question: should we start packing up and get ready to leave Earth? While it is impossible to migrate to a planet over 1 000 light-years away, people are starting to take the question seriously, and the Mars One Organisation has got people excited about the possibility of life elsewhere. With many uncertainties as to the long-term future of our planet, protecting Earth as if it were the only one we will ever have should be the collective and primary goal of every man, woman and child that calls Earth their home.

Yet the problems we face are becoming more noticeable, as more and more resources are needed to support our ever-growing human population. This is putting extreme pressure on the planet's ability to provide and meet our demands. With around seven-billion people living on Earth seeking better living conditions, the consequences of such increase in consumption are often matched with increasing damage to the natural environment and severe depletion of natural resources. Sustainable development over the long-term will remain by far our biggest challenge in years and decades to come. If success is to be truly achieved, it will take the collective vision and collaboration of every living person.

It is obvious that governments and local authorities should take lead and push for transformation, but companies, communities and individuals should increasingly be involved and work together to achieve this goal. Arup has been working with many city governments to help them share successful practices that lead to a higher level of efficiency and sustainability. Furthermore, our research department helps to raise awareness and educate people on such issues through the C40 organisation. One of the main reasons for our involvement is to ensure that any proposed strategy for urban transformation is able to successfully and effectively address key issues needed to ensure a sustainable future. Therefore, for stakeholders and civic authorities to have a clear and holistic understanding of such issues would be vital in order for any proposal to hold value.

Environmental education without a doubt holds the key to to ensure long-term sustainability and prosperity for mankind and the planet. If we remain unaware and oblivious to the crisis taking place around us, any significant action to reverse the effects is unlikely to occur. Whether you are a politician, government official, a company executive, an activist or a student, we all share a great responsibility to steward the planet for both ourselves and countless generations to come.

What makes this book so unique and appealing is that so much has been written about environmental consciousness, across a multitude of industries and sectors. Not only that, but it has been prepared by two enthusiastic young persons who have seen the need for greater public education and understanding in this area. The book is amazingly readable and comprehensively reveals the true facts about sustainability. It helps to clear up the misconceptions around the topic in a method that is both highly stimulating and engaging. If you are looking to get down to the fundamentals of these increasingly relevant issues, you are in for an amazing journey.

Dr. Ricky Tsui
Director of R&D and East Asia Arup University Leader,
Ove Arup & Partners HK Ltd

PREFACE

We live in an age where the world around us is constantly changing and evolving. This transformation is taking place at a rate never seen before in the history of mankind. We are continually faced with a feeling of uncertainty, and much of this concern has to do with the future of the planet. How our concerns for the future will play out in reality remains a mystery. We can't predict the future, but we do have the opportunity to influence it.

The transformation our world is presently undergoing is a direct result of two extraordinary forces, never before experienced at its current magnitude: population growth and technological innovation. Together, these forces are radically changing the way in which we live. But the trade-off is that they place incredible demands on the natural environment and its invaluable resources. Human consumption and impact is at an all-time high. There is no denying this.

We are experiencing a radical demise and depletion of the environment across the globe. Climate change, deforestation, urban pollution, species extinction, water contamination, soil degradation and ecological destruction are just some of the many problems that have come about as a result of our inability to properly steward and protect the Earth. In addition, our depletion and destruction of the environment has given rise to major problems moving forward in meeting the growing demands of increasing global population levels. Rising fuel costs, global food shortages and human health challenges are just a few of the consequences ahead. It is clear that change is needed.

Thankfully, many corporations, industries, governments and individuals are committed to finding and adopting sustainable solutions to these problems. As we innovate, educate and begin the transition toward sustainable alternatives, we can indeed have hope for a brighter future for ourselves and generations to come.

If education holds the key to our future, then environmental education can be considered one of the most vital and relevant needs of our day. We have made it our mission to provide people of all ages with an ethical understanding of the environmental issues that affect their lives and of those around them.

"WHAT YOU DO FOR YOURSELF DIES WITH YOU WHEN YOU LEAVE THIS WORLD, WHAT YOU DO FOR OTHERS LIVES ON FOREVER."
-KEN ROBINSON

WHY WE WROTE THE BOOK

Environmental consciousness is a popular debate these days, and has become the centre of much conversation and debate. Although we recognise the value of this widespread acknowledgement of environmental issues, we have identified a growing problem across both industry and society at large with the trend of 'greenwashing'. If something simply looks environmentally friendly, whether by association, branding or even colour, we automatically assume it to be better for the environment, and as a result, a contributor to a more sustainable world.

Due to the pitfalls in public education and its failures in creating a real and authentic understanding in the areas of sustainability and environmentalism, both the general public and industry alike has been left to make their own assumptions of what it means to make a positive impact in this area. From coffee cups to buildings, water bottles to organic food, things that are simply labelled 'eco-friendly' or 'green' are thought to be better for the environment than their counterparts, prompting people to feel like they are doing 'their bit' for the environment. Although it can often be true, it is not always the case.

It is exactly for this purpose that we have named the book "Green is Not a Colour". We wish to clear up the general misconceptions of what it really means to be sustainable, and ultimately see authentic, sustainable and environmental practice implemented across industries and daily

life. It is only through the medium of education that we can stimulate a change in mindset, and expect real transformation to take place.

The value we gain from education cannot be emphasised enough. It is often said that education is the most important investment anyone can make. We believe in this statement, and when it comes to the topic of environmental education, it becomes of critical importance. The future of both humanity and our planet is at stake.

Education provides people with a sound knowledge of their surroundings, and helps them to become flexible and adaptable in a changing world. It transforms the way people think, the way they behave, what they fight for and what they stand for. It challenges the way they perceive their very surroundings. It can be confidently said that education is the most powerful tool we can use to change the world.

For too long, people have remained closed-minded and viewed environmental education merely as a subheading of science education. This needs to change urgently. After all, environmental education could very well prove to be the reason humans continue living on Earth for many years to come. Environmental education needs to be transformed in a way that fosters an understanding of our responsibility towards the Earth. A dramatic mindset change is needed, and it is only through education that we can achieve this.

"ONE OF THE MAIN DRIVERS OF BEHAVIOURAL CHANGE IS KNOWLEDGE. IF PEOPLE DON'T KNOW, THEY CAN'T ACT."
–BJARKE INGELS

"EDUCATION IS THE MOST POWERFUL WEAPON
YOU CAN USE TO CHANGE THE WORLD."
-NELSON MANDELA

STRUCTURE & METHODOLOGY

In order to make an actual difference in the areas of environmentalism and sustainability, we need to cut to the very root of the problems. Ultimately, these problems lead back to a number of industries such as energy, transport, agriculture, manufacturing and construction. These industries, as a means of providing much-needed products and services to a growing world population, place high demands on Earth's natural resources. This, in turn, results in severe degradation to its ecosystems. If we, as a society, are able to shift the practices and behaviour of these industries to more environmentally friendly and ecologically sustainable methods of production, we can effectively reduce mankind's environmental footprint on Earth. Significant transformation in these industries is the most viable solution if we are to restore environmental harmony and secure a sustainable future for the Earth.

We have worked to create a highly enriching and engaging resource that takes a realistic and sophisticated approach to the issues stemming from these industries. We do not push for a particular agenda, but rather give an honest and sober-minded overview of the realities at hand. Throughout this book readers should actively engage with, and absorb the information presented. Ultimately, the aim is to formulate your own educated opinion on the matters at hand. We have provided a broad overview of the sectors we consider to have the greatest impact and influence upon the future of our planet.

What you are about to experience is a stimulating and engaging learning resource that is non-technical and simple to read. The book provides readers of all ages and backgrounds with an enriched understanding of environmentalism and sustainability. The book can be read in the traditional fashion, that being front to back. It can also be read informally, as readers can open up onto any page and learn something new and relevant in a matter of minutes.

The book is broken up into six chapters, each providing an exploration into a particular aspect of one of five industries. The first chapter, 'The world as we knew it' provides a foundation and outline of mankind's relationship with the environment, as well as a breakdown of the most important forces influencing our world. Chapter's two to six discuss the five prevailing industries that can be regarded as the main instigators of our environmental problems. The industries discussed are that of Energy, Transport, Food and Agriculture, Consumer Products, as well as Buildings and Cities. The book ends with the afterword titled 'The Tipping Point', which reflects on the topics discussed throughout the book, and provides clarity on the path we must take to ensure a sustainable future.

THE WORLD AS WE KNEW IT

OUR PLANET EARTH.
WHAT IS THE ENVIRONMENT? THE
INDUSTRIAL REVOLUTION.
POPULATION GROWTH AND INCREASED
DEMAND. WHAT IS GLOBAL
WARMING AND CLIMATE
CHANGE? THE VICIOUS CYCLE.
THE STATE OF THE PLANET.
WHAT IS SUSTAINABILITY?

"WE LOVE OUR PLANET EARTH. WE SHOULD – IT IS OUR HOME, AND THERE'S NO PLACE LIKE HOME. THERE CAN'T EVER BE A BETTER PLACE THAN EARTH."

–DIMITAR SASSELOV

OUR PLANET EARTH

Earth is the third planet from the Sun in our solar system of nine planets. Earth's name comes from the ancient language of Germanic, as well as Old English, and it essentially means 'ground' in both languages, whilst all the other planets derive their names from Roman and Greek mythology. But apart from the uniqueness of Earth's name, it is also the only planet in our solar system that is able to support and sustain life. All the others, despite their outer beauty, are no more than desolate wastelands of rock and gas on which life cannot exist. Earth, however, is home to both humans, as well as billions of other species of animals and plants.

Earth is a haven where life and biodiversity flourish. From great deserts to lush tropical forests, majestic mountain ranges and extensive grasslands, Earth is a playground for all forms of life to thrive and coexist. Looking at the tiny blue dot from space, it is hard to imagine the enormous complexity of daily activity that takes place on Earth.

But the earliest images of Earth, taken from space exploration satellites in the mid-20th century, allowed us to see just how small and seemingly insignificant our planet appears in the vast reaches of space. For the first time ever, humans realised the fragility of our Earth in the greater scheme of things.

Like millions of settings on a machine, Earth's systems are perfectly calibrated. Earth's specific distance from the sun and the gaseous composition of its atmosphere, are both perfectly set to allow life to thrive here. If a single factor goes out of sync, life on Earth would be impossible, like all the other planets in our solar system.

Because of this, it is crucial that we think seriously about protecting and preserving our planet. Earth is the only home we have ever known, and the only planet within our reach that can safely support both human life and the life of the biodiversity that surrounds us.

DID YOU KNOW?

About 71% of Earth's surface is covered by water. The ocean holds over 90% of all water found on Earth.

WHAT IS THE ENVIRONMENT?

Although the term 'environment' has a broad range of definitions, meanings and interpretations, at the most basic level it can be viewed as the sum total of everything that Earth provides.

The environment is fascinating, inspiring and thought provoking. The beauty of nature is embedded within its mystery. Much like gazing upon a beautiful painting, or listening to the melodic sounds of an orchestra, we can study the various parts of nature that make up its whole, yet always be utterly and profoundly mesmerised by the harmonious way they come together.

Earth is organised into four unique spheres or layers. These four spheres – the lithosphere (land), hydrosphere (water), biosphere (living things) and atmosphere (air) – are incredible interconnected. If it weren't for these four spheres and their unique roles and characteristics, life on Earth would be unable to take place. They provide the carefully balanced conditions of sunlight, oxygen, food, water and heat to take place on the planet.

Everything that is naturally occurring on Earth, whether living or non-living, is essentially part of the environment. From the sunlight that warms our world, the cycles that purify and filter our water, and the ongoing supply of life-supporting oxygen, the environment is an ever-evolving and adapting mechanism.

Ecologists find that life on Earth is organised into an extremely complex, yet interconnected, set of ecosystems. Many call this ongoing connection and relationship the 'circle of life'. The environment thrives on the interactions between plants, animals, soil, water, temperature and light. Life on Earth takes many different forms, shapes and sizes, which is an incredible testimony to its rich biodiversity. The term biodiversity refers to the incredible range of life found on Earth. This

"THE ENVIRONMENT IS EVERYTHING THAT ISN'T ME"
– ALBERT EINSTEIN

DID YOU KNOW?

Ecology is the study of organism's & the environments in which they live. An ecologist would not only study a fish, but also the water, temperature & food supply relative to that fish.

includes both plants and animals. It is estimated that there are approximately 8.8-million species in the natural world, but the total amount out there may be significantly larger than that. Some studies estimate the number to be as high as 100-million species.

The rainforests of the world, situated around the equator, are home to most of the planet's plant and animal species. Although rainforests cover less that 2% of Earth's total surface area, they are home to almost 50% of all plant and animal life. Our oceans, which cover an incredible 71% of Earths surface, also hosts some of the richest and most diverse collections of life. The ocean sustains over one-million species of plants and animals, but scientists estimate that there may be as many as 9-million ocean species we have yet to discover.

The environment is vital to the health and prosperity of humanity. Not only does the environment provide us with an abundance of natural services, but studies have proven that our engagement and experience of nature heightens our sense of wellbeing and allows for faster recovery from various forms of sickness, stress and injury.

The environment is constantly undergoing change and transformation. This is a result of both natural and human-related causes. Change brought about by natural events, such as volcanoes, earthquakes or hurricanes, can drastically alter or damage the environment. At the same time, human-related causes, such as deforestation or pollution, can heavily alter the natural world as well. Generally, the environment is able to restore itself over time, thus bringing about balance to the natural order. However, under extreme and ongoing cycles of damage, many existing ecosystems have become unable to respond to such overwhelming events.

We are currently living in an era known as the 'anthropogenic age'. The term 'anthropogenic' essentially refers to any effect on the environment that results from human-related activities. The anthropogenic era is said to have begun 150 to 200 years ago, and its influence has increased drastically over the past few decades.

As our modern society has progressed, many believe we have lost our connection to the natural world, and as a result lost our sense of respect, dependence and responsibility toward it. Despite how disconnected we may have become, the environment is undeniably linked to our survival and prosperity. Our relationship with the natural world is determined by two inextricably linked mediums: natural resources and ecosystems.

DID YOU KNOW?

Natural services play a vital role in the global water cycle, as they regulate the flow & purification of water.

NATURAL RESOURCES

A natural resource is simply anything that we can use and consume that comes from the earth. The planet provides many resources for mankind that we simply cannot provide for ourselves. Every single thing we use is made up of materials and energy that has been harvested or extracted from the earth at some point during production. Examples of valuable resources we use from the earth include wood, water, fuel, soil, wind and oxygen.

There are two types of natural resources: renewable resources and non-renewable resources. Renewable resources never run out, and can be constantly resupplied without any loss from the environment. These resources include rain, wind and heat from the sun. Even resources such as wood, water and fertile soil can be considered renewable if we use sustainable methods of harvesting and extracting them. Through natural processes, these resources have the ability to replace and replenish themselves over time.

Non-renewable resources, on the other hand, are those that are unable to replenish themselves shortly after they have been used, either by human efforts or natural processes. Even those that do have the ability to be replenished would only be able to do so over thousands, if not millions, of years. Examples of such non-renewable resources include coal, oil, gold, diamonds and shale gas. Once these resources are extracted, modified and consumed from the earth, they are gone forever and never to be replaced — or at least not in our lifetimes. At the rate we are consuming such resources, it is inevitable we will eventually run out of many of them, whether in the next 20 years or the next 100. In addition to their limited nature, such resources cannot be reused or recycled once consumed. Unfortunately, due to our growing consumption patterns, even resources that were once believed to be completely renewable, like topsoil, are being used up so rapidly that they now fall into the bracket of non-renewable resources.

"NATURAL RESOURCES ARE SO VAST THAT NO SINGLE INDIVIDUAL OR BUSINESS IS GOING TO PROTECT THEM; THEY DON'T HAVE AN INCENTIVE TO."
-WILLIAM WELD

DID YOU KNOW?

We have lost 50% of the planet's original forest cover, mostly in the last 30 years. Rainforests once covered 14% of the Earth's surface, now they cover a mere 6%.. On average, forest areas the size of a football field are cleared every second!

8.8 MILLION

THE ESTIMATED NUMBER OF SPECIES ON EARTH.

"OUR CHALLENGE FOR THE FUTURE IS TO REALIZE THAT WE ARE VERY MUCH PART OF EARTH'S ECOSYSTEMS. WE MUST LEARN TO RESPECT AND LIVE ACCORDING TO THE BASIC BIOLOGICAL LAWS OF NATURE."

– JIM FOWLER

ECOSYSTEMS

Ecosystems are systems of living and non-living things that coexist and interact with one another within a given area. The role of each species is often vital to maintaining the natural balance within the ecosystem. Ecosystems can be as small as a garden or pond, or as large as an entire rainforest or ocean.

A forest consists of many living and non-living things that are essential to the health and well-being of the ecosystem. The range of living organisms in a forest ecosystem boasts a range of animals and plants Non-living elements include water, the air, rainfall, sunlight and the temperature. These non-living things allow trees to grow and produce the fruit that animals eat, as well as shelter. The proper maintenance and functionality of the ecosystem depends on how all these living and non-living things interact. When a species is no longer part of an ecosystem, either as a result of extinction or migration, an imbalance occurs in the natural food chain. When forests are cut down or forest fires occur, the trees that once provided food and shelter for the animals are lost, causing significant damage to the once-thriving ecosystem. Thus, any disturbance has profound impacts.

Ecosystems can be disrupted and damaged easily as they are highly sensitive to change. Severe floods, forest or veld fires, changes in temperature, natural disasters, species loss, invasion by alien plant life, pollution or contamination can drastically damage the delicate balance of an ecosystem, sometimes causing irreversible and permanent damage.

DID YOU KNOW?

The rapid loss of species we are seeing today is estimated by experts to be between 1,000 & 10,000 times higher than the natural extinction rate.

THE INDUSTRIAL REVOLUTION

The Industrial Revolution, which began in Europe and America towards the end of the 18th century, marked the beginning of a dramatic and fundamental shift in the relationship between humans and the environment, and humans with one another. Up until this time, humans had a relatively low impact on the planet, and our consumption of natural resources was fairly insignificant in the grand scheme of things. The Industrial Revolution was characterised by several important changes in human behaviour that took place over this time. The most significant of these changes were mass production and rapid urbanisation – the mass movement of people from the countryside to live in towns and cities, along with technological innovation and globalisation.

Breakthroughs in modern science allowed these significant transformations in society to take place. Famous inventors such as Nikola Tesla, Henry Ford and Thomas Edison all lived during this period and they came up with some of the greatest inventions that the world has ever seen. Some of these notable inventions include the steam engine, the light bulb, the telephone and the harnessing of electricity. These inventions completely transformed the way human beings lived, worked and engaged with one another. They also allowed international trade to flourish and human wealth to increase.

People who had previously lived in rural farmlands began to move into towns and cities as work opportunities in factories became more abundant. This caused the cities to expand significantly, and established them as the key engines of economic wealth and prosperity. Factory workers used newly invented machinery, which allowed them to produce goods and services for the public at far greater

DID YOU KNOW?

Before the Industrial Revolution, raw materials & finished goods were transported by horse-drawn carts & wagons, as well as by boats & sailing ships along canals, oceans & rivers.

DID YOU KNOW?

Britain is credited as the birthplace of the Industrial Revolution. It had great deposits of coal & iron ore & was the world's leading colonial power, which meant that its colonies could provide raw materials & become the marketplace for manufactured goods.

DID YOU KNOW?

Although the Industrial Revolution improved the standards of living for many, the working class & poor often lived & worked in grim conditions.

speeds, and at much lower prices. Soon enough, everything from clothing and food to housing and medicine became more affordable and readily available. For the first time, importing goods from far-off countries, as well as exporting them, became a commonplace reality, as improved transportation methods and international trade relations strengthened by the day.

For all the wealth, benefits, and conveniences the Industrial Revolution brought about for humankind — such as medical advancements, improved living standards and an abundance of food and resources — it also brought with it many negative impacts, especially upon the environment.

The manner in which humans have continued the process of industrialisation has resulted in extreme exploitation of Earth's resources and severe damage to our ecosystems and atmosphere. Over the last 250 years, the impact of humans on the environment has increased at a rate far

beyond what the planet is naturally able to withstand. Deforestation, pollution, toxic waste, global warming and species extinction are just some of the environmental problems humans have created as a result of rapid industrialisation. Every aspect of the natural world, including our forests, rivers, oceans and even deserts, has been drastically affected as a result of industrial activities over the past 250 years.

Although the breakthroughs that came with the Industrial Revolution have allowed individuals and societies to prosper in previously unimaginable ways, many of the leaders and pioneers who steered the Industrial Revolution did not consider the limited nature of Earth's resources, or the drastic effect our methods and practices would have upon the planet over the long run. Although we have become reliant on all the advancements brought about since the beginning of the Industrial Revolution, it is now clear that under our current practices, we cannot sustain ourselves or the environment forever.

POPULATION GROWTH
& INCREASED DEMAND

DID YOU KNOW?

The average life expectancy is 80 years old for people in industrialised nations – 30 years more than a century ago!

Nobody knows exactly how many people planet Earth can sustain, however it is clear that Earth's resources are limited. In 1960 there were about three-billion people on the planet. At the time of writing this book, 55 years later, there are over seven-billion, more than ever before in human history, with the number increasing year after year. It is predicted that by 2050 Earth will have to support a global population of nine-billion people – with the majority of the additional population coming from developing countries that are still undergoing industrialisation. The challenge of providing for and supporting such an overwhelming number of people in the near future is of great concern.

Mankind is already pushing the limits of what the planet is able to provide and its ability to replenish itself. Western societies are largely consumer societies, where people depend on their ability to buy and sell goods, rather than, for example, growing their own food. This consumer behaviour places excessive strain on the natural environment and its ecosystems, as we continue to take from the planet the resources and land we deem necessary to satisfy our way of life. The continued practice of extracting Earth's resources, modifying them, consuming them and disposing of what remains, has resulted in many negative environmental impacts in

the form of, for example, pollution and greenhouse gases. But over the past few decades we have seen developing countries, such as China, India and Brazil, undergo their own process of modernisation and industrialisation. Except this time it is taking place on a far greater and more rapid scale.

In the past, it was only developed countries that had a significant impact on the planet as a result of industrialisation and consumerism, and most of these were western nations. However, rapid population growth in Europe and North America from the Industrial Revolution onwards began to decrease in the second half of the 20th century. Today, most of the population growth we are seeing is taking place in Asia, Africa and South America. More and more developing countries on these continents are now firmly involved in industrialisation, in order to catch up to the level of development Europe and America have already achieved. As this process continues, the number of people engaged in a high level of consumerism will increase as well.

China has a population of over 1.3-billion people. Now try to imagine the impacts on Earth when a nation of this size scales up the process of industrialisation. China is achieving the same levels of industrialisation in a period of a few decades, that nations like France, England and the US took over 250 years to achieve. Take into account the fact that these western nations have populations a fraction of the size of countries like China or India. To put this into perspective, China alone has consumed more concrete in the last three years than the US used in the entire 20th century. All this has gone into building its new cities, in the form of buildings, bridges and roads to cater for its rapidly industrialising and growing population.

Although the process of industrialisation and modernisation provides many opportunities for improving people's standards of living, the effects of this process on Earth are disastrous. As emerging nations continue to undergo these processes, consider the sheer amount of resources such as steel, concrete, plastic, coal, food and water that must be used every day to satisfy the rising living standards of millions – or even billions – of people.

What is interesting to note is that although we are collectively consuming more resources and emitting more pollution than ever before, as modern individuals we are consuming less than we did in the past.

This is because our production methods are becoming more efficient. Over recent decades, we have found ways of producing the same goods, with the same or better standard of quality than before, and using less energy and resources to do so. In other words, our products and processes have become considerably more efficient and higher performing.

These advancements have allowed industries to produce more or better goods by using fewer resources. This has allowed for both good business and better stewardship of Earth's resources to take place. These are earmarks of the principles of efficiency and performance. Performance is about increasing output, whereas efficiency is about producing something at the same rate, by using less – whether it be energy, time or materials. If industries are able to increase the performance of goods and services by using less time, energy and materials in the process, we have a recipe for a more sustainable future.

Although we are producing and using products and services with higher output and greater efficiency than ever before, there still remains the challenge of high population growth and increasing

DID YOU KNOW?

Many developed countries are actually experiencing zero or even negative population growth. An ageing population can be a threat to a country as there are not enough working-age citizens to drive & grow the economy, nor take care of the elderly.

DID YOU KNOW?

By the early 20th century, the United States had become the world's leading industrial nation.

DID YOU KNOW?

Developing countries account for 97%
of global population growth due to
high birth rates & young populations.

THE NUMBER OF PEOPLE ON THE PLANET HAS DOUBLED SINCE 1960, AND IF CURRENT GROWTH RATES CONTINUE, THE GLOBAL POPULATION WILL REACH 9 BILLION BY THE YEAR 2050.

consumption patterns. The rate at which populations are industrialising completely overshadows these steps in innovation. Even though the wealthier and developed countries are levelling off in terms of consumption, many developing countries are in the process of catching up. A significant difference has been made by efficient technologies that reduce the amount we individually consume; yet we are consuming more and more, collectively, as the global population continues to increase and developing nations continue to industrialise. Producing concrete, for example, may use far less energy and resources today compared to the past, but the sheer increase in demand for this highly sought-after material completely outweighs the significant improvements in production. We have reduced the environmental impacts of such materials, but we have not solved the problem.

However, there is hope in this dark scenario. While the developed world continues to look for ways to rectify the unsustainable behaviour resulting from industrialisation, the emerging nations of the 21st century have the opportunity to skip past these flawed methods right from the start and put in place more sustainable and environ-

mentally friendly methods whilst industrialising. For example, instead of building toxic, coal-fired plants, developing countries have the option of building infrastructure for renewal energy, such as solar and wind farms. Or, in place of new telephone and internet cables, they can skip straight to wireless technology. If developing nations are able to 'leapfrog' the pitfalls of the industrialisation process, they then have the opportunity to either reduce or completely avoid contributing to the environmental issues that many other countries before them have created.

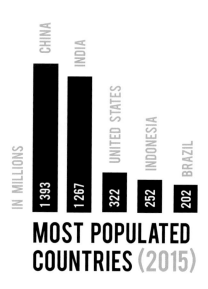

MOST POPULATED COUNTRIES (2015)

IN MILLIONS

CHINA	INDIA	UNITED STATES	INDONESIA	BRAZIL
1 393	1 267	322	252	202

WHAT IS GLOBAL WARMING & CLIMATE CHANGE?

Human impact on the environment takes two major forms. Firstly, we extract and consume valuable resources from the earth to satisfy consumer needs and wants. These valuable resources come from established and flourishing natural ecosystems such as forests, oceans and lakes. Over-consumption of these resources causes imbalances and destroys the natural order of these ecosystems, often far beyond the point from which they can recover.

The second effect occurs when we turn these natural resources into goods or services. When we use natural resources, they undergo processes of extraction, modification, consumption and disposal. More often than not, these processes produce solid waste that pollutes the Earth, or harmful gases such as carbon dioxide that affects the health of the planet and destroys the balance of gases in the atmosphere. Gases such as carbon dioxide and methane are called greenhouse gases, as they act like a blanket around the Earth by trapping the sun's heat in the atmosphere to warm the Earth. This contributes to the naturally occurring phenomenon known as the greenhouse effect.

Our planet is carefully calibrated to allow just the right amount of suns rays to be absorbed. These suns rays allow all life on Earth to take place. They provide warmth, light and the process of photosynthesis to take place in all plant life. Greenhouse gases in the atmosphere trap these rays of light in the atmosphere to regulate Earth's temperature and keep it consistent. The rays that are not absorbed by the Earth's oceans and plants are reflected back into space. However, when excess greenhouse gases are emitted into the atmosphere, the gas particles accumulate and absorb more of the suns rays that are either entering or leaving the atmosphere. When this happens, more of the heat emitted from the sun is kept within Earth's thin atmosphere, gradually heating it up in the process. It is simple: the more greenhouse gases we release, the more heat is trapped within the atmosphere as opposed to escaping it.

As industrial processes such as the burning of coal in coal-fired power stations emit more and more heat-trapping gases into the atmosphere, we are effectively turning the Earth into an oven. As humans, we have been contributing to this process

"GLOBAL WARMING IS NOT ONLY THE NUMBER ONE ENVIRONMENTAL CHALLENGE WE FACE TODAY, BUT ONE OF THE MOST IMPORTANT ISSUES FACING ALL OF HUMANITY."
– LEONARDO DICAPRIO

DID YOU KNOW?

Since 1870, global sea levels have risen by about 20cm.

TOO MUCH NEGATIVITY ABOUT CLIMATE CHANGE WOULD MEAN THAT WE WOULD NOT BE ABLE TO ATTRACT THE CREATIVE PEOPLE WHO BUILD THE SOLUTIONS.

since the beginning of the Industrial Revolution, and have hastened this effect by burning more and more fossil fuels such as coal, oil and natural gas. We have further intensified the greenhouse effect by destroying vast areas of forest and plant life, which have the natural ability to absorb carbon dioxide, and as a result, reduce or even reverse the heating of the atmosphere. As the Earth heats up, the ice caps at the North and South Poles melt, sea levels rise and temperatures reach record-breaking highs and lows. The process of the Earth's surface heating up is referred to as global warming.

As a result of the global warming that Earth is experiencing, we have another dangerous problem to deal with: climate change and climate variability. Due to the imbalance in the Earth's temperatures, the world's weather systems are beginning to undergo drastic changes. Storms are becoming more severe, and droughts and floods are becoming more common. Oceans, once full of rich biodiversity, are warming and becoming more acidic as they absorb higher levels of carbon dioxide from the atmosphere. Sensitive ecosystems that are well established are becoming severely damaged or disrupted with even the smallest change to climatic conditions. Scientists agree that if this process is left unchecked, we are likely to be dealing with a climate crisis that has a negative effect on every ecosystem on the planet. Animals may no longer follow their natural migration patterns, lush grasslands may turn to desert due to lack of rainfall and lakes may

dry up completely. The effects of climate change, if unchecked, will be felt in every corner of the world.

Skeptics of climate change say nothing is certain. True, we do not yet fully know if the Earth will be two degrees or 10 degrees warmer in the next 50 years. Yet it is clear from scientific evidence that the Earth's climate is indeed warming and changing, and scientists, using state-of-the-art climate models, are able to say with a very high degree of certainty that these changes are imminent. And we cannot deny human involvement in this process, considering the changes have occurred since the dawn of the Industrial Revolution, and the immensity of these changes in the last 40 years.

There is too much at risk for us not to act. It is obvious to many that the fight against climate change and global warming should be on the world's top priority list. Some argue that it should be the most important collective goal of humanity. Thankfully, we are seeing significant transformations in environmental policy, industrial practices, and public thinking, which give significant hope for a better future. Organisations such as the International Panel of Climate Change, the United Nations and the G8 are becoming highly involved in this area. Through greater research, awareness, policy change and industry innovation we can hope to see significant transformation in the near future.

DID YOU KNOW?

As of 2015, the hottest years ever recorded have been 2005, 2010 & 2014.

THE VICIOUS CYCLE

Humans are highly dependent upon the natural world. The environment provides an abundance of natural resources and services that are of great value to our survival. As a result of industrialisation, rapid population growth and increased demand, our methods of consuming these resources has put the natural environment under great threat and turmoil. This ultimately ends up affecting our own ability to thrive on Earth.

Our consumption patterns and our behaviour towards the environment create a vicious cycle. Our needs are satisfied by the resources Earth provides, but we demand too much from it. We extract, modify, consume and dispose of these resources in such ways that deplete, pollute and damage Earth to an extent beyond its ability to replenish itself. As a result of our depletion of natural resources and ongoing damage to the environment, the Earth spins into chaos. The flourishing ecosystems we are so dependent on perish, the air we breathe becomes polluted, the water we drink becomes contaminated and the fertile land we depend on suffers from soil erosion, flooding, drought and acid rain.

Toxins released into the ocean poison the many fish species we depend on for food. When we eat these fish, we take in the hazardous contaminants the fish carry. When we destroy forests to make space for the expansion of cities, we reduce the amount of oxygen the trees naturally release into the atmosphere. By doing so, we lower the quality of the very air we breathe.

"THE FORCES THAT ARE IN PLAY ON CLIMATE CHANGE ESSENTIALLY REVOLVE AROUND THE GENERATION OF POWER, THE TRANSPORTATION OF GOODS, SERVICES & PEOPLE, AND THE SORTS OF MATERIALS THAT WE USE TO FUEL THE WHOLE OF OUR CIVILISATION."
-PETER GARRETT

"WE ARE LIVING ON THIS PLANET AS
IF WE HAD ANOTHER ONE TO GO TO."
– JERRI SWEATINGEN

DID YOU `KNOW?`

What most people fail to realise is that we will
never truly destroy the Earth. The planet will
always remain & its nature will change &
adapt to new conditions. We can only
destroy humanity.

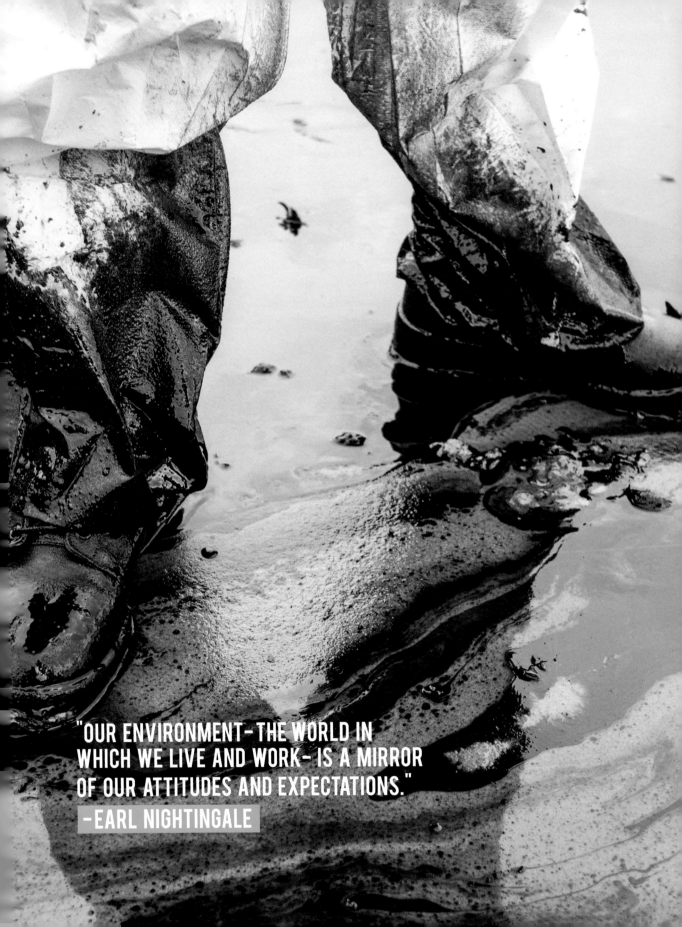

"OUR ENVIRONMENT-THE WORLD IN WHICH WE LIVE AND WORK- IS A MIRROR OF OUR ATTITUDES AND EXPECTATIONS."
-EARL NIGHTINGALE

DID YOU KNOW?

Global warming has the ability to cause an ice age. Ice at the north pole & Greenland is melting, causing the Gulf stream to become unbalanced. This cools America & Europe instead of warming it.

We are overstepping the limits of endurance of two of Earth's critical systems: the climate and the planet's ecosystems. This is especially worrisome because we run the risk of creating a chain reaction of destruction, ultimately shifting the Earth into an alarming state of decay. If we raise the planet's temperature enough to cause ice sheets to collapse, more and more of the sun's heat will be trapped in our atmosphere. This accelerates the warming process, as less ice is available to reflect the sun's rays back into space. If we chop down enough rainforests, what remains will become savannah, removing all the benefits that rainforests provide. If we continue to pollute the ocean, we will destroy one of the planet's largest and most effective carbon absorbents.

Ultimately, what affects the environment, affects us. When the planet suffers, we end up suffering too. Natural environments and ecosystems have an incredible ability to heal and replenish themselves when loss or damage occurs. Yet the excessive rate at which we are damaging the Earth's systems prevents them from counterbalancing these effects. If this cycle of damage continues into the future, we could end up with a completely depleted, hostile and resource-scarce planet to call home.

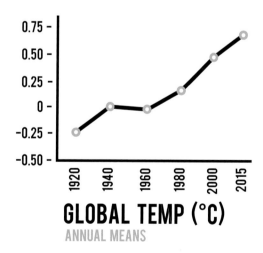

GLOBAL TEMP (°C)
ANNUAL MEANS

THE STATE
OF THE PLANET

Geologists speak of the era we're living in as anthropocentric — the 'Age of Man'. Today, humans are the greatest force of power and influence on the planet. We dam rivers, pollute the oceans and cause deforestation and desertification on frightening levels. It has been proven that we have the capacity to cause massive and irreversible impacts on the planet for many years to come. It is with little doubt that the state of the planet is in a sheer and ongoing crisis.

The existing relationship between mankind and the planet is paradoxical and disconnected. While a larger majority of humans are living more prosperous lives than ever before, the health of the natural environment is at an all-time low. Over the past 200 years man has accelerated his impact on the environment as a result of overconsumption and industrialisation. The most devastating impacts have been experienced through biodiversity and topsoil loss, deforestation and desertification, atmospheric pollution, and the depletion of our oceans.

One of the greatest concerns, for which we are directly responsible for, is the rapidly increasing levels of carbon in the atmosphere. A potent greenhouse gas that plays a vital role in regulating Earth's temperature through the greenhouse effect, the concentrations of carbon in the atmosphere have increased significantly throughout the past 200 years. Since the dawn of the Industrial Revolution, carbon dioxide levels have increased from 280 parts per million to 400 parts per million. The increases are said to be the consequences of our unsustainable consumption of fossil fuels, amongst other human activities, such as deforestation. To make matters worse, atmospheric carbon dioxide levels are currently rising at a rate of approximately two parts per million every year, and accelerating. Carbon in

DID YOU KNOW?

To limit the increase in average global temperature to within 2°C by 2100, emissions of greenhouse gases worldwide will have to be cut by 50% by 2050.

"WE HAVE BECOME SO SUCCESSFUL AT CONTROLLING NATURE THAT WE HAVE LOST OUR CONNECTION TO IT."
—AL GORE

"OUR CLIMATE IS CHANGING. AND IT'S CHANGING IN WAYS THAT THREATEN OUR ECONOMY, OUR SECURITY AND OUR HEALTH. THIS ISN'T AN OPINION, IT'S A FACT."
-BARRACK OBAMA

the atmosphere is widely acknowledged as the direct cause of climate change and global warming, both of which will have catastrophic impacts on the natural world and humanity.

The increases in atmospheric carbon is leading to the gradual warming of the planet. Nine of the ten hottest years humans have ever recorded, which dates back over 100 years, have been in the last 16 years. 2014 marked the 38th consecutive year where temperatures were above average since first recorded. Out of the many consequences of global temperature rises, perhaps the most devastating is the ongoing melting of Earth's polar ice caps. These sheets of ice contain around 70% of all fresh water found on Earth. Only about 0.036% of the planet's total water supply is found in lakes and rivers. From 1979 to 2006, melting of the ice caps over the summer season increased by 30%, reaching a new record in 2007. If the polar ice caps completely melted, our sea level could rise by as much as 75m. We would also lose an overwhelming amount of valuable freshwater supplies as well as countless low-lying areas of land. It is expected that we will lose approximately 30-40% of our global freshwater supplies by the year 2050.

Many low-lying communities and even entire nations may need to relocate as a result of rising sea levels. It is predicted that around 77% of the entire land surface of the Maldives will be completely underwater by the end of the 21st century. On average, most of the islands that make up the Maldives are only 1.5m above sea level. As the sea level is predicted to rise between 0.8 and 2m, the Maldives will become the first state in history to be completely consumed by the ocean. Many of the world's largest and most important cities such as New York, Guangzhou, Miami and Mumbai are also in danger of rising sea levels. As such cities are located along the coast and barely above sea level, they will inevitably face heavy flooding which will have damaging effects on its infrastructure and citizens. The future of these cities and their importance as both living environments for millions of people and as centres of production, trade and commerce will suffer greatly.

The forests of the world, most notably the tropical rainforests that form a belt around the equator in regions such as Brazil, Central Africa and South East Asia, host some of the planet's most diverse ecosystems and provide vital oxygen to the world. The Amazon Rainforest alone provides approximately 20% of the world's oxygen. Although these tropical forests cover less than 7% of Earth's surface, they are home to approximately 50% of all living things on the planet. Unfortunately, the growing demands for farmland, timber products and urban living space are the driving forces behind rapid rates of deforestation that continues to shrink these vital ecosystems. It is estimated that globally, we are losing as much as 18-million acres of forest every year – equal to the entire area of Switzerland. We have already lost half the world's forests, and are losing an estimated 36 football fields worth of trees every minute. Tropical deforestation is now responsible for approximately 20% of world greenhouse gas emissions. A single tree can absorb as much as 21 kg's of carbon dioxide per year, whilst provide a supply of oxygen for two people. A large tree can also lift up to 380 litres of water out of the ground and discharge it into the air. Adding to this, deforestation also severely impacts biodiversity, soil quality and the hydrological cycle – all of which are vital for life.

Another prevailing issue we face heading into the future deals with our topsoil resources. Topsoil is one of the most important natural resources we find on Earth. It provides the necessary nutrients for plants to grow. Due to our unsustainable farming techniques, and along with the rapid rates of deforestation, it is estimated that we have about 60 years of fertile topsoil remaining on our planet. Adding to this, approximately 40% of the soil used for agriculture is severely degraded. On average, we are using up soil at rates between 10-40 times faster than the environment can naturally replenish itself. Topsoil has traditionally fallen within the renewable resource bracket. However, due

to our sheer unsustainable overuse of topsoil, it has since moved into the non-renewable bracket.

Amongst the most devastating effects of mankind on the natural world is the severe depletion and pollution of our oceans and marine ecosystems. Due to the vast amounts of pollution that we have discarded to the planet's ocean over the last two centuries, the health of this environment is dropping rapidly. Coupled with this, our fishing methods have become so unsustainable that we are predicted to run out of all commercial fisheries by the year 2048. Around 85% of global fish stocks are over-exploited, depleted, fully exploited or in recovery from exploitation. Unfortunately, less than 1% of the ocean is protected, and so these trends are likely to continue in the foreseeable future. The deterioration of our oceans shows a direct result of our inabilities to steward the planet. The sad reality is that once we have caused drastic damage to the ocean, it will be extremely difficult, maybe even impossible, to get the oceans back to the healthy levels that they once were.

The facts show that we have caused immense damage to our planet across all spheres of the environment, from our atmosphere to our forests, oceans and soils. If we are to give the planet the chance it needs to heal itself and overcome the damage we have inflicted upon it, we need to find ways of reducing our overconsumption and wastage of natural resources, bring an end to our overbearing cycle of pollution, and protect our environment from further damage. If we are to bring an end to this ongoing destruction of the natural environment, we must look for more sustainable ways of living.

DID YOU KNOW?

Between 2003 & 2008, up to
2 trillion tonnes of ice in
Greenland, Antartica &
Alaska melted.

WHAT IS
SUSTAINABILITY?

The mainstream version of 'sustainability' has been around for about three decades. Yet the fundamental principles of sustainability have existed for hundreds of years. Amongst the thousands of scientists, environmentalists and academics alike around the world, a uniform definition of the concept has still not been reached. The topic soon became central to government agendas, media campaigns and business strategies form the 1970s onwards when people began to realise the incredible impact humanity was having on the environment.

Some people define sustainability as a process in which we use the resources we need now without compromising the ability of future generations to meet their own needs as well. For instance, we should not consume excessively high amounts of resources that we know are limited in supply and can positively influence our lives, such as fossil fuels. Others see sustainability as a way of consuming what we need in such a way that we do not diminish the planet's ability to replenish and restore itself. These groups argue that our overuse of resources is jeopardising the ability of future generations to survive. These include resources such as fertile soil and healthy and stable fish populations. All in all we can view sustainability as a way of living and consuming that allows for the continuation of natural systems and processes. Becoming sustainable as a society today matters a great deal. Every decision we make and every action we take has a profound impact on the future of others. We have to see ourselves as stewards of the Earth, not owners. Other generations will inherit it after us, and the

48 THE NUMBER OF COUNTRIES WITH RENEWABLE ENERGY TARGETS IN 2004

144 THE NUMBER OF COUNTRIES WITH RENEWABLE ENERGY TARGETS IN 2014

"WE ALL HAVE TO DO OUR PART TO RAISE AWARENESS ABOUT GLOBAL WARMING AND THE PROBLEMS WE AS PEOPLE FACE IN PROMOTING A SUSTAINABLE ENVIRONMENTAL FUTURE FOR OUR PLANET."
–LEONARDO DICAPRIO

"THE ONLY WAY FORWARD, IF WE ARE GOING TO IMPROVE THE QUALITY OF THE ENVIRONMENT, IS TO GET EVERYBODY INVOLVED."
-RICHARD ROGERS

condition of the planet they receive will have everything to do with the way we leave it to them.

The common model of sustainability is based on three interlinking circles: environment, social and economic. The concept behind this approach is that we cannot achieve economic growth without tapping into the resources the environment provides. And we cannot achieve social development without achieving positive economic growth simultaneously. Some sustainability experts have now included a fourth circle in this model: future generations. By doing so, it emphasises the long-term thinking that is needed for sustainability to effectively take place.

The fundamental principles of sustainability boil down to three Rs: Reduce, Re-use, and Recycle. This approach to sustainability involves reducing the amount of resources, energy and products we consume, re-using what we can, and recycling the things that can be used again and again, whether for the same or different purpose. These principles are too often neglected by both industries and individuals in their everyday habits and consumption patterns.

For many, the concept of positive economic growth taking place whilst environmental impact is minimised can seem like an impossible mission. Since the beginning of the Industrial Age some 250 years ago, humans have learnt to match the exploitation of natural resources with positive economic growth. But it does not have to be this way. It is becoming increasingly clear that with the aid of modern technology, economic prosperity can indeed take place whilst significantly reducing environmental degradation. In fact, if we are to see a prosperous future for ourselves in any scenario, it becomes vital to address the environmental aspect of sustainability. If not, economies with eventually collapse due to the depletion of resources and services it so vitally depends on.

There has never been a more urgent need for sustainability than our present time. While we cannot undo our past actions, we do have the chance to learn from our mistakes and make a difference for our future, and the futures of generations to come. Collectively reducing and even reversing the devastating impact we have inflicted upon the natural world will be one of our greatest challenges, but if we succeed, it will become one of our greatest achievements. These issues have an affect on every living person. As severe as the issues may be, they provide us with an incredible opportunity to unite around a common cause.

"THE DEBATE IS SETTLED: CLIMATE CHANGE IS A FACT. AND WHEN OUR CHILDREN'S CHILDREN LOOK US IN THE EYE AND ASK IF WE DID ALL WE COULD TO LEAVE THEM A SAFER, MORE STABLE WORLD, WITH NEW SOURCES OF ENERGY, I WANT US TO BE ABLE TO SAY 'YES, WE DID.'"
–BARACK OBAMA

ENERGY

WHAT IS ELECTRICITY?
WHAT ARE FOSSIL FUELS? **WHAT ARE THE PROBLEMS WITH CONVENTIONAL ENERGY SOURCES?** WHEN WILL FOSSIL FUELS RUN OUT? **DO WE HAVE ALTERNATIVE ENERGY SOURCES?** IS GREATER EFFICIENCY WITH FOSSIL FUELS ENOUGH?
WHAT IS RENEWABLE ENERGY? ARE THERE ANY PROBLEMS WITH RENEWABLE ENERGY?
WHAT ABOUT NUCLEAR ENERGY?

WHAT IS
ELECTRICITY

AND HOW DO WE MAKE IT?

Electricity is a form of energy that has great value to mankind. Humans have become so dependent on electricity that it becomes rather daunting to imagine a world without it. We have been using electricity for well over a hundred years, and it has played a highly influential role in shaping the way our societies appear and function today. It can be said with all surety that without the discovery of electricity, many of mankind's greatest inventions and technologies would never have come to fruition. Electricity has steered technology, communication, transport and security into the modern era.

Electricity has become a modern convenience and everyday necessity in many places around the globe. Electricity is highly versatile, can be easily controlled, and has numerous uses ranging from lighting, heating and cooling to telecommunication and transportation. Without it, humans would be forced to use other forms of energy that are considerably less efficient, such as candles for lighting, wood for heating and cooking and mail for communication.

Humans did not invent electricity. Rather, it is a natural form of energy that has been around since the beginning of time. Following the expansion of the human ingenuity and innovation that took place around the time of the Industrial Revolution, humans started to understand the processes involved in harnessing and generating electricity. No one in particular can be credited with the discovery of electricity, or the most efficient way to generate it. But noteworthy individuals such as Thomas Edison, Benjamin Franklin and Nicola Tesla have all been credited with making valuable contributions to the advancements of electricity production, control and use. What the pioneers of the Industrial Revolution were able to achieve was the ability to create an electric current through particular processes and materials. They realised that in order to achieve this, energy had to be converted from one source to another.

DID YOU KNOW?

A lightning bolt has enough energy per strike to keep alight about 100 000 lamps for an entire day, or make 200 000 peices of toast.

"WE FORGET HOW PAINFULLY DIM THE WORLD WAS BEFORE ELECTRICITY."

-BILL BRYSON

DID YOU KNOW?

The first power plant was owned by Thomas Edison & opened in New York City in 1882.

The creation of the electric current required to generate electricity can be achieved by converting other sources of energy into electrical energy. Fossil fuels hold great energy potential and are a commonly used resource for electricity generation. The three predominant fossil fuels used for electricity generation are coal, oil and natural gas, but there are other methods that can also be used, such as renewable energy and nuclear energy.

The energy releasing potential of fossil fuels is enormous as they produce large amounts of heat energy which, when burned, can be converted into electrical energy. The heat released from the burning of fossil fuels is used to boil large tanks of water. The steam passes into a turbine containing thousands of propeller-like blades. The steam released from the boiling water spins the blades, causing the turbine to rotate at high speeds. A generator is mounted at one end of the turbine and consists of carefully wound wire coils. The friction process creates an electrical current, and the energy produced is then stored as electricity. After passing through the turbine, the steam is condensed and cooled through cooling towers, and finally returned to the boiler to be heated once again.

Other types of technologies, such as renewable and nuclear energy, effectively generate electricity in a similar process, except they manage to spin the blade of the turbine without burning any fuels.

Renewable technologies, such as solar energy, convert natural heat from the sun into usable heat, which is predominantly a substitute for the heat generated from burning fossil fuels. Nuclear energy, on the other hand, uses highly advanced technologies to capture the heat exchanges between atoms to spin the turbine.

All in all, electricity can theoretically be produced by spinning a large turbine engine around a generator to produce an electric current. While the processes required to meet the growing demands for electricity are by no means an easy task, the methods we have created in producing electricity have become extremely efficient. Conventional energy sources, in the form of fossil fuels, are significantly more efficient than most other sources and are able to generate the large amounts of electricity modern society demands. There are, however, numerous problems with these methods, as the process involved in extracting fossil fuels and producing electricity from them is becoming increasingly expensive, and has profound negative effects on the natural environment.

"ELECTRICITY IS REALLY JUST ORGANIZED LIGHTNING."
– GEORGE CARLIN

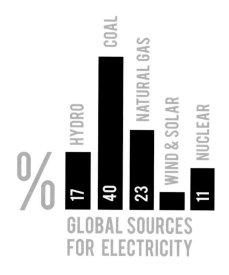

GLOBAL SOURCES FOR ELECTRICITY

HYDRO 17
COAL 40
NATURAL GAS 23
WIND & SOLAR
NUCLEAR 11

WHAT ARE
FOSSIL FUELS?

The majority of our daily activities involve the consumption of fossil fuels in one way or another. Many people assume the use of oil to power our cars is the only time we consume fossil fuels as individuals. But the truth is, our fossil fuel consumption goes beyond transport, and is an integral part of almost every modern convenience. Most of the electricity used in our homes, offices, hospitals and schools has come from power plants that have used large quantities of coal to generate electricity. The food we eat and the cell phones we own have all undergone numerous manufacturing process that require electricity and fuel, most of which are harnessed from unsustainable sources. Without fossil fuels, the cars, ships, trains and airplanes that transport these goods would have no source of power and would therefore be unable to transport these resources from one point to another. Almost every product we consume has, one way or another, made use of fossil fuels.

Fossil fuels are not man-made resources; they are natural and from the earth. Scientists estimate that the fossil fuels we use today were formed between 280 and 300-million years ago, and came to exist when living organisms, such as trees and plants, died and fell to the ground. Over

DID YOU KNOW?

When fossil fuels are burned, they release greenhouse gases into the atmosphere & can cause severe air pollution & serious health problems.

"WHAT HAS BECOME CLEAR FROM THE SCIENCE IS THAT WE CANNOT BURN ALL OF THE FOSSIL FUELS WITHOUT CREATING A VERY DIFFERENT PLANET."
– JAMES HANSEN

"FIRE MADE US HUMAN, FOSSIL FUELS MADE US MODERN, BUT NOW WE NEED A NEW FIRE THAT CAN MAKE US SAFE, SECURE, HEALTHY AND DURABLE."

– AMORY LOVINS

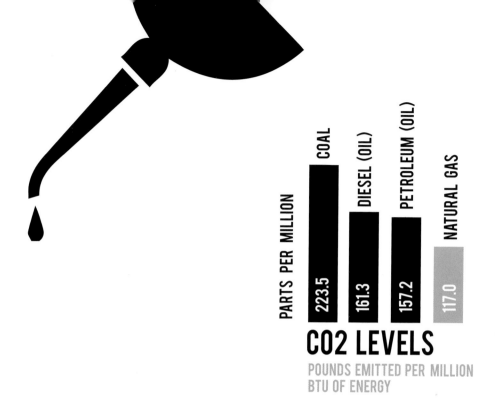

CO2 LEVELS

POUNDS EMITTED PER MILLION BTU OF ENERGY

PARTS PER MILLION

COAL	DIESEL (OIL)	PETROLEUM (OIL)	NATURAL GAS
223.5	161.3	157.2	117.0

time, oceans, rocks and other sediments covered the organic matter and compressed it. As the organic matter fell under greater pressure, it turned into a substance called peat. Over time, more rocks and other sediments piled on top of the peat and the weight above increased. Eventually, the pressure squeezed out the water particles in the peat. Add a few more million years to this process, and the water-less peat transformed into various forms of fossil fuels.

All fossil fuels are composed of hydrocarbons - compounds made up of hydrogen and carbon atoms. When fossil fuels are burned in the presence of oxygen, the hydrocarbon compounds are released as carbon dioxide and water. This is why carbon dioxide is the primary greenhouse gas responsible for the deterioration of the atmosphere. Greenhouse gases such as methane and nitrous oxide are also hydrocarbons. When they are burned, carbon dioxide is released. Methane, for instance, is comprised of four parts carbon and one part hydrogen. What is interesting to note is that when natural gases are released into the atmosphere due to mining activities, animals waste or decomposing organic matter, they are more harmful to the atmosphere than when they are burned to form carbon dioxide.

Fossil fuels exist in three states: solid, liquid and gas. There are three types of fossil fuels, each existing in one of these natural states. Coal, oil and natural gas are the three predominant types of fossil fuels, and all have different uses and applications, yet all are potent sources of energy and are highly flammable.

COAL

Coal is the world's most abundant fossil fuel, and the most commonly used source of energy for generating electricity – contributing to around 40% of global production. Coal is extracted from beneath the ground either by surface or underground mining.

Coalification refers to the degree of change undergone by coal as it matures from peat to anthracite – the purest form of coal. The process has an important effect on the physical and chemical properties of coal, often referred to as the different 'ranks'. The quality of coal depends on a number of factors, such as the type of vegetation the coal originated from, the temperatures and pressures exerted on the coal reserve, and the length of time the coal has been undergoing change.

The biggest advantages of using coal are its efficiency, reliability and cost. Coal is by far the most efficient source of energy available to us, and can be used to produce vast amounts of electricity, outperforming every other type of fossil fuel for electricity production. People who support the use of coal argue that despite its negative effects on the environment, it is the only source of energy within reach that is sufficiently abundant and able to keep up with our enormous and growing demand for electricity. Coupled with this, new and emerging technologies are making it possible to increase the performance and output of coal, making it more efficient as a source of electricity generation.

Despite the many positive economic factors in using coal as an energy resource, the negative aspects cannot be ignored. Firstly, coal is non-renewable and cannot be reused. It is a limited natural resource that humans cannot recreate. Many who push for the elimination of coal as an energy source argue that the excessively high carbon content released when burning coal to make electricity is a primary contributor to climate change and global warming. Coal contains large quantities of carbon, and research has linked carbon levels in the atmosphere as a key contributor to the greenhouse effect, and Earth's increasing temperatures. To make matters worse, an overwhelming majority of countries around the world use coal to generate electricity. In China, for example, coal powers approximately 80% of the electricity grid, which is growing faster than anywhere else in the world at unrelenting rates.

DID YOU KNOW?

Underground coal mining is considered one of the most dangerous jobs in the world.

"BURNING CARBON-BASED SUBSTANCES LIKE OIL, GAS, AND ESPECIALLY COAL, PRODUCES BILLIONS OF EXTRA CARBON DIOXIDE EACH YEAR."

- BILL NYE

DID YOU KNOW?

Nigeria, which recently overtook South Africa as the continent's largest economy, owes 78% of its export success to petroleum.

DID YOU KNOW?

Oil is measured in barrels, which is equal to 159ℓ. The United States consumes more oil than any other country - 19 million barrels per day.

OIL

Oil is a liquid hydrocarbon that formed when organic matter was subject to immense heat and pressure. Unlike coal, which is used directly with little processing, oil is generally refined and chemically altered to meet different uses, such as jet fuel for aeroplanes or petroleum for cars. Oil is predominantly used as a fuel source for transportation, but also has other uses such as mechanical lubrication and electricity generation, as well as an ingredient in a number of products, most notably plastics.

There are many different types of oil. These oils are defined according to their viscosity (oil's resistance to flow), volatility (rate at which oil evaporates into the air), and toxicity (how poisonous the oil is to people and animals). The different kinds of oil depend on the amount and degree of heat and pressure the organic material has endured over the years.

Oil's reputation in the news and media is becoming increasingly worse due to rising and fluctuating prices around the globe, political tension and conflict, its negative effects on the atmosphere when burned for fuel, as well as recurring spills in the oceans, lakes and on land that cause vast environmental damage.

There are however considerable advantages to using oil as a fuel source. First and foremost oil has traditionally had a greater performance in its ability to move vehicles faster and over greater distances than almost any other fuel source. Oil can also be stored and transported with relative ease, which is convenient for many countries and industries around the globe that lack sufficient supply of the resource and have a need to import it. Many industries today have been using oil for over a hundred years, and so the technology has evolved and become more efficient with greater performance.

THERE ARE, ON AVERAGE, TWENTY-SEVEN OIL SPILLS EVERY DAY ON EARTH.

NATURAL GAS

Coal and oil have a particular use in certain industries: coal is used mostly for generating electricity, while oil is used as the primary energy source for transport. While they do have other uses, these are their predominant respective uses. Natural gas, on the other hand, has numerous uses, ranging from electricity production, heating and cooling households, gas for cooking and running transport systems. Natural gas includes methane, shale gas, tight gas and coal seam gas.

Natural gas has traditionally been one of the easiest fossil fuels to extract from below Earth's surface. But scientists have recently discovered that most of the easily accessible natural gas has now been extracted and consumed over the years. However, there is one particular form of natural gas which is found in abundance: shale gas. The process of extracting shale gas, hydraulic fracturing (or commonly known as 'fracking'), has caused major controversy over the years, especially in terms of its environmental impacts. Shale gas is located between cracks in rocks that are many kilometres below Earth's surface. A mixture of water and other chemicals is pumped with extreme force to crack the underground rocks. The gas slowly seeps through the cracks and is captured at the top of the well.

In the last few years, mining for shale gas has received a great deal of attention in international media. Many 'anti-fracking' campaigns have been established, with the intention of completely banning the process and bringing an end to the fracking industry. Although a contested debate, many scientists argue that the hydraulic fracturing process causes significant environmental damage, such as polluting valuable underground water resources and the clearing away of landscapes. In addition, although there is no evidence yet, many scientists firmly believe that hydraulic fracturing is linked to the triggering of earthquakes. There is ongoing research into the relationship between hydraulic fracturing processes and whether or not they trigger earthquakes.

Many people strongly feel that natural gas should be the fossil fuel of choice moving forward. When burned, natural gas is cleaner than its counterparts, as it has a lower carbon content. The carbon content of natural gas is 117 pounds per million British thermal units (Btu), as opposed to coal (223.5) and oil (157.2).

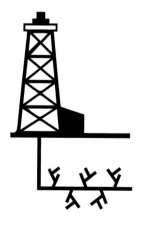

"I DON'T FEAR FRACKING. I FEAR CARBON."
– RUSSELL GOLD

WHAT ARE THE PROBLEMS WITH CONVENTIONAL ENERGY SOURCES?

Although fossil fuels are highly efficient as an energy source, they still have their disadvantages. One of the biggest disadvantages is that fossil fuels are non-renewable and limited in supply. As they take millions of years to form, we cannot create them ourselves, nor rely on them forever. Most industries are still completely reliant on fossil fuels as a source of energy, which is a major cause for concern. 80% of vehicles today run on oil, making the transport industry highly dependent on fossil fuels. The energy industry still makes use of coal as the primary energy source for electricity production. The simple reality is that we cannot rely on fossil fuels to sustain us forever. Fossil fuels will eventually run out, and we therefore need to find and adopt alternative sources of energy and fuel.

It has always been known that the extraction methods used to obtain such resources are degrading the planet. Surface mining, oil drilling and hydraulic fracturing all have disastrous impacts on the natural environment, and often cause irreversible and permanent damage to ecosystems. When we extract oil by drilling

into Earth's surface (whether on land or sea) entire ecosystems can be wiped out. Hydraulic fracturing, the process used to extract shale gas, is said to pollute underground water supplies severely. When we mine for coal, whether on Earth's surface or deep underground, entire landscapes are destroyed and reduced to barren wastelands.

Over the past 30 years, we have learnt that these processes of extracting fossil fuels not only have an impact on Earth's surface, but are also contributing to another dangerous impact on the natural environment. The carbon released by the burning of fossil fuels is immense, and contributes greatly to atmospheric pollution. As a result, this contributes to the greenhouse effect, leading to climate change and global warming. Research has shown that there is a direct relationship between the increase in the carbon dioxide content in the atmosphere and the rise in Earth's temperature. In many ways, this damage to the environment could potentially have a far broader and more devastating impact for Earth than the clearing away of vegetation and upheaval of land in mining processes.

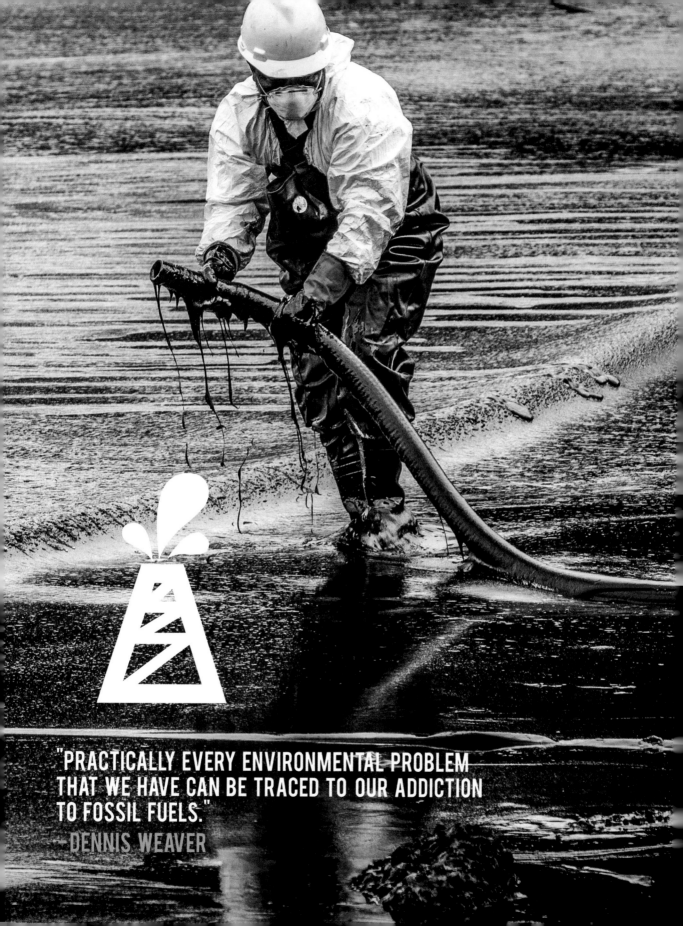

"PRACTICALLY EVERY ENVIRONMENTAL PROBLEM THAT WE HAVE CAN BE TRACED TO OUR ADDICTION TO FOSSIL FUELS."
—DENNIS WEAVER

DID YOU KNOW?

The oil crisis of the 1970's revealed the delicate nature of fossil fuels as a source of energy for the world. As a result, research into alternative & renewable forms methods of generating energy gained momentum.

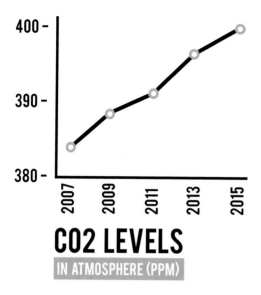

CO2 LEVELS
IN ATMOSPHERE (PPM)

Whether it be oil for our cars, coal for electricity production, or natural gas for heating, every time we consume fossil fuels, carbon dioxide is released into the atmosphere. Instead of carbon remaining underground in the form of fossil fuels, we are effectively releasing it into the air, where it accumulates and contributes to the natural greenhouse effect. We are not creating more carbon when we burn fossil fuels. Rather, we are releasing the embodied carbon within the fossil fuels into the air when burned.

It is important for us all to become aware that the era of easily accessible fossil fuels is over. It is becoming far more difficult to locate and extract these resources, as we have already extracted and consumed all the easily accessibly ones. Mining companies are now having to dig even deeper, expand their operations further afield and invest in more and more advanced and expensive machinery to extract these harder-to-reach resources. This increases both the cost of these operations and the price of the electricity and fuel they create. Fracking operations have escalated in recent years as a direct result of the ongoing high costs of coal and oil mining operations. It is clear that we are in the middle of a transition between a bygone period of cheap, easily accessible fossil fuels, to an age of high resource extraction challenges and costs.

As we look to the future, it will be crucial that we manage the consumption of fossil fuels in an efficient and responsible manner. The value of fossil fuels to humans cannot be over emphasised. They are the resources we have depended on since the start of the Industrial Revolution, and have steered us into the modern world we live in today. Yet at the same time our use of them continues to cause severe damage to the environment and threaten our future.

DID YOU KNOW?

We burn 100 times more fossil fuel today than we did in 1850. As industrialisation has increased across the world, we now need to produce enough energy to serve the world's population of over seven billion people.

WHEN WILL FOSSIL FUELS RUN OUT?

Even with our modern equipment, technologies and research methods, no one on Earth can predict with certainty when fossil fuels will run out. And it is possible that we will never know exactly. But as technology and research has improved significantly over the years, we have become more equipped to make more accurate estimations on the remaining supplies.

Some studies estimate that we have somewhere around 50 years worth of fossil fuels remaining. Other studies suggest the figure is more in the range of 100 to 200 years. All these projections are based according to data collected on many factors such as the current and predicted future consumption, along with the known reserves remaining. But in truth, we cannot predict our consumption of fossil fuels moving into the future. Oil shocks, wars and environmental crises have all occurred before, and will likely occur again. All of these occurrences influence our consumption levels of fossil fuels.

In addition, estimations vary between the three main types of fossil fuels. Some say we have more oil than natural gas, or more coal reserves than oil deposits. For example, it is estimated that at our current consumption rates, the remaining coal reserves we know of will last us until 2088, and oil will last until 2052. But these are merely the known reserves; we do not know how much else is out there. Regardless of which estimate is correct or which we choose to believe, the reality is fossil fuels will inevitably run out, whether in the next 50 years, 100 years or 200 years.

To complicate the matter further, the world's energy demands are certainly not going to decrease in the foreseeable future. With accelerating population growth, the demand for energy will increase, meaning we will use fossil fuels at a much higher consumption in the future. Whether we can adequately substitute our reliance on fossil fuels with other sources of energy is still unknown. But it can be confidently said that fossil fuels will still play a central role in global energy consumption for some time.

"ENERGY IS THE ABILITY TO DO WORK; POWER IS THE RATE AT WHICH WORK GETS DONE. PUT ANOTHER WAY, ENERGY IS AN AMOUNT; POWER IS A RATE."

- ROBERT BRYCE

IS GREATER EFFICIENCY WITH FOSSIL FUELS ENOUGH?

The first solution to reducing our heavy reliance on conventional energy sources is energy efficiency. This does not involve finding a new source of energy, but rather involves being smarter and more efficient with our consumption of it. The principle behind energy efficiency is to use the energy sources that we have sparingly. Energy efficiency is generally considered to be the first and perhaps easiest step in the move toward to a sustainable energy future.

Energy efficiency makes use of modern technologies that are generally more efficient than older technologies. These require less energy to produce the same results. An energy-saving light bulb, for example, uses less electricity to produce light when compared to a conventional light bulb, yet the light energy levels are more or less the same. Take note of fuel-efficient cars too; new car models have better designed engines that use less fuel per kilometre than cars built 20 years ago.

Energy efficiency not only involves adopting and installing energy-saving technologies; leading more sustainable lifestyles plays its part too. It is focused on changing the way we think about our need for and use of energy. This includes getting people to make simple decisions about energy-saving, such as turning off lights when leaving a room. Simple, yet effective, decisions such as these decrease the environmental impacts of using fossil fuels, as they essentially reduce the need to produce unused or wasted electricity.

The adoption of energy-saving technologies is becoming a necessity for many industries that produce significant amounts of carbon dioxide. This is because many governments are implementing carbon taxes for any pollution above a stipulated level. This type of taxation is based on the principle of 'the polluter pays', and is considered an effective method for governments to curb their country's cumulative carbon emissions.

DID YOU KNOW?

Some new refrigerators are so energy-smart that they use less electricity than a light bulb.

"WE MUST CONTINUE TO RESEARCH INTO NEW FORMS OF ENERGY AND INTO MORE EFFICIENT USE OF EXISTING ENERGY SOURCES."
-MAC THORNBERRY

Since no company wants to pay additional taxes for polluting the atmosphere, companies are adopting energy-saving technologies that produce the same results as traditional technologies, yet require less electricity to operate.

Reducing the consumption of fossil fuels will result in less pollution and ecological destruction. By adopting energy-saving technologies, industries are able to produce the same output without being penalised. Energy-saving technologies include household appliances such as energy-saving lightbulbs, motion lighting systems, heat pumps, solar geysers and energy efficient refrigerators. The adoption of energy-saving technologies benefits both people and the environment. This is why energy efficiency is considered to be such a promising solution to our energy crisis.

On an industrial scale, becoming more efficient in how we produce electricity from fossil fuels is extremely important. This is

particularly the case in developing countries where existing power plants are less efficient in producing electricity. As a result, a higher coal consumption is required in order to meet demands. It is estimated that a 1% improvement in the efficiency of a conventional coal combustion plant results in a 2-3% reduction in carbon dioxide emissions.

Although energy efficiency is an absolute necessity for the time being, humans need to continue searching for alternative sources of energy. We urgently need to adopt energy-efficient practices while we continue to find and develop alternative sources of energy. Unfortunately, no matter how efficiently we use fossil fuels, they are still considered non-renewable and their supply is limited. We therefore need to find other sources of energy to ensure a sustainable future for mankind and the planet. Thankfully, we have discovered viable alternative sources of energy.

"THE ECONOMIC PROSPERITY OF THE MODERN WORLD HAS BEEN BUILT ON TWO DEADLY BUT ENERGY-RICH HYDROCARBONS: COAL AND OIL."
-RICHARD BRANSON

DO WE HAVE ALTERNATIVE ENERGY SOURCES?

There are two alternative sources of energy in particular that are proving to be viable solutions for the future. These are renewable energy and nuclear energy. Each one has its advantages and disadvantages, from economic, social and environmental perspectives. Neither of these options provide a complete solution on its own, but rather should be used in tandem with other resources and processes to diversify the energy mix. Having a number of ways to produce electricity, such as coal-based power stations, nuclear energy and renewable energy, allows countries to improve their energy security and the reliability of their energy supply.

In order to reduce our dependency on carbon emitting fossil fuels, it will be necessary to integrate the different solutions in the most efficient and effective manner, depending on the resources available to each country and their demands. For example, countries with an abundance of coal will place a great focus on coal-fired plants to meet their base electricity demands whilst transitioning to a sustainable energy system. In other words,

the solutions will differ between countries depending on their unique situation and the natural resources available at their disposal. Also, as research advances and technology improves, some options will emerge as more attractive and effective than others. However, it is unclear which methods will benefit from advances in technology and to what extent or point this will happen. It would therefore be a mistake to adopt one approach in particular whilst completely neglecting others.

It needs to be noted that the power generated from fossil fuels is, for now, significantly more efficient and reliable when compared to other technologies. While this situation is changing rapidly, it is still

"WHETHER IT IS TO REDUCE OUR CARBON DIOXIDE EMISSIONS OR TO PREPARE FOR WHEN THE COAL AND OIL RUN OUT, WE HAVE TO CONTINUE TO SEEK OUT NEW ENERGY SOURCES"

– MARTIN REES

"THE PROGRESSIVE DEVELOPMENT OF MAN IS VITALLY DEPENDENT ON INVENTION. IT IS THE MOST IMPORTANT PRODUCT OF HIS CREATIVE BRAIN."
– NIKOLA TESLA

important that the transition to a low-carbon, or even zero-carbon, energy supply is managed correctly and strategically. Diversifying the energy mix will take a long-term planning framework that slowly but surely reduces the reliance on fossil fuels, whilst simultaneously developing and investing in the low-to-zero carbon solutions.

The reality is that, for the time being at least, we cannot meet the growing energy and fuel demands with renewable and nuclear energy alone. Fossil fuels will undoubtedly play a key role in meeting energy demands for the foreseeable future, at least until renewables and nuclear energy become more efficient and affordable.

Because renewables have been relatively expensive (historically speaking), most investments in them have come from wealthy and developed countries. Poorer and less developed countries have generally been unable or unwilling to afford these energy sources, and in a hasty attempt to bring their nation up to speed with the rest of the world, have resorted to non-renewable sources of energy to meet their needs. Oil rich countries, many of which are well suited to solar, haven't invested nearly enough into renewables either, as they have resorted to buying cheap and highly available oil instead.

Another important point to note is that many countries cannot adopt certain types of renewable energy technologies, even if they are willing to, as they do not have the necessary natural conditions, or logistical challenges lie in the way. For example, Scandinavian countries are unlikely to install solar plants to meet their energy demands, as it is mostly dark during large portions of the year. For these countries, wind or hydro-electric technologies would be a smarter strategy. On the other hand, a country such as South Africa that has great solar radiation would likely target solar technology. South Africa is an extremely water scarce country, so hydro-electric power could understandably be overlooked. For other countries, constantly importing coal could prove too expensive and unreliable, so an option such as nuclear energy could be the most appropriate. The underlying point is that different countries will likely opt for technologies that can produce the most efficient and affordable results possible according to their available resources and weather conditions.

"EVEN IF WE DIDN'T HAVE GREENHOUSE GASES, WE'RE GOING TO HAVE TO MOVE AWAY FROM FOSSIL FUELS, AS WE'RE GOING TO RUN OUT. THEY'RE FINITE, WHEREAS SOLAR AND WIND ARE INFINITE."

– TED TURNER

DID YOU **KNOW?**

China is already gearing up to be the world's renewable energy superpower, with the largest installed base of wind & solar photovoltaic (PV) power, as well as by far the world's largest manufacturing system for wind turbines & solar photovoltaic cells.

WHAT IS
RENEWABLE ENERGY?

The first of the two viable energy solutions for the future – renewable energy, can simply be explained as an energy resource that cannot be overused or depleted: there is an unlimited supply of it. We can consume as much as we want of it, we can use it over and over again, and, unlike fossil fuels, it will never ever run out. There are five basic types of renewable energy: solar, wind, hydropower, biomass, and geothermal.

Thanks to advancements in modern technology, we have discovered ways to convert naturally recurring energy sources (such as the energy derived from the sun) into something we can benefit from: heat or electrical energy. The technology that humans have developed to harness such energy is not free, and is still considered relatively expensive. This has been a major obstacle to the widespread adoption of solar power and other types of renewable energy programs. Because the energy produced from fossil fuels is relatively cheap, renewable energy has battled to become mainstream. However, over the past ten years, the price of renewable energy has decreased significantly. In addition, the price of energy from conventional sources has increased due to the overconsumption of energy and the depletion of fossil fuel reserves. This has led to renewable energy becoming a very attractive 'alternative'. From an environmental perspective, this is encouraging, as renewable energy does not degrade the environment nearly as much as fossil fuels do.

Because the costs of generating electricity from renewable sources are becoming

increasingly more competitive, and renewable energy sources have considerably less impact on the environment, people are starting to opt for renewables as a source of energy over conventional sources. Governments and organisations are rapidly adopting and promoting renewable technologies, as the cost of producing renewable energy is becoming competitive with the cost of conventional energy sources, and the widespread environmental benefits are being realised.

Renewable energy is now amongst the fastest growing markets in the world, on par with industries like construction, financial services and digital technology. While some types of renewable energy technolo-gies are proving to be more attractive than others, they are all receiving significant funding for research and development, which is making the technologies increasingly cost-competitive with conventional sources of energy. For example, the price of a single watt of electricity produced from solar technology in 1976 was $76.00. In the year 2015, it was sitting at $0.30.

A world powered completely by renewable energy is possible, but it will undoubtedly be a long term transition; one that will take decades, not just years. However, the resiliency of the renewable energy sector in the face of low oil, gas and coal prices is a sign that the sector has a great future.

99.99%

THE AMOUNT OF SOLAR ENERGY IN SOLAR RADIATION THAT GOES TO WASTE.

DID YOU KNOW?

Hydropower is the most efficient way to generate electricity. Modern hydro turbines convert as much as 90% of the available energy into electricity. Fossil fuels are only about 50%.

SOLAR

The energy given off by the sun is called solar radiation. Solar powered technology allows us to directly capture some of the sun's radiation and convert it into various forms of energy. Solar power is one of the most popular and promising renewable energy technologies today. This technology has improved dramatically over the past few decades, to a point where we can now capture the sun's radiation and convert it into electricity. To demonstrate the improvements in efficiency, experts estimate that conventional solar panels will increase in efficiency by 2% over the next 7 years. This may not seem like much at first glance, but an additional increase from 16% to 18% is large enough to boost electricity output by about 12%.

Completely free of carbon emissions, solar technology can produce electricity in two common ways. The first method makes use of Concentrated Solar Power (CSP) technology. This is a process whereby hundreds of large mirrors are strategically placed to concentrate the sun's rays onto either a central tower or a series of pipes. The central tower or pipes contain fluids, generally oil or a mixture of water with other minerals. The concentrated solar rays are so powerful and immensely hot that they heat up the tank of liquid water until it has reached boiling point. The steam stemming from the boiling water is then used as a power source to spin a turbine, thereby producing electricity in the process. The second way to produce electricity from solar radiation is by using solar panels called photovoltaic panels, or PV panels. This sophisticated technology does not concentrate the sun's rays onto a central point, but rather converts light energy from the sun into electrical energy – a process called the photovoltaic effect.

Solar energy provides a significant opportunity for the future. The technology is becoming cheaper and more efficient each year, making it more appealing to investors. The cost of solar power has reached a tipping point, having dropped below the price of fossil fuels in many countries around the world in the last few years. Globally, the price of solar PV modules has dropped as much as 75% since 2009, making it amongst the fastest growing markets in the world.

Having said that, there are challenges to overcome. The biggest challenge with solar energy, at least for the immediate future, is the intermittent generation of power. Solar panels do not operate with optimal efficiency unless the conditions for solar radiation are perfect. Seasons or days experiencing cloud cover, rainfall, or even dust blown from wind, can all reduce the efficiency of solar panels. On a cloudy day, a typical solar panel will only produce between 10-25% of their full capacity. The fact that solar panels still generate electricity even in the absence of direct sunlight is testimony to the sophisticated technology.

"ALMOST THE ENTIRE PLANET IS SOLAR POW-
ERED. WHAT WE ARE TALKING ABOUT IS TAKING
A SMALL AMOUNT OF THAT POWER AND TURN-
ING IT INTO ELECTRICITY."
– ELON MUSK

WIND

Humans have harnessed wind power for thousands of years. The ships that were used to explore the furthest corners of the world in the 15th and 16th centuries did not have engines that ran off fossil fuels, but rather used sails to harness the power of the wind to move their boats. Windmills, which have been used for over 2 000 years to process grains and foods, are another great example. Humans have always understood the opportunities associated with wind power and have capitalised on these. However, it was only recently that we began to use wind to generate electricity.

Electricity from wind turbines is produced in a similar way to electricity from fossil fuels. Instead of burning fossil fuels to spin a turbine and produce electricity, wind energy uses the power of the wind to spin the blades of tall windmill-like structures. Strong wind forces blow upon the blade of the turret, forcing them to spin. The blades spin an engine around a small generator, which is located at the top of the tower, which generates electricity.

Although the processes of manufacturing and installing wind turbines consume a certain amount of resources and energy, the process of generating electricity through wind turbines emits zero pollution and is a completely clean source of energy. Wind power, along with solar power, is also becoming increasingly cost-competitive with fossil fuels, with the price of wind power generation reducing annually.

From an environmental point of view, one of the biggest issues with wind power is that the wind turbines occupy extremely large areas of land. When built on solid ground, existing trees and other obstructing vegetation need to be cleared in order for the wind turbines to be erected. Even when located offshore they can have an influence on marine ecosystems. Some argue that wind turbines are not the most responsible or profitable use of land, with agriculture perhaps being more necessary moving into the future.

DID YOU KNOW?

Wind turbines are quiet. An operating modern wind farm at a distance of 750 to 1000 feet is no noisier than a kitchen refrigerator.

"LARGE OFFSHORE WIND FARMS CAN BE INSTALLED FROM START TO FINISH IN LESS THAN TWO YEARS, A CRUCIAL ASSET GIVEN THE PRESSING THREAT OF CLIMATE CHANGE."
–GLOBAL WIND ENERGY COUNCIL

DID YOU KNOW?

Norway produces more than 99%.
of its electricity with hydro power.

HYDROPOWER

Hydropower harnesses the energy of moving water. Similar to wind, humans have been harnessing energy from lakes, rivers and the ocean for over 2 000 years. The ancient Egyptians realised that flowing or falling water has enough force to spin an object, such as a barrel or wheel. They used this form of hydropower to process foods, such as converting grain into flour through a grinding action.

Fast-forward to present day, and humans have developed the technology needed to produce electricity from the power of moving or falling water. In order to generate electricity from hydropower, a large dam with a significant amount of stored water is necessary. The water is contained in the dam by large controllable dam walls. When electricity needs to be generated, the gates of the wall are opened, which releases the water. As a result of gravity, the water flows down the dam wall, falling with immense power. Located beneath or at the bottom of the dam walls are turbine engines. The force and weight of the moving water then spins the turbine engines around a small generator, producing large amounts of electricity in the process.

Hydropower is one of the cleanest methods of producing electricity, and is also one of the cheapest, once the dam has been built. The ability of hydropower to generate large amounts of electricity when demand is high, or save the water when demand is low, is another major advantage of the technology. Hydropower is considered an extremely efficient method of producing electricity, especially in regions that have large inland bodies of water and experience perennial high rainfall.

Despite its advantages, research has shown that building large dams can have many negative impacts on the environment. The dams are also expensive to build, and need to be of a high standard in order to allow electricity to be generated efficiently. The construction of large dams can cause serious geological damage, as well as alter the natural water table level. Despite this, hydro-electricity is a carbon-free source of power and omits zero pollution whilst generating electricity.

HYDROPOWER IS THE LEADING SOURCE OF RENEWABLE ENERGY. IT PROVIDES MORE THAN 97% OF ALL ELECTRICITY GENERATED BY RENEWABLE SOURCES.

WASTE-TO-ENERGY

By and large, waste-to-energy is generally excluded form the renewable energy list, but can still be argued to be a renewable energy source. Waste-to-energy can best be explained as the process of generating energy, in the form of electricity or heat, from the incineration of leftover waste. Energy from waste offers a safe, efficient and sustainable means of generating power while simultaneously disposing of waste.

In order to generate energy from waste, municipal waste, mostly in the form of hard trash, is delivered to a facility where it is stored. The waste is transferred to a combustion chamber where a large fire is maintained at extremely high temperatures. The heat released in the burning of waste from the combustion chamber is then used to boil water, which produces electricity in a similar process to the burning of fossil fuels. During these processes certain gases, notably methane, are released and then captured. The gases are then used for a number of applications, such as heating, cooking and cooling in households.

The sheer amount of waste produced in many of the world's largest cities provides an incredible opportunity for waste-to-energy generation. Sweden, for example, is the world leader in waste-to-energy, having set up 32 waste-to-energy plants around the country. Sweden converts up to 50% of all its waste into energy. It is estimated that less than 1% of Sweden's garbage ends up in landfill sites. Incredibly, these waste-to-energy plants provide about a million homes with heating and over a quarter of a million homes with electricity. Not only is Sweden's fossil fuel consumption reduced significantly, but the problems of waste disposal are too.

Unfortunately, some products contain materials that cannot be recycled or safely burned, so the use of landfills are still necessary. However, the opportunity remains for most other forms of waste to be used as a sustainable resource in electricity generation.

DID YOU KNOW?

For every ton of trash processed by a waste-to-energy plant in place of a landfill, approximately one ton of carbon dioxide emissions are avoided.

DID YOU KNOW?

In the United States, waste-to-energy plants recover more than 700 000 tons of ferrous metals for recycling annually. Recycling metals saves energy & avoids CO_2 emissions that would have been emitted if virgin materials were mined & new metals were manufactured, such as steel.

ARE THERE ANY PROBLEMS WITH RENEWABLE ENERGY?

It is easy to recognise the environmental advantages of utilising renewable sources of energy, but we must also be aware of the disadvantages associated with it. Although power generated from renewable sources will play a pivotal role in the future of energy supplies, there are still some obstacles that need to be overcome.

Perhaps the biggest challenge facing renewable energy technologies is inconsistent weather conditions. For example, a wind turbine's blades cannot spin and produce an electrical current unless there is a sufficient supply of wind. A solar panel cannot produce optimal electricity unless there is sufficient sunlight available. A hydro-electric plant cannot produce electricity unless there is sufficient and consistent rainfall to maintain the body of water needed to be released through the dam walls. In truth, renewable energy technologies are not nearly as efficient as conventional methods unless weather conditions are ideal.

It needs to be ensured that renewable energy projects can produce an ongoing and constant supply of electricity. When considering performance, renewable energy generally cannot provide the same quantity of power as traditional energy technologies, such as coal-fired plants. If a renewable power source is unreliable and unable to supply an ongoing source of power, then governments, industries and citizens may opt for non-renewable energy sources instead. It is crucial that projects are located in suitable and favourable regions with reliable weather conditions all year round to ensure wide-scale adoption of renewable energy. Only through careful and strategic planning can we overcome this challenge and propel renewables into a dominant energy source.

THERE'S BASICALLY ONE THING HOLDING SOLAR BACK:
STORAGE

DID YOU KNOW?

A marginal gas or oil well has a power
density at least 22 times that of a wind
turbine, while a nuclear power plant has
a density that is more than 8 times that
of a solar photovoltaic facility.

Those opposed to the adoption of renewable energy argue that when compared to the prices of electricity generated from fossil fuels, renewable energy is too expensive. The initial capital costs of the technology needed to convert renewable energy into electricity, such as solar panels or wind turbines, are high, especially when compared to the electricity that can be purchased from conventional sources. It often takes a few years for the investment to pay itself off, and many investors are unwilling to wait it out. In contrast, the technology and infrastructure needed to convert fossil fuels into electricity is well established and therefore cheaper. But it cannot be denied that the price of renewable energy is reducing rapidly, and is continuously dropping with rapid innovation, while the prices of conventional sources rise simultaneously. Once the initial capital investment has paid itself off, whether that be three years or ten, the electricity is generated for free with zero environmental impact.

Renewable energy technologies cannot, at this present time, produce the excessively large quantities of electricity that conventional sources of energy are able to produce. Unless a significant amount of wind turbines or solar panels are installed, the efficiency of renewables cannot match up with conventional sources. The only solution to overcome this challenge for the time being would be to rapidly ramp up the production and construction of renewable energy technologies. By doing this, the mass production and large-scale adoption of such technologies would make them both cheaper as well as provide the industry with the necessary funding to advance the technology and improve its performance.

One of the greatest challenges that has traditionally held renewable energy back is the issue of storing the electricity produced. The electricity produced from solar panels, for example, needs to be used instantaneously and cannot be stored overnight without the use of electricity-storing batteries. The batteries have traditionally been too expensive or have been unable to store a sufficient amount of electricity. Thankfully, this situation is rapidly changing. New battery technologies are becoming capable of storing more and more electricity. The storage capabilities of batteries are reaching a point whereby we will be able to supply power to our homes, cars, offices and factories for days, or even weeks, on a single charge.

In total, although there are challenges ahead, renewable energy technologies are showing substantial promise and potential, as research and development continues to improve the technologies in every way possible. Whether it be the intermittent or inefficient generation of electricity compared to conventional sources, or the storage of generated electricity, the drawbacks of renewable energy are being overcome rapidly with new technological advancement and innovation.

DID YOU KNOW?

Though solar energy is used on a wide scale, it only provides a small fraction of the world's energy supply.

"ALL THE WASTE IN A YEAR
FROM A NUCLEAR POWER PLANT
CAN BE STORED UNDER A DESK."
– RONALD REAGAN

WHAT ABOUT
NUCLEAR ENERGY?

Nuclear energy is another alternative source of energy that is currently available to generate electricity, and is considered a relatively clean and safe method of doing so, if managed properly. Unlike renewable energy that converts energy from the sun, wind and water, nuclear energy comes from energy stored in the nucleus of atoms.

Everything is made up of atoms. Inside each atom is a small part called a nucleus. The nucleus contains tiny particles called protons, neutrons and electrons. The protons are positively charged, the neutrons have no charge, and the elections are negatively charged. Nuclear energy is essentially the force that holds all the parts together in an atom. There are two ways in which humans can manipulate these atoms to produce electricity: fusion and fission. All nuclear processes make use of a natural resource called Uranium when generating electricity. Uranium is found in rocks and is extracted from the earth through mining activities, similar to those used for coal.

Fusion is a way of harnessing energy by combining atoms. When atoms are forced together they create unstable neutrons. These neutrons are essentially an excess form of energy. This excess energy is then released as heat or light energy, which is then captured and used to generate electricity.

Fission is the opposite process of fusion. Fission energy is released when an atom is split up into two smaller atoms. The two smaller atoms don't need as much energy to hold them together as the larger atom, so the extra energy is released as heat and radiation. This excess heat is then converted into electrical energy.

Similar to the processes used with conventional sources of energy, nuclear reactors utilise the heat from fusion and fission to produce steam, which spins a turbine around a generator and ultimately produces an electric current, thereby generating electricity.

Nuclear energy is widely considered to be a low-carbon source of power generation, but it's credibility as a renewable source of energy is an ongoing issue of debate. Some scientists argue that it is a renewable source of power, whilst others argue it is not. Nuclear energy makes use of the natural resource Uranium, which needs to be mined and extracted from below Earth's surface. This natural resource, according to all scientific organisations, is considered to be non-renewable, much like coal, oil and natural gas.

Although a low-carbon power source, many people are against the adoption of nuclear energy for varying reasons. Nuclear power reactors produce large amounts of radioactive waste in the process of nuclear power generation. If the waste comes into direct contact with humans, plants and animals, it can be deadly, depending on the severity of contact, and the health consequences can essentially last for decades. And while nuclear power reactors have strict regulations for containing radioactive waste, the reality is accidents do occur. The Chernobyl disaster, for example, was a deadly nuclear incident that occurred in Ukraine in 1986. A large explosion in one of the reactors at the Chernobyl Nuclear Power Plant led to the release of large quantities of radioactive dust into the nearby environment. Many people died from the accident and major health problems throughout the country continue to this day. Chernobyl was shut down and the area around it is now uninhabited by humans and exists as nothing more than a radioactive wasteland. It is believed that it will take around 1 000 years before the area is safe for human habitation again. More recently, the tsunami that hit the coast of Japan in 2011 led to an explosion in the nuclear power plant at Fukushima, leading to the melt down of three of the plant's six nuclear reactors.

With this in mind, advances in modern technology continue to make the production of nuclear energy safer and more efficient. Although there are risks, the regulations for containing the toxic radioactive waste produced by nuclear energy reactors are strict and the possibilities of disaster are relatively small. Nuclear energy is considered a reliable source of energy, and although radioactive waste has leaked into the atmosphere in the past, it still remains far less damaging to the environment than fossil fuels.

Although nuclear energy is considered an expensive power option, it still has many advantages such as its ability to efficiently produce electricity and it is a low-carbon power source. From a long-term perspective nuclear power can become an increasingly efficient source of energy, but there are some setbacks. One of the biggest is they are widely perceived by the public to be unsafe and dangerous. And while they are relatively cheap to run, they are highly expensive to build.

NUCLEAR REACTORS
UNDER CONSTRUCTION WORLDWIDE
(AS OF 2015)

THERE ARE OVER

430

NUCLEAR ENERGY PLANTS IN THE WORLD TODAY...

WITH ANOTHER 70 UNDER CONSTRUCTION.

DID YOU KNOW?

Nuclear energy was first developed in the 1940's. During World War 2, research initially focussed on producing bombs by splitting atoms of either uranium or plutonium.

FOOD & AGRICULTURE

WHAT IS THE HISTORY OF MODERN AGRICULTURE?
WHAT EFFECT IS POPULATION GROWTH HAVING ON THE FOOD INDUSTRY?
HOW DOES INDUSTRIAL FARMING AFFECT THE ENVIRONMENT? WHAT IMPACT ARE WE HAVING ON MARINE LIFE?
HOW WILL CLIMATE CHANGE AFFECT FOOD PRODUCTION?
ARE WE CONSUMING MORE THAN THE PLANET CAN PROVIDE?
WHAT METHODS CAN WE ADOPT TO SOLVE THESE ISSUES? HOW CAN WE CONSUME MORE SUSTAINABLY?

WHAT IS THE HISTORY OF MODERN AGRICULTURE?

Humans have been using Earth's resources for as long as we have been on the planet. It was only after about 10 000 BC that human communities began to produce, rear and cultivate food rather than hunt and gather from the wild. People discovered that the production of fruit, vegetables and grains could actually be controlled, nurtured and maximised through certain techniques and practices. Slowly, animals were also domesticated. Cows, goats, chickens and pigs were used as a food source in the form of meat, eggs and milk. This practice of controlled food production – known as agriculture – provided a steady, reliable and consistent source of food. Farming made life significantly better for people.

With an abundance of food, people had more time to devote to the development of new technologies. With time, great inventions, such as the wheel, provided opportunities to create better farming equipment, such as the ox-driven plough. People were able to share farming techniques and methods, leading to greater innovations and improvements to existing systems, for example fertilisation and irrigation. Villagers dug large canals and complex systems of ditches, delivering water from distant sources to where it was most needed. Agriculture remained relatively stable with few inventions for thousands of years.

Very little drastic transformation took place in agriculture up until about 1700, during which a fundamental shift took place that changed man's relationship to food forever. The Agricultural Revolution, as it was known, occurred in Europe and North America between 1700 and 1800 and was a period of development that saw a massive and rapid increase in agricultural productivity and vast improvements in farming technology. The Agricultural Revolution preceded the Industrial Revolution. But unknown to many, it was the drastic transformations during the Agriculture Revolution that helped kickstart the Industrial era and remained crucial to its success thereafter.

In the 1850s, the Industrial Revolution spilled over into agriculture with new mechanised methods and technologies. Before the Industrial Revolution, farmers had to do field work by hand or with horse-drawn equipment. This work would

take a long time to complete, which meant that farms were smaller because farmers could only work so much land. It also meant that production was lower, meaning less food could be produced. The inventions and technologies of the Industrial Revolution, such as the steam-powered engine, brought a whole new dimension to the production of food from crops and livestock. Produce could now be transported to distant locations where it was demanded, which allowed the industry to expand. Fewer workers were now needed to cultivate farms, as machinery replaced less efficient human labour. Reliable and fast motorised vehicles replaced horses, while irrigation systems replaced seasonal rainfall. Crops could be grown consistently, predictably and efficiently. The advancements in agriculture, both in technology and method, allowed food to become increasingly bountiful, available and profitable.

The growth of global trade experienced after the Industrial Revolution had a significant impact on agriculture. The trading of food dates back thousands of years, when civilisations in Asia, North Africa and Europe traded spices, such as salt, pepper and cinnamon. During these times, spices were so valuable that they even became a currency. It was only until around 200 years ago that global food trade really started to have an influence on agriculture. The evolution of transport has had a significantly positive impact on agriculture throughout the globe. Food trade has helped provide greater quantities, wider variety and better quality to increasing numbers of people.

Around the mid-20th century, agriculture entered the modern era. Incredibly, there has been more change to agriculture in the last 50-100 years, than the last 10 000 years. Agriculture has moved from small, subsistence farms to ones that cover thousands of acres, cultivating hundreds of crop varieties. To put this into perspective, the average farm size in North America in 1900 was 147 acres. In 2015, the average farm is 441 acres.

Thanks to technological advances, natural systems such as rainfall patterns don't play an important role in determining crop yields anymore. Threats of pests, disease and drought are reduced significantly thanks to advancements in insecticides, genetic modification, extensive irrigation systems and satellite images. Coupled with this, the technology farmers can use to harvest foods, such as tractors and grain processors, have improved dramatically, which has increased productivity on the farm. For instance, in the 1930s, a farmer with the help of farm workers, could harvest, on average, 100 bushels of corn by hand in one day. Today, with the aid of machinery, farmers can harvest 100 bushes of corn in approximately seven minutes. This has increased efficiency by over 8 000 times.

It can be confidently said that modern agriculture has improved our lives tremendously. But while the modern methods of agriculture are successful in meeting the ever-growing demands for food intensified by the world's increasing population, in reality the system is extremely broken and, environmentally speaking, highly unsustainable over the long run.

DID YOU KNOW?

If our global population is to reach 9 billion people by 2050, then food production will need to increase by 60% in the next few decades.

WHAT EFFECT IS POPULATION GROWTH HAVING ON THE FOOD INDUSTRY?

The reason for the rapid boom in global population over the last 200 years, and more specifically the last 70 years, can be attributed to both industrialisation and significant advancements in agriculture and medicine. As World War II came to an end in 1945, enormous focus was placed on increasing agricultural productivity. With Europe undergoing major recovery programs from the devastation of the War and countries like the United States (US) growing in power and wealth, heavy investment in agriculture took place. Underdeveloped countries in Asia, Africa and South America also began major processes of industrialisation, dedicating more and more resources to food production. Following World War II, increasing both the scale and efficiency of food production became the dominant focus.

Increasing agricultural output and productivity is often said to be the very first goal of any nation attempting to advance economically. Industrialisation, agricultural productivity and medical advancements are undoubtedly the most important factors that are leading to population growth. The simple reality is that being able to feed more people runs alongside an increasing population. More food means more people, which means a greater workforce. And a greater workforce often means a more prosperous society. This is especially true for developed countries, which are able to match population growth with both a greater supply of food, as well as a greater supply of medicine. But with the end of World War II, these agricultural and medical technologies and practices became more available to the less developed parts of the world.

The reason for such high birth rates in developing nations such as China, Brazil and India, and the significant stagnation and decline in birth rates in the more developed nations over the last 70 years, has a lot to do with these historical events. In developing nations it has traditionally been expected to have large families with many children. As most of these societies had their livelihood invested in agriculture, larger families meant more assistance on the farm. But there was another significant reason for high birth rates. With so many children dying at birth in the early years of life, it was not uncommon for a woman to bear 10, 15 or even 20 children over the course of her life. The culture and tradition of having many children did not automatically come to an end with the introduction of medicine and agricultural technology. Over the past 70 years many of these societies have continued to bear large families. As a result of the availability of medicine and food to these nations, the global population has skyrocketed.

The relationship between population growth and agriculture has resulted in great challenges moving forward. We are facing exponential population growth, yet have a limited supply of natural resources. With approximately 200 000 people being added to the world every day, we are faced with the incredible challenge of providing food to nearly 75-million additional people every year. With the global population expected to increase by 3-billion by 2050, each and every one of these new people will require a constant supply of food in order to live strong and healthy lives.

The global middle class is also becoming wealthier, which means their food preferences are changing. More and more people are demanding protein-rich foods such as beef, poultry, eggs and milk – all of which come from livestock. These types of foods have a higher environmental footprint as they require more energy, land, water and time to cultivate. Livestock leads to substantially faster rates of deforestation, soil erosion and greenhouse emissions when compared to crop farming. Livestock also consume large quantities of grain as food that could otherwise be used to feed the world's population. In fact, it is estimated that as much as a third of the world's entire food supply is used to feed livestock. Fish are another protein-rich food that is demanded by the growing middle class. The environmental impact linked to livestock and fish consumption is considerably higher than traditional crop farming.

There are contested issues amongst the world's leading scientists and environmentalists as to how population growth will influence agriculture in the future. Some stress concern over our rapidly increasing population, stating that the higher the number of people, the greater our environmental impact. Others believe that it is not the our growing population, but rather the changing patterns of consumption that is the area of greatest concern.

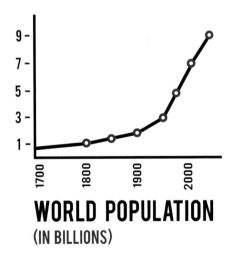

WORLD POPULATION
(IN BILLIONS)

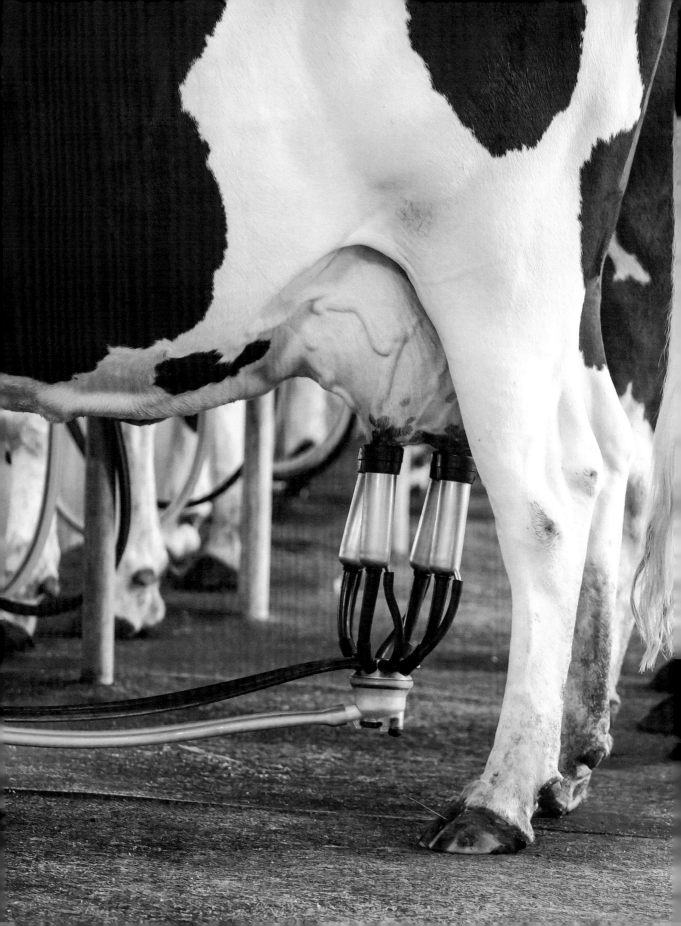

HOW DOES INDUSTRIAL FARMING AFFECT THE ENVIRONMENT?

Sustainable agriculture is a set of ideas and principles whereby farmers not only take from the land, but they also give back. Unfortunately, most industrial farming methods today completely disregard the need for such a balance. Crops are seldom rotated in ways that grant the soil the ability to be replenished with nutrients, which leads to infertility. Forests are often cleared to create space for livestock grazing or crop farming. Water is consumed in enormous amounts in order to sustain extensive fields of crops and livestock. Fertilisers and pesticides pose a threat to soil and groundwater streams through chemical contamination. The list of environmental concerns surrounding industrial agriculture activities is broad and severe.

Industrial agriculture is now one of the leading forces behind some of the most daunting environmental challenges we face. These include climate change, global warming, soil infertility, ecosystem destruction, biodiversity loss, as well as water scarcity and contamination. But at the same time, agriculture is the most important industry to man, as it provides the food we need to survive.

The environmental effects of industrial agriculture are both direct and indirect, and can often result in irreversible damage to our soils, water resources and ecosystems. There are many problems with industrial agriculture, but there are five issues in particular that will have a major impact on our future. These are deforestation, soil degradation, livestock-related issues, unsustainable farming techniques as well as water wastage and contamination. They all pose a significant threat to the long-term sustainability of the food industry, which will undoubtedly affect both humanity and the planet.

"AGRICULTURE IS THE MOST
DESTRUCTIVE INDUSTRY THAT WE
HAVE. MORE THAN COAL MINING AND
OTHER EXTRACTIVE INDUSTRIES."
- ALLAN SAVORY

"IF WE PLANTED TREES ON LAND CURRENTLY USED TO GROW UNNECESSARY SURPLUS AND WASTED FOOD, THIS WOULD OFFSET A THEORETICAL MAXIMUM OF 100% OF GREENHOUSE GAS EMISSIONS FROM FOSSIL FUEL COMBUSTION."

– TRISTRAM STUART

GLOBAL DEFORESTATION
(IN BILLIONS OF HECTARES)

2BLN –
1.5BLN –
1BLN –

1800 1850 1900 1950 2000

DEFORESTATION

Modern agriculture is recognised as the biggest driver of deforestation. Farmers and industrial food companies around the world continue to cut down forests to provide additional land for farming operations. Other direct causes of deforestation include logging activities, mining operations and urbanisation. The most common methods of deforestation include the burning and clear cutting of trees – activities that leave the land completely barren.

Natural forests still cover an estimated 30% of the world's land surface, but they are being cleared at alarming rates. It is estimated that at the current rate of deforestation, the world's rain forests could completely vanish within the next 100 years. Tropical forests are largely confined to developing countries, but as a result of global interest and trade, they are being used to supply more than just local or national needs. Instead, the global demand for forest resources are bearing down on them as well. Forests worldwide are in danger.

Industrial agricultural operations are speeding up the process of deforestation drastically, as farmers and food companies continue to search for new land to farm crops and livestock. Millions of acres of forest areas are unsustainably cleared every year for these agricultural purposes. But the problem isn't restricted to industrial farming operations alone. Subsistence farming – in other words self-sufficiency farming in which farmers focus on growing enough food to feed themselves and their families – is another major contributor to the clear cutting of forest areas. This is especially the case in poor, developing countries where it is estimated that subsistence farming is responsible for 48% of deforestation compared to industrial farming which sits at 32%. To put these numbers into perspective, commercial logging operations that clear trees to create paper and timber products is only responsible for 14% of deforestation in these countries.

Trees and plants are crucial as they have the incredible ability to absorb carbon dioxide and produce oxygen for the planet. They have a vital role to play not only in reducing the amount of carbon dioxide in our atmosphere, but in providing a richly oxygenated environment for us to thrive. The major rainforests of the world, located around the equatorial regions of South East Asia, South America and Central Africa, produce the largest quantities of oxygen for the planet, and are known as the lungs of the world. As a result, deforestation is now amongst the leading causes of global warming as we are clearing the very resource that has the ability to counteract our carbon dioxide emissions.

SOIL EROSION

Soil is a mixture of minerals, air, water and organic matter – all the ingredients necessary for our plant life to flourish. In fact, soil is described as Earth's fragile skin that anchors all life on the planet, as it is home to a countless number of species that create a dynamic and complex set of ecosystems. Soil is unquestionably one of the most precious natural resources we have. However, many people are unaware that soil can be damaged to a point that it becomes completely infertile and life cannot be sustained. The activities involved in industrial agricultural are in many ways responsible for this, as they directly lead to increased soil erosion.

Because soil formation is an extremely slow process, soil erosion creates major problems. The erosion of soil can cause fertile land to become completely unusable for agricultural purposes. In many cases, severe soil erosion can lead to desertification – an unwanted process which causes arid soil to become completely barren and incapable of sustaining plant growth. Even small amounts of soil erosion can severely damage the quality of agricultural land. Soil erosion not only reduces the water-holding capacity of soil, but it also strips away vital nutrients and organic matter.

Deforestation, due to agricultural operations, is now amongst the leading global causes of soil erosion. Removing trees deprives the forest of its ability to provide shelter, shade and protection, which blocks the sun's rays during the day and holds in heat at night. These changes in temperature can be harmful to both plant and animal life. Over-exposure to these elements, such as wind and rain, damages the quality of the soil severely. Because tree roots also hold the soil together and retain water in an ecosystem, deforestation sets in motion the cycle of soil erosion. It is estimated that Costa Rica loses 860-million tonnes of valuable topsoil every year due to the rapid rates of deforestation the country is experiencing. In Madagascar, so much topsoil is lost that the rivers run blood-red with soil, staining the surrounding Indian Ocean.

The preservation and protection of soil is something most often overlooked in industrial agriculture practices. Soil is used repeatedly without being rested or rotated. Soil is in fact said to be a non-renewable resource, as it generally cannot be recreated in a human lifetime, especially not in such high volumes as are needed.

DID YOU KNOW?

Annual soil loss in South Africa is estimated at 300-400 million tonnes, nearly three tonnes for each hectare of land.

LIVESTOCK-RELATED PROBLEMS

As much as modern farming has benefited the world, and provided great food security and diversity to the global population, there are significant issues of concern, much of which arise from our demands on livestock.

The first major problem with livestock farming is the incredibly high amount of greenhouse gases that are produced from the industry. The faming sector contributes a staggering 18% of all global greenhouse gases, more than the entire transport sector. Although it only contributes around 9% towards carbon dioxide emissions, it generates around 65% nitrous oxide and 35% methane from human-related activities, which has 296 times and 21 times the global warming impact of carbon dioxide respectively. Most of the greenhouse gas emissions from the agriculture industry are directly linked to livestock. Because it is humans who raise these vast amounts of livestock for food purposes, it is ultimately our responsibility to solve this environmentally harmful issue.

To put the greenhouse gases of the industry into perspective, consider that there are an estimated 1.5-billion cows on Earth. The average cow emits between 70 and 120 kg's of methane gas per year as part of their natural digestive system. Because of the potency of methane, this amount is equivalent to 2 300 kg's of carbon dioxide. This is equal in comparison to the burning of around 1 000 litres of petrol. Now imagine the collective amount of greenhouse gases released from all the other billions of livestock, such as sheep, goats, chickens and camels.

The second major problem with industrial livestock operations is an ethical one, that deals with the controversial ways we farm these animals. With the widespread concept of approaching farming like an assembly line in a factory – in order to increase production and output – farmers have created 'factory farms'. Under such conditions, animals are kept permanently indoors with little space, if any, to move or walk freely. The belief is that by raising the animals purely for the production of food, they can exist in an assembly line environment, which will increase efficiency and productivity of the animals. The situation is so severe that in the US alone over 99% of farm animals are raised in these industrial environments. Many of these animals are fed corn based diets, instead of their usual diet of grass, seeds and plants. By taking thousands of animals and confining them to a tiny space and depriving them of their natural instincts and diets, it can also lead to the start of diseases. This is especially the case when farms are not as sterile as they should be. When diseases start, such as salmonella and swine flu, they tend to spread easily.

"10% OF RICH COUNTRIES' GREENHOUSE GAS EMISSIONS COME FROM GROWING FOOD THAT IS NEVER EATEN."
– TRISTRAM STUART

FARMING TECHNIQUES

Modern farming methods, technologies and techniques are increasingly being adopted in an urgent attempt to meet the world's growing demand for food. However, closely coupled with such modern techniques is environmental damage. The leading environmental impacts arise from two widespread farming techniques: the use of pesticides and out-of-season farming.

In general, a pesticide can be any chemical or biological substance that is used to warn off pests – such as birds or locusts – that pose a threat to the cultivation of plants or rearing of livestock. Where we once used dogs or scarecrows, we now use chemical substances, as they prove to be more effective, especially on large-scale farms. However, the use of pesticides in commercial farming raises a number of environmental concerns. 'Pesticide drift' is one of the biggest issues, whereby toxic pesticides that are suspended in the air are carried elsewhere by winds, rivers or groundwater systems. These substances contaminate both water and soil supplies. It is estimated that over 98% of sprayed pesticides reach a destination other than their target species, simply because they are sprayed across entire crop fields. In addition to these environmental challenges, the use of pesticides also reduces biodiversity, destroys natural habitats (especially for birds) and threatens endangered species, as many of the chemicals can be toxic. Over time, pesticides have become less persistent and more species-specific, reducing their environ-

mental impact. However, the global adoption of pesticides has increased significantly, offsetting the improvements in chemical ingredients in the products.

Before the birth of industrial agriculture and all the modern technologies and opportunities it brought with it, farmers were only capable of growing certain crops seasonally, when the climatic conditions were just right to support growth. Natural elements, such as rainfall, temperature and humidity were only ideal in certain seasons throughout the year. However, with the help of technology, controlled irrigation systems and a host of chemicals, farmers are now able to grow almost any crop throughout the year, regardless of seasonal conditions. This is due to advancements in irrigation technology and infrastructure, where dry areas can receive water supply for farming from distant locations. The problem with out-of-season farming is that it is not dependent on seasonal rainfall. As a result water must often be sourced from elsewhere. With a disregard for natural growing conditions, industrial farmers grow crops all year round.

Although in many ways this is extremely beneficial to food yields and supplies, the soil becomes greatly overused as a result of insufficient rest. Soil is not given sufficient time to replenish itself with vital nutrients for the following season. From a water and soil perspective this method is extremely unsustainable.

WATER WASTAGE & CONTAMINATION

Water is without a doubt the single most important resource for agriculture. Absolutely nothing can grow or survive without a constant supply of this precious asset. A generous and consistent supply of water for our crops and livestock is vital in order to keep up with both local and global food demands. But the industrial-scale cultivation of crops and livestock requires intensive amounts of water to grow and produce food, which magnifies the pressure on our already overstretched water resource.

Agriculture has always consumed a staggering amount of water. Irrigation has been used for thousands of years to increase crop yields and keep food production consistent during dry seasons when there is little rainfall. But since industrial agricultural operations skyrocketed some 60 years ago, technological advancements in the form of mechanical irrigation pumps and sprinkler systems have allowed us to cultivate and exploit more land that would otherwise be impossible to farm. Irrigated farming is now the single largest consumer of water globally, consuming about 70% of the planet's accessible freshwater.

The second major problem relating to water is contamination and pollution. Ironically, industrial agriculture, an industry in particular that requires copious amounts of water for survival, is considered amongst the leading causes of water pollution today. The relationship between industrial farming and agriculture is often plagued by overuse, waste and contamination.

Although industrial agriculture pollutes and contaminates water in numerous ways, its impact is mainly attributed to the overuse of fertilisers. Nutrients, such as nitrogen and phosphorous, are the minerals in fertiliser that most industrial farmers use to promote plant growth. Because fertiliser has almost become industry standard, far more nitrogen and phosphorous have been used across larger crop fields. However, too much of it degrades ecosystems by making water or soil too acidic, which can easily destroy certain plants while promoting the growth of others.

A good example of how acidic water can destroy ecosystems would be the process of eutrophication. When water becomes acidic, it promotes the growth of bacterial algae. This algae grows on the surface of water and essentially forms a blanket over ponds, lakes and reservoirs. This blocks sunlight and oxygen from entering the water source to the plants and aquatic life below. The algae also absorbs more oxygen than other aquatic plants, thereby reducing the amount available for fish and plant life.

MARINE FISH STOCK

(600 MONITORED SPECIES)

- 3% UNDEREXPLOITED
- 20% MODERATELY EXPLOITED
- 52% FULLY EXPLOITED
- 17% OVEREXPLOITED
- 7% DEPLETED
- 1% RECOVERING FROM DEPLETION

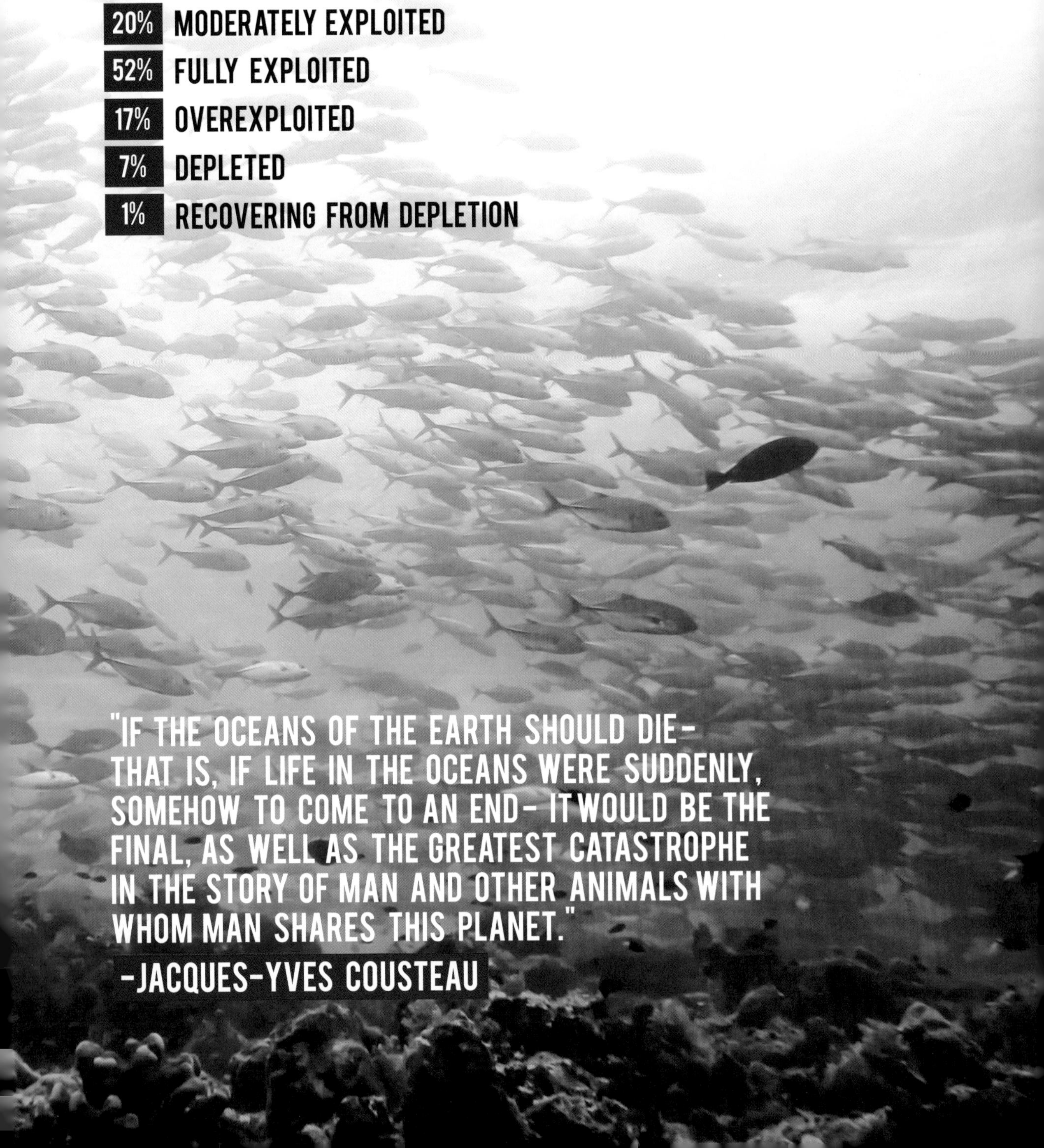

"IF THE OCEANS OF THE EARTH SHOULD DIE-
THAT IS, IF LIFE IN THE OCEANS WERE SUDDENLY,
SOMEHOW TO COME TO AN END- IT WOULD BE THE
FINAL, AS WELL AS THE GREATEST CATASTROPHE
IN THE STORY OF MAN AND OTHER ANIMALS WITH
WHOM MAN SHARES THIS PLANET."
-JACQUES-YVES COUSTEAU

WHAT IMPACT ARE WE HAVING ON MARINE LIFE?

Food supplies from marine ecosystems differ significantly from the food sources we get from crops and livestock for one important reason: we cannot sufficiently control or monitor marine food supplies. When we catch fish from the ocean, we are effectively catching creatures from the wild. We cannot control their movements or breeding habits, nor can we domesticate them. Fish are elusive creatures and require vast amounts of ocean to flourish and multiply.

The ocean covers 71% of the world's surface and hosts some of the most diverse ecosystems on our planet. Because the ocean is such a delicate environment and because marine ecosystems provide us with such an abundance of food, it becomes vitally important that we protect, preserve and steward the world's marine ecosystems.

Seafood is a dominant source of protein for many cultures and people groups. Many nations such as Japan, India and Bangladesh rely on fish as their main source of protein. Due to the widespread demand for fish and seafood around the world, large-scale commercial fishing operations exist to provide for the high demand. Our large-scale commercial fishing activities are extremely unsustainable, and along with the excessive amount of pollution we inflict upon the ocean, we are seeing the universal demise of this beautiful ecosystem. Unless we can bring significant and long-lasting transformation to our ocean-based activities, we will soon witness both the collapse of one our most important and largest ecosystems, as well as the entire fishing industry. This will have an irreversible effect on the world's food supply. Both the issue of overfishing and ocean pollution must be resolved.

DID YOU KNOW?

Large areas of seabed in the Mediterranean & North Sea now resemble a desert - the seas have been expunged of fish using increasingly efficient methods such as bottom trawling.

OVERFISHING

Over the last 100 years, fishing operations have expanded to all corners of the ocean. Millions of people around the world depend on the ocean for their livelihoods. Whilst this has allowed the global supply of seafood to increase and become more available, it has placed immense strain on marine populations. As the fishing industry has aggressively expanded, and with it the amount of fish species taken from our oceans, we have reached a point whereby our food demands have exceeded the ability of marine populations to adequately replenish their numbers. By exploiting the ocean's fish reserves beyond a point of natural replenishment, we have caused significant imbalance in the natural food chain and witnessed the populations of countless fish species dwindle. What has resulted is an unsustainable and catastrophic exploitation of our oceans.

During the 20th century, relaxed governmental policies, coupled with the growing demand for protein-rich foods, led to a rapid rise in industrial fishing operations. Extremely large commercial fleets became highly aggressive with their fishing activities and yield targets, scouring the oceans

and developing increasingly sophisticated technologies and methods for finding and extracting their target species. Consumers soon became accustomed to a wide selection of seafood available at affordable prices, which resulted in the ongoing demand for industrial fishing operations.

The fishing industry reached its peak in 1989, when about 90-million tonnes of catch were taken from the world's oceans. Since then, most fishing operations have slowly declined or stagnated, due to increased pressure by environmental organisations and governmental policies. However, in many cases this transformation has come too late. Many marine populations are battling to replenish and sustain themselves. It is believed that the population levels of sought-after fish species such as the Chilean Sea Bass and the Bluefin Tuna have decreased so heavily that their number stands at a mere 10% of their pre-industrial population.

Because numerous fish populations have declined and collapsed, industrial fishermen now return with lower yields. As such, fishing operations are having to venture

DID YOU KNOW?

On average, people eat four times as much fish now than they did in 1950.

"ONE FIFTH OF ALL FISH THAT ARE CAUGHT ARE THROWN OUT BEFORE THE BOATS EVER GET TO THE DOCK."
– PETER LENHER

DID YOU KNOW?

Around 85% of global fish stocks are over-exploited, depleted, fully exploited or in recovery from exploitation.

"40 TO 60% OF ALL FISH CAUGHT IN EUROPE ARE DISCARDED- EITHER BECAUSE THEY ARE THE WRONG SIZE, SPECIES, OR BECAUSE OF THE ILL-GOVERNED EUROPEAN QUOTA SYSTEM."
-TRISTRAM STUART

deeper into the uncharted areas of the ocean and further below the surface in an attempt to locate and capture what remains of the fish populations. The fishing industry has developed vessels that can travel further out, cast wider nets and reap a greater volume in order to reach their target. Many of these fleets are unregulated and their operations are having a heavy impact on the basic functioning of marine ecosystems, causing permanent damage and changes to the ocean.

Unfortunately, many fishing operations are not concerned with which methods they adopt to catch fish. Even in the face of dwindling fish populations, many commercial fishing boats now cast large nets that sweep across ocean floors, trapping absolutely anything that they can get. Referred to as 'bottom trawling', these activities are responsible for some of the most catastrophic damage to marine landscapes and ecosystems. Trawling the ocean floor is often compared to a bulldozer, whereby nets or containers of around 60m long are pulled for as far as 20 km's, picking up turtles, coral and anything else, destroying the forests of plant life along the ocean floor. It is estimated that the bycatch — unwanted fish and other ocean life — thrown back into the sea can amount to as much as 90% of the total trawl's catch. But this unsustainable activity also wrecks havoc on ecosystems and coral reefs. It is estimated that the area of the ocean floor that has been transformed from 'ocean forest' to mud is equivalent to the area of all the land-based forests that have ever been cut down in the history of humanity. This has all taken place within the last 150 years.

DID YOU KNOW?

The total number of discarded fish is 7.3 million tonnes per year - nearly 10% of all fish caught in oceans.

POLLUTION

The ongoing and widespread amount of pollution that is released into our oceans in the form of hard trash, hazardous waste and airborne gases is testimony to mankind's irresponsibility and disregard for the natural environment. Until the 1970s, chemicals and garbage waste was deliberately dumped into the oceans by businesses, governments and individuals. It became a common practice for disposing everything, assuming that the effects would be insignificant compared to the vast expanse of the world's oceans. However, this train of thought has in time proved to be entirely wrong. It is now clear that our oceans have suffered a great deal at the hands of mankind. Marine life is dying, and as a result the whole oceanic ecosystem is threatened by pollution.

It is estimated that 80% of pollution that enters the marine environment comes from the land. Such pollutants include pesticides, herbicides, chemical fertilisers, detergents, oil, sewage, plastics and other garbage. The introduction of such pollutants into our oceans is often the result of careless disposal. Oftentimes, people illegally dump their waste into the oceans. Other times rainfall picks up contaminants left in our streets, yards, farms and landfall sites, and they flow into the sea via rivers or sewers.

The pollution that we dispose of in our oceans can be broken into two categories. The first is hard trash in the form of plastics, metals or any other solid. It is estimated that around 300 000 dolphins die each year as a result of becoming tangled in discarded fishing nets. When not responsibly disposed of, plastic products can do much harm to our sea life. Plastics are not a naturally occurring substance; they are highly engineered materials. They are often extremely strong, durable, non-biodegradable and poisonous if consumed. Any animal that gets tangled in, trapped in, or swallows plastic products can suffer serious harm or even death.

Apart from direct pollutants caused by mankind in the form of oil spills or plastic trash, biological pollutants are another form of pollution that can be traced back to man's interference with the ocean. When pollution such as nitrogen and phosphorus from pesticides or fertiliser used in farming activities makes its way into our oceans, it provides ideal growing conditions for invasive species of algae and bacteria. When this happens, algae plants grow rapidly and uncontrollably, spreading over the ocean floor and choking the existing coral reefs and plant life, where fish and other marine animals feed.

"IF YOU WERE TO DRAG ALL THE OCEAN GYRE FOR PLANKTON, YOU WILL FIND 6 TIMES MORE PLASTIC THAN PLANKTON."
–NADYA ZHEXEMBAYEVA

DID YOU KNOW?

At least 10% of the 100 million tons of plastic we use every year end up in the oceans. This is equivalent to the weight of 700 billion plastic bottles.

China alone dumped nearly 5 billion pounds of plastic waste into the ocean in 2010.

Plants cannot perform photosynthesis, as sunlight cannot reach them through the thick layer of algae covering them. Adding to this, algae plants extract huge amounts of oxygen from the water. This removes the oxygen for fish to breathe. Even when oxygen levels decrease slightly, it has drastic affects on the survival of marine animals.

It is estimated that approximately 10-20% of the world's coral reefs have been completely destroyed due to human activities. These richly diverse marine ecosystems are also destroyed by boat anchors, large fishing nets and dredging activities that oftentimes wipe out entire areas of coral reef. It has been estimated that human related activities have resulted in the complete destruction of nearly half of the Great Barrier Reef – the world's largest reef in the world.

Due to ocean winds and currents, areas far from human activity are threatened by pollution. The North Pacific Gyre, an area of ocean located off the coast of California in the US, is known as the largest garbage site in the world. Commonly known as the North Atlantic garbage patch, the area is known to have as much as 200 000 pieces of debris per square km. The debris zone shifts by as much as 1 600 km's north and south, depending on the season, ocean currents and prevailing winds. As such, any marine animal within a 2 000 km radius of this zone is in danger.

Ocean pollution is having an incredible impact on marine life and the health of our oceans, whether it be through a chemical imbalance in the water, or a poison to their digestive system when consumed. Despite its overwhelming size and incredible power, the ocean is a sensitive ecosystem, whereby a careful chemical and ecological balance must be maintained for life to flourish.

TOTAL PLASTIC DEBRIS SENT TO OCEAN (2010)
(IN POUNDS)

HOW WILL CLIMATE CHANGE AFFECT FOOD PRODUCTION?

Both agriculture and fisheries are highly dependent on specific climate conditions. In order to maximise growth and in turn productivity, the precise conditions under which crops, livestock and marine life flourish must be maintained. However, climate change is threatening the stability of such conditions. Climate change will make it significantly more challenging to grow crops, raise animals and catch fish in the same manner we have done so in the past.

Regions that have historically allowed us to successfully cultivate a wide range of healthy crops over thousands of years may become unable to do so with the drastic changes in weather and climate the planet could experience. Diverse marine ecosystems that have up until now been unaffected by human-related activities such as overfishing may be unable to deal with the devastating effects climate change could bring.

The agriculture industry is already facing huge challenges to provide food for the growing global population. With the additional challenges brought about by climate change, it will become all the more important to reduce our carbon emissions. If we fail to do so, the great transformation in weather and temperature Earth will undergo could devastate our ability to harvest food on land and from the ocean.

"IN THE NEXT 24 HOURS, DEFORESTATION WILL RELEASE AS MUCH CO2 INTO THE ATMOSPHERE AS 8 MILLION PEOPLE FLYING FROM LONDON TO NEW YORK. STOPPING THE LOGGERS IS THE FASTEST AND CHEAPEST SOLUTION TO CLIMATE CHANGE."
–DANIEL HOWDEN

AGRICULTURE

The effects of climate change could have devastating impacts on crop and livestock farming around the world. The expected changes in temperature, carbon dioxide levels and frequency and intensity of extreme weather will prompt significant challenges for farmers.

In terms of crops, climate change could reduce or alter rainfall patterns, increase or decrease temperatures, increase levels of carbon dioxide and shift the timing of seasons. Extreme temperatures and precipitation can prevent crops from growing entirely. Such weather events, coupled with the shifting of seasons, will bring about unwanted conditions during sensitive and vital stages of a plants lifecycle. For instance, most plants germinate during early spring when the weather conditions are ideal to support growth. Due to expected changes to the climate, these times could be met with severe weather events such as rain, hail or drought that would completely destroy the sensitive plant life. This type of incident was witnessed along the banks of the Mississippi River in the US in 2008. Severe floods occurred just before the harvest period, causing significant damage to crops. There was an estimated loss of an enormous $8-billion for farmers. Although this may not have been attributed to climate change, and could have been a rare weather event, it does show daunting consequences as to what we could expect from drastic and hostile weather events that will be expected to occur more frequently as our climate changes.

A large number of studies have shown that weeds, pests and fungi thrive under warmer temperatures, wetter climates and increased levels of carbon dioxide in the air. Climate change will amplify these ideal conditions. Weeds, pests and fungi will thrive, meaning more farmers will be forced to make use of chemicals, such as pesticides and fertilisers. It may become increasingly difficult to farm using sustainable, organic methods as a result of these growing problems.

Temperature increases will create significant problems for livestock farming. Heat waves, projected to increase drastically as a result of climate change, could directly threaten the health and livelihood of livestock. There have been cases where a single heat wave has killed thousands of farm animals. In India, a heat wave in 2015 led to the death of as many as 17-million chickens in the month of May alone. The loss of such a food source dealt a huge blow to the Indian poultry industry. In 2011, a heat wave in the US killed as many as 6 500 cows across three states. Livestock, like humans, have a core temperature that must be maintained to ensure productivity. Any deviations from this can cause the animal to become stressed or fatigued, which in turn can disrupt the health and fertility of the animal, limiting the animals' ability to produce meat, milk or eggs. Heat stress is another concern for the livestock industry. Over time, heat stress can increase animals' vulnerability to disease, reduce fertility and reduce milk production.

DID YOU KNOW?

The increased frequency & severity of droughts resulting from projected climate change is likely to further exacerbate desertification.

DID YOU KNOW?

Catches in the tropics are expected to decline a further 40% by 2050, & yet some 400 million people in Africa & Southeast Asia rely on fish caught to provide their protein & minerals. With climate change expected to impact agricultural production, people are going to rely more than ever on fish for their nutritional needs.

MARINE LIFE

On the surface, the world's oceans appear to be perfectly stable, an unchanging and expansive world unaffected by the exploits of humans. However, the drastic effects that climate change and global warming bring are starting to impact on our oceans and marine life significantly. These changes in temperature and climate have the ability to drastically reduce our marine food supplies as well as the oceans natural ability to absorb carbon.

Climate change will have an impact on both living and non-living organisms in the ocean. Many marine species can only survive in very specific water temperatures. Cod in the North Atlantic, for example, require water temperature conditions below 12 degrees Celsius in order to live and reproduce. Cod will struggle to adapt above that. Climate change will cause changes to water temperatures and oceanic currents, which could completely wipe out the fish species that are unable to adapt to such thermal changes.

Increased concentration of carbon dioxide in the oceans will lead to greater ocean acidification. Since the Industrial Revolution, the ocean has become 30% more acidic. Many fish species, especially shellfish, are extremely vulnerable to water acidity. Such populations of fish will not be able to survive or reproduce sufficiently in water that is becoming increasingly acidic. The increase of carbon content in the water is also reducing the ocean's role as a natural carbon absorbent. In other words,

the oceans are becoming overly saturated with carbon, reducing its ability, like trees, to absorb carbon from the atmosphere. This is concerning considering the ocean contains more than 50 times as much carbon as the atmosphere. If the oceans are not drawing in carbon dioxide, more will drift into the atmosphere increasing the greenhouse effect.

Coral reefs are life-supporting ecosystems in the ocean and host amongst the greatest biodiversity on Earth. As the climate and ocean temperatures change, coral bleaching – the process whereby coral becomes completely white and unable to support other marine life – occurs as a result. When corals experience bleaching they are subject to decay and stress. As a result the fish populations that depend on them are also affected. In 2005, the US lost half of its coral reefs on the Caribbean coastline in one year due to a massive bleaching event caused by changing weather patterns that brought about colder temperatures in the water.

The melting of the polar ice caps as a result of global warming is another concern which is sending extremely large amounts of freshwater into the world's oceans. It is estimated that global sea levels could rise as much as 75m if the Arctic ice caps melted. Such melting would have devastating effects for low-lying coastal ecosystems throughout the world, especially mangroves, swamps and lagoons, where many juvenile fish are born.

ARE WE CONSUMING MORE THAN THE PLANET CAN PROVIDE?

Currently, there is enough food to feed as many as 10-billion people – more than the global population we expect to reach by 2050. In fact, for the past two decades, the rate of global food production has increased faster than the rate of global population growth. In spite of the incredible amount of food produced around the globe, there are still close to one billion hungry people on the planet. 21 000 people die every day from hunger-related causes. That's one person every four seconds. The reason behind the world hunger crisis is not due to a lack of global food production. Rather, it is a result of the fact that as much as one-third of the food we produce is used to feed animals, while another one-third goes to waste. Despite widespread beliefs and assumptions, the reality is we do not need to place endless pressure on Earth to provide enough food for the world, at least not for the foresee-able future. Inequality is the prevailing reason for world hunger and starvation.

Although we produce so much food, more than we actually need, the agricultural system is neither environmentally nor economically sustainable. Our troubling system provides half the world's population with an overwhelming access to food, whilst the other half struggles to provide for its most basic nutritional needs. As much as 40% of the food in the US alone is thrown away or left uneaten. This culture of waste is experienced across the food industry from the farm to the fork. This is especially the case in wealthy societies where food is affordable and in abundance. In grocery stores, meats, fruits and vegetables are thrown in the garbage and sent to landfills if they pass the expiry date. At the farm, if produce appears unappeal-ing due to shape or blemish, they are

"IT TAKES TWENTY-ONE POUNDS OF PROTEIN FED TO A CALF TO PRODUCE A SINGLE POUND OF ANIMAL PROTEIN FOR HUMANS. WE GET BACK LESS THAN 5 PERCENT OF WHAT WE PUT IN."
- PETER SINGER

"FOOD WASTE HAPPENS BOTH AT THE PRODUCTION LEVEL AND THE CONSUMPTION LEVEL. FROM FARM TO FORK."
– DR. PATRIZIA LA TRECCHIA

usually thrown in the trash, with the expectation that consumers wont purchase the product. And in our homes, we throw away incredible amounts of food instead of preserving, consuming or recycling it.

The truth is the Earth is perfectly capable of supplying the needs of our current population and more. But sadly, due to our existing consumption habits and farming methods, this will not be sustainable in the long run. We can provide for a surplus of food now, but may not be able to do so in the future.

The consequences of our unsustainable consumption habits and farming methods will drastically impact marine ecosystems, perhaps more than any other. As it stands, around 30% of edible fish and seafood species have declined by 90% since the Industrial Revolution. Unfortunately, this drop means that the collapse of these fisheries is imminent. At current rates, it is expected that all commercial fish will be lost by the year 2048. The unsustainable and aggressive nature of the fishing industry must come to an end if we are to see a future for this food source and the entire marine ecosystem.

Topsoil is another important factor to discuss. We tend to think of soil as a renewable resource – one that is constantly being replenished by decaying matter. But worldwide trends suggest that we may need to rethink that common understanding, not because our scientific knowledge is incorrect but rather because our behaviour has resulted in depletion at rates that exceed a natural rate of replenishment. Unsustainable farming operations that lead directly to deforestation and soil erosion are the prevailing reasons we are losing more topsoil every year. It is estimated that at the current rates of soil degradation, we have around 60 years of usable topsoil remaining, while some 40% of soil used for agriculture around the world is said to be degraded. Because of unsustainable farming operations that strip the soil of carbon, making it less fertile, topsoil is being lost at between 10 and 40 times the rate at which it can naturally be replenished. As a result, our farmland will become less and less productive. This situation of soil degradation will mean that we will produce 30% less food over the next 20-50 years, at a time when demand for food is expected to increase by 50%.

Then there is the challenge of the growing middle class. As more and more people in countries like China, India and Brazil become wealthier, their demand for meat and other protein-rich products derived from livestock will naturally increase. Already, as much as one-third of the food we produce goes towards feeding livestock, and with such an increased demand for livestock-related products, this will need to triple by mid-century. If the trend continues, such a situation will lead to more devastating rates of deforestation, greenhouse gas emissions and soil erosion.

WHAT METHODS CAN WE ADOPT TO SOLVE THESE ISSUES?

The next few decades that lie ahead will prove to be an extremely challenging time for the agriculture industry. In order to ensure a healthy and sustainable future for our planet, we need to find the means to provide an incredible amount of food for our global population of seven-billion people. Not only that, but we will need to increase production immensely as the world population is set to increase to over nine-billion by 2050. At the same time, we need to do so whilst reducing our impact on the environment and our atmosphere. Both of these objectives will place a great amount of responsibility and pressure on modern agricultural practices. The future of the food industry will depend on our ability to meet demands without depleting or degrading the capacity of the planet to produce food in the future.

It becomes necessary for us to 'sustainably intensify' our farming practices. But doing so could be extremely difficult given the non-renewable nature of many of the resources that are fundamental to agriculture, such as sufficient land space, nutritional soil and a clean water supply.

Fortunately, there are innovative technologies in place and in development that provide us with the opportunity to reduce the pollution and wastage of resources within the agriculture industry. There are four promising technologies and practices already available that can greatly assist us in overcoming some of the challenges that lie ahead. These include genetic modification, hydroponic agriculture, precision agriculture and organic farming.

"ALL THE WORLD'S NEARLY ONE BILLION HUNGRY PEOPLE COULD BE LIFTED OUT OF MALNOURISHMENT ON LESS THAN A QUARTER OF THE FOOD THAT IS WASTED IN THE US, UK AND EUROPE."
– TRISTRAM STUART

HYDROPONIC AGRICULTURE

One of the more pressing issues surrounding the future of agriculture is the quality of our topsoil is degrading by the day. Currently, land capable of growing crops only occupies around 3% of Earth's surface. Due to our unsustainable industrial farming operations, rapid urbanisation and population growth, the amount and quality of topsoil is quickly reducing. Fortunately, a new technique of farming known as hydroponic farming is allowing us to grow crops whilst alleviating the heavy burden on the world's non-renewable topsoil resources. Hydroponics is the fastest growing sector of agriculture, and could very well become a leading form of agriculture in the future.

Through experience, humans have understood over the centuries that if you give a plant exactly what it needs, when it needs it and in the right amount, then the plant will be as healthy as possible. Hydroponic agriculture has the incredible ability to achieve just that. Hydroponic farming is an innovative method of growing plants and crops using mineral nutrients solutions in water, and is done in the complete absence of soil. Certain nutrients that enhance plant growth, such as calcium or magnesium, are injected into water, which is then fed to plant roots. This approach allows the plant to absorb nutrients more efficiently and with far less effort than soil-based farming.

A variety of plants can be grown in a hydroponic environment. As these plants are usually grown in a greenhouse facility, the conditions can be tightly controlled for maximum food production. High-quality foods can thus be produced almost anywhere in the world, regardless of weather, soil conditions and seasons. Farmers have the ability to constantly monitor the temperature, humidity and water acidity of the plants environment – essential factors that influence crop growth.

With the problems posed by pests, hail, frost, floods and soil erosion removed, and with a rich supply of nutrients, food production in hydroponic environments is significantly higher than traditional farming methods. Hydroponic farming has also been used to enhance the nutritional value of the foods grown.

Hydroponic farming also requires less water compared to traditional farming methods. Hydroponics crops use as little as 5% of the amount of water as a regular farm to produce the same amount of food. Through the advancement of hydroponics agriculture, we are now ultimately accelerating the rate of growth and nutritional value of crops whilst reducing the consumption and wastage of two vital resources – water and soil. Hydroponics is also suitable for environments with limited land, as it produces about three to six times the harvest of traditionally farmed crops. Hydroponic technology will play a valuable role in the future of agriculture. As the world's population grows and its spending power increases, this technology will be essential to ensure that we maximise food supply and reduce the wastage of precious resources.

HYDROPONIC FARMING
USES UP TO:

50% **90%** **60%**

LESS LAND   LESS WATER   LESS FERTILISER

TO GROW THE SAME AMOUNT OF CROPS
AS SOIL BASED FARMING

GENETIC MODIFICATION

Surprisingly, genetic modification is not a recent breakthrough in agriculture. People have been manipulating the genetic make-up of plants and animals for countless generations using crossbreeding and cross-pollination strategies. Aided by technology, however, the processes involved in selecting and replicating crops with the most desirable characteristics, such as disease resistance and nutritional value, has become even more accurate and advanced. Manipulating genetics to create more superior, durable and nutritional foods is incredible testimony to human ingenuity and creativity.

Technology has improved so dramatically of late that we are now able to produce crops of far greater yields, higher nutritional value and greater resistance to pests and diseases. Through genetic modification, we are also granted the opportunity to drastically improve the efficiency of food production systems. From a food security point of view, this is a promising step forward.

Advances in genetic engineering have massive potential to help us meet the world's growing food demands by resolving the issues of food scarcity and security. At the same time, the biotechnology can reduce the negative environmental impacts of industrial agriculture. For example, by creating pest and disease deterrent foods, we can reduce the need for pesticides. We can also create crops that require less water to grow. The environmental benefits of the biological advancements also results in less total carbon dioxide emissions. In 2012, it was estimated that those biologically modified crops resulted in the removal of 27-billion kg's of carbon dioxide from the atmosphere. This is equivalent to removing 11.9-million cars from the road for one year.

Another advantage of genetic engineering that will be essential for the future is that it will allow us to grow crops in a much shorter space of time. Cultivating a potato variety through conventional methods, for example, can take up to 15 years. In contrast, producing a potato with a superior genetic code can take less than six months. Because the growing threats of climate change, soil degradation and water scarcity all pose significant threats to the agriculture industry, such benefits could prove extremely valuable to humanity.

PRECISION FARMING

Throughout the history of agriculture, farmers have learnt through research and experience how to observe and anticipate weather patterns, soil conditions and pollination processes, all of which contributed to the betterment of crop production. Over time, the technology used to monitor such conditions has improved dramatically, allowing farmers to use precise tactics to increase their crop yields. Fortunately, these skills and technologies can assist us by ensuring more sustainable and efficient methods of crop production for the future.

One such approach is known as precision agriculture. This advanced approach to farming makes use of progressive technologies that help farmers manage their crops and livestock and increase productivity substantially. With precision agriculture, farmers are able to use resources such as soil and water more efficiently and effectively with the aid of modern technology. Farmers are able to take extremely large fields of crops and manage them as if they were smaller fields. This reduces the mismanagement of time and resources and increases the performance of the land.

One of the more promising tools for precision agriculture is that of geographical information systems (GIS). By using digital maps retrieved from aerial imagery from satellites, farmers can single out areas where natural conditions are best for farming. Farmers can visually identify critical factors like soil quality and types, water drainage levels and land contours through such images. By understanding these conditions, farmers can be more strategic of which land to cultivate, and for what purposes.

The opportunities these technologies provide helps farmers take large fields and divide them into smaller management zones for more precise treatment and attention. Using small management zones reduces the resource wastage whilst increasing crop yields. If the soil in one area is able to retain water better, crops can then be planted more densely and irrigation can be used more sparingly. With precision agriculture technology, farmers are now able to identify these 'hot spots' and change their farming methods accordingly to maximise production.

In an ideal situation, each plant or animal should be managed according to its own unique conditions and circumstances. This would maximise efficiency. Unfortunately, due to the sheer amounts of food demanded from industrial agriculture, farmers cannot tend to every individual crop or animal. However, if a farmer can manage a progressively smaller group, then there is huge potential to increase productivity. Precision farming methods can help farmers achieve this goal.

DID YOU KNOW?

organic farming consumes up to 40 percent less energy than conventional industrial farming, & support higher levels of wildlife on farms. Buying more organic food can reduce your food footprint by around 15 percent.

ORGANIC FARMING

In the wake of both the devastating environmental impacts and health concerns related to industrial agricultural operations, the organic food market has grown substantially over the last 15 years. Organic farming is a method of growing crops and rearing livestock that attempts to do so without the use of pesticides and fertilisers. The organic farming movement seeks to be environmentally sustainable and socially responsible. There is strong focus on soil regeneration, water conservation and animal welfare. Other fundamental principles include the reduction of agriculture-related pollution and biodiversity maintenance within the system.

Dissatisfied with the increasing problems of industrial farming practices, organic farmers seek to improve the quality and health benefits of foods by reducing unnatural and unsustainable farming methods. Organic farming looks to more pre-industrial ways of farming foods, whereby the negative effects of industrial farming are reduced or completely removed. Organic farmers take a holistic approach to agriculture that respects and harnesses the power of natural processes to build healthy systems across the ecology of the farm. Crops are rested and rotated, fertilisers are made from organic matter as opposed to engineered substances, crops are grown seasonally, and plants are left to flourish in their natural habitat. There is a greater respect for and conservation of water, far less exploitation of land and topsoil, and an increase in biodiversity and cross-pollination on farms by plants and animals. The approach seeks to reduce the environmental impact of the industry, and increase the nutritional value and health benefits of our foods.

Free-range farming, an extension of organic farming concentrating on livestock, focuses on improving the livelihood of farm animals, and in so doing, improves the quality of food they produce. Animals are granted access to roam freely in open fields and eat their naturally preferred diets of grass, as opposed to being held in captivity and fed corn-based diets. Although on many farms the outdoor roaming area is fenced off, they are generally large enough to offer the opportunity for the animals to experience a measure of freedom. This provides them with exposure to clean outdoor air and sunlight, as well as the opportunity to socialise with their kind. Such methods allow livestock to live relatively happy and pleasant lives.

In essence, free-range farm animals live stress-free lives. Due to the natural environments the animals find themselves in, free-range animals are significantly healthier than those kept in captivity. A recent study showed that organic milk has on average 68% higher levels of the essential fatty acid omega-3 than non-organic milk.

HOW CAN WE CONSUME MORE SUSTAINABLY?

Consuming more sustainably starts with one simple realisation. Governments, organisations and individuals worldwide must begin to recognise that the natural environment upon which we continuously place heavy demands has very real limits. The environment has a particular threshold that, if surpassed, will be unable to supply us the fundamental ingredients needed to continue producing food. The decisions we make regarding food and agriculture, both in the long term and on a daily basis, large or small, need to take into account the limited nature of life-supporting resources.

The technologies we develop and adopt, the strict policies and economic structures that governments set in motion, as well as the final decisions that the individual consumer make, will all contribute towards making the food industry more sustainable. This will also lessen our environmental impact as the dominant consumers on the planet.

Human ingenuity has saved us time and time again in the past. If it weren't for the sophisticated and effective technology that has been developed over time, we undoubtedly would not have nearly enough food to feed the world's growing population. Technology has been the invaluable tool that has allowed us to produce food in abundance. It will be critical for us to find ways of living within Earth's limits, and technology can help us reach that point. We have already developed certain technologies and methods of farming that can reduce our environmental footprint – precision agriculture, genetic modification, hydroponic farming and organic farming. Such technologies and methods need to consistently improve, become more reliable, and most importantly, produce greater yields whilst reducing their environmental impact. Investing in technology and smart practices is likely the only solution that will allow us to operate sustainably in a resource-constrained world.

DID YOU KNOW?

Currently less than 1% of the ocean is protected, although by 2020, the international community has agreed to raise this to 10%.

"THE GREAT CHALLENGE OF THE TWENTY-FIRST CENTURY IS TO RAISE PEOPLE EVERYWHERE TO A DECENT STANDARD OF LIVING WHILE PRESERVING AS MUCH OF THE REST OF LIFE AS POSSIBLE."

- EDWARD O. WILSON

"THE AVERAGE SUPERMARKET IN THE U.S. WASTES 10% OF ITS FOOD."
– PETER LENHER

DID YOU KNOW?

Meat is four times more demanding than grains. If consumers would gravitate toward less intesive foods, energy use would drop.

As these technologies bring about greater yields and volumes of foods, some may take advantage and offset the environmental benefits by abusing these technologies. For instance, bigger and better fishing vessels can capture larger quantities of fish, so fishermen can return with far greater yields than in the past. Or, more extensive irrigation systems will allow for more extensive fields of crops to be watered more easily, leading to an abuse and exploitation of our water resource. While these technologies may lead to increased food yields, they are unsustainable over the long run and ultimately disastrous from an environmental perspective. This is where governments need to step in and intervene.

Governments are regulators that have the power to set in place strict policies that can prevent certain activities from happening. Governments have the ability to protect depleting fish species by putting in place strict regulations on fishing permits, limits, zones and types of fish being caught. This has been highly effective in many countries such as Canada, Australia and Norway. These countries have reversed the decline of fish population, simply because of government intervention. Brazil once had the highest rates of deforestation in the world. However, when the Brazilian government realised the devastation it was causing in the early 1990s, they decided intervention was necessary. Since then, the rate of deforestation in Brazil dropped by 20% between 1995 and 2013, when demand for forest products and land for pastures soared. Governments have the power to penalise, tax or incentivise any activity or company that they feel could be either harmful or beneficial to the environment.

Unfortunately, economic theory of supply and demand can overcome government policy. If certain products are in extremely

2400 LITRES
THE AMOUNT OF WATER NEEDED
TO PRODUCE A 150G HAMBURGER

135 LITRES
THE AMOUNT OF WATER NEEDED
TO PRODUCE ONE EGG

13 LITRES
THE AMOUNT OF WATER NEEDED
TO PRODUCE ONE TOMATO

"25% OF ALL THE WATER THAT IS CONSUMED IN THE U.S. IS USED ON CROPS THAT NOBODY WILL EVER EAT."
– PETER LENHER

high demand, a penalty or tax imposed by governments on producers may be insufficient in reducing or deterring harmful activity. The final solution therefore boils down to the very consumer.

Most of the time, we have the ability to choose which foods we purchase and consume. When this is the case, we are indirectly supporting the products that we buy. For instance, if we purchase eggs that have been delivered by chickens in a factory farm, essentially we are supporting unethical forms of farming. On the other hand, if we were to purchase eggs that have been delivered by chickens that are free-range, we are able to support healthier and more ethical farming methods. If we eat at a restaurant and choose to eat a particular fish that is highly endangered, we are contributing to the demand of such species and to the further depletion of their populations. The continuation of unsustainable agricultural operations hinges on the very decisions made by the everyday consumer.

If we care for animals and wish to see the recognition of animal rights, then we should be aware of what livestock products we are buying, and then act appropriately. This concept doesn't only apply to animals, though. If we care for the health of the environment, and wish to contribute towards the stewarding of the planet, then we should become regular buyers of local, organic and seasonal foods. With enough collective action, eventually the demand for food from unsustainable operations will be reduced and the re-adoption of sustainable methods of farming could once again become industry standard.

DID YOU KNOW?

In general, cheaper fruits & vegetables require less fertiliser, pesticide, land & energy than more expensive ones. For instance, switching from strawberries to oranges in your fruit salad cuts pesticide use by half and fertilizer use by a factor of 10.

TRANSPORT

HOW DOES MODERN TRANSPORT DIFFER TO THAT OF THE PAST? WHAT IS THE RELATIONSHIP BETWEEN GLOBALISATION AND TRANSPORT?

WHAT OPPORTUNITIES DOES MODERN TRANSPORT PROVIDE? WHAT ARE THE PROBLEMS WITH MODERN DAY TRANSPORT?

ARE THERE MORE ECO-FRIENDLY WAYS TO TRAVEL? WHAT FUEL-EFFICIENT TECHNOLOGIES ARE AVAILABLE?

CAN TRANSPORT BECOME MORE SUSTAINABLE?

HOW DOES MODERN TRANSPORT DIFFER TO THAT OF THE PAST?

The world of transport is dynamic and has evolved over centuries as a result of historic breakthroughs in technology. Without a doubt, the wheel, invented in about 3 500 BC, has been the most significant invention in the history of transport. The invention of the wheel led to the horse-drawn carriage, the bicycle, the steam engine and the automobile. Even airplanes use wheels, and would be unable to take off or land without them. The nature of transportation is that it continues to evolve and transform as more effective and efficient technologies emerge. Every breakthrough in transport technology has built upon the technologies of previous inventions. For example, the steam train led to the electric train which evolved into the bullet train, and the sailboat led to the steam-powered ship. A fascinating characteristic of modern-day transport is that while the modes have remained somewhat similar, the technologies are becoming more efficient and higher performing. Transport today represents the pinnacle of all the prior innovations and achievements that have ever emerged in the field.

Another significant step in the evolution of the transportation industry has been the discovery and adoption of fossil fuels. Early explorers and traders used natural sources to power their vessels and vehicles; they harnessed wind energy to sail their ships, or used horses to pull their carriages. But the discovery of fossil fuels and the newfound ability to harness their explosive power changed this completely. It became clear that fossil fuels had an abundance of energy that could be harnessed when burned.

DID YOU KNOW?

Henry Ford is often credited with making cars affordable through the mass production of vehicles. He developed the assembly line of production which revolutionised the industry.

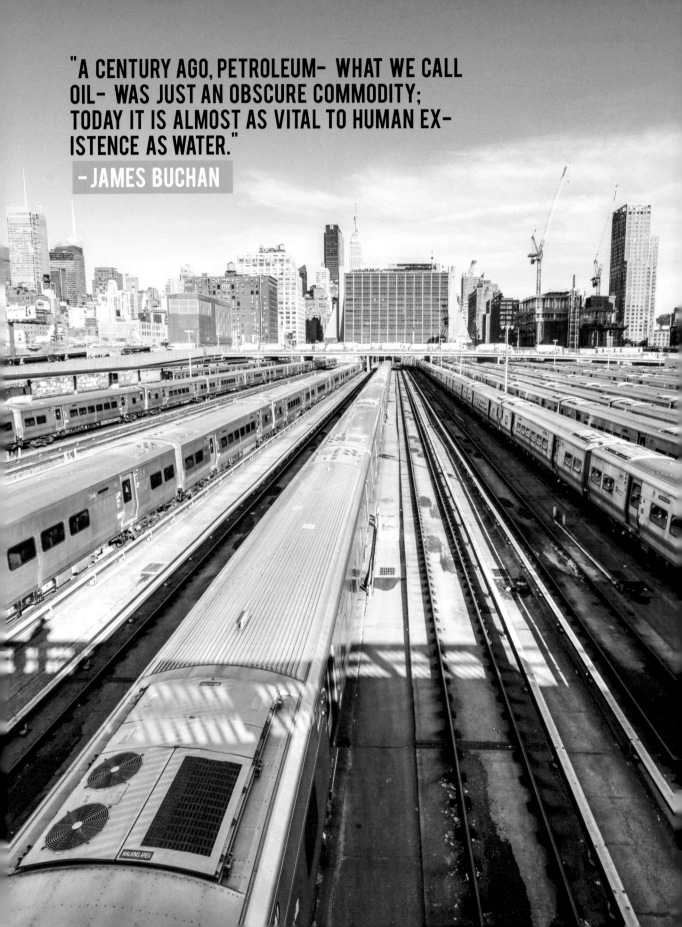

"A CENTURY AGO, PETROLEUM— WHAT WE CALL OIL— WAS JUST AN OBSCURE COMMODITY; TODAY IT IS ALMOST AS VITAL TO HUMAN EXISTENCE AS WATER."

– JAMES BUCHAN

This energy from fossil fuels was more than sufficient to power vehicles, and could also be stored and harnessed at will. Fossil fuels also provided a more reliable and consistent source of energy than wind energy or horse labour. This discovery drastically transformed the speed and efficiency of transportation. For example, steam-powered ocean liners in the 19th century were able to cross the Atlantic in 15 days, compared to the two months it took for sailing ships that used wind power to power their boats during the 16th century. Today, the performance and reliability of fossil fuels as a power source has evolved to a point where almost all transportation is completely reliant on them.

Not only have our methods of transport continued to evolve over time, but so too has the nature of transport. Transportation today consists of a lot more than just the movement of people, although it is estimated that there are around 500 000 people flying across the world at any given moment. The movement of raw materials, food and other consumer goods are now key components in the global transportation system. Raw materials such as timber or coal, as well as food, water and consumer products such as clothing, furniture, and electronics are transported around the world in large quantities every day. Transport continues to become more effective and affordable, which has allowed the importing and exporting of goods to become easier and cheaper. The concept of a 'global product' is becoming more widespread, which is increasing the demand for goods and materials to be delivered across the world. In the global transportation system, this is referred to as commercial transport, and its importance in the global economy has increased substantially in recent times. This has fuelled the need to improve upon existing modes of transport by increasing performance.

DID YOU KNOW?

There are already around 2 billion cars & commercial vehicles on the world's roads, and nearly 100 million new vehicles are being added every year!

IST
Palma Mallorca
Moskau DME
Brüssel
Helsinki
Doha
Helsinki
Rimini
Amsterdam
Frankfurt

WHAT IS THE RELATIONSHIP BETWEEN GLOBALISATION AND TRANSPORT?

Although transportation predates globalisation, the impact of globalisation on modern transportation has been profound. Both people and goods have been moving around the globe for hundreds of years. What has become evident in recent times, though, is that globalisation has set a higher standard for the volumes, speed, capacity and efficiency of transportation systems. The relationship between globalisation and transport is complex, yet they are completely dependent upon one another. Transportation is one of the least obvious, but most critical, components of the global economy, and is referred to as the enabling factor that allows globalisation to progress. Without the high efficiency of transport systems today, the world would not be as connected as it now is. The influence of modern-day transport on our everyday lives is therefore more significant than we may imagine.

Even today, no nation on Earth is completely self-sufficient. Every country is involved, to some degree, in international trade. This is a result of the fact that no single country has internal access to every natural resource within its borders.

Consider a natural resource such as coal. Some countries have large coal reserves, while others have none at all. Coal is a highly valued natural resource as it has many important uses, most notably to produce electricity. Countries without coal need to gain access to it, and so they trade with countries that do. This leads to the demand for the importing and exporting of coal between nations. Clothing is another example of a globally traded commodity. For example, cotton or raw silk may be harvested in Brazil, transported across the world for manufacturing in China, then transported to your location as a finished product. The same process takes place for almost every other product available in our supermarkets or department stores nowadays.

Global products such as these are the driving forces behind global transportation. Global products are the result of our ability to use modern transport systems to obtain global resources. Manufacturing companies continually search for the most affordable materials, labour and locations, regardless of geographical whereabouts. A company may discover that development and delivery costs are lower in a foreign country, as a result of the lower wages of foreign employees. This may lead the company to close its local factories and use the foreign location for manufacturing, before importing the finished products back to their own country. However, international trade cannot take place without an effective global transportation network.

Globalisation drastically transforms nations, as well as the individuals and communities that live within them. Take China, the most populous country on Earth. China has become one of the most powerful economies in the world, second only to the US. This is a result of the fact that it has taken advantage of the globalisation of consumer goods. In 2011, China alone produced over 320-million personal computers. This accounted for over 90% of all personal computers made that year. China also made seven out of every ten pairs of shoes that year, accounting for 70% of all shoes made. China has indeed become the world's manufacturing powerhouse and taken full advantage of modern transportation.

But these goods are not consumed only in China; they are distributed to markets across the world. Producing billions of products in China and delivering them worldwide every day requires an extensive and sophisticated transportation network. Globalisation has indeed been the spearhead in transforming China's economy. But without advances in transportation, this globalised network would be unsuccessful. Globalisation advances transportation, and vice versa.

The influence of transport on international trade has had a greater impact on our lives than just the availability of international products. It has also significantly improved the standard of living and quality of life for millions of people on Earth. Without international trade, people would be limited to and solely dependent on the resources available within their countries or local areas. Globalised transportation makes a vast array of products and services available across the world. Many of these are vital for human health and development, such as medical supplies, food, education, financial services, technology and building materials.

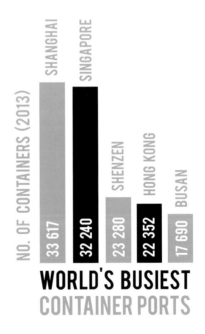

NO. OF CONTAINERS (2013)

SHANGHAI 33 617
SINGAPORE 32 240
SHENZEN 23 280
HONG KONG 22 352
BUSAN 17 690

WORLD'S BUSIEST CONTAINER PORTS

"MEASURED IN TIME OF TRANSPORT AND COMMUNICATION, THE WHOLE ROUND GLOBE IS NOW SMALLER THAN A EUROPEAN COUNTRY WAS A HUNDRED YEARS AGO."

– JOHN BOYD ORR

WHAT OPPORTUNITIES DOES MODERN TRANSPORT PROVIDE?

Over the centuries transport has evolved into a powerful tool to meet human needs. It has also expanded our horizons and the opportunities associated with travel. When Christopher Columbus discovered the Americas in 1492, having led an expedition of only three ships, it was a groundbreaking moment in human history. Without question, that discovery, and the skills and effort it took to get there, was a remarkable achievement. Shortly thereafter, Vasco de Gama's successful voyage around the southern tip of Africa opened up the sea route trade between Europe and India for the first time. Prior to this, all trade between east and west had taken place via overland routes. Ocean travel thus transformed global trade between east and west.

In light of these achievements, think of the abundance of opportunities that modern transport provides today. In 1969, 477 years after Columbus's famous voyage, humans left our planet's atmosphere and landed on the moon. It was not only the bravery and ambition of the astronauts that made this possible, but the technology that was created to get them there. Today, humans can live in space for months at a time at the International Space Station. Visionary companies involved in space travel such as Virgin Galactic and Space X are now researching ways to make space exploration commercially viable. As space travel has historically been incredibly expensive, the vision of these companies and the challenges they are set to overcome may allow us to reach far beyond what we thought was possible. It will allow us to make new discoveries and provide a commercial future for space travel.

Transport allows us to expand our knowledge of the world and connectivity with others. It allows us the remarkable opportunity to engage with other cultures, countries, languages, technologies, and now, even our solar system. Incredible opportunities arise, purely as a result of the knowledge and experience we gain from travel.

DID YOU KNOW?

The world's largest container ship – the CLSC Globe – is 400m long, 60m wide, & can carry up to 19000 standard containers.
If stacked end to end, the containers would be 5 times the height of mount Everest.

"I THINK WE ARE AT THE DAWN OF A NEW ERA IN COMMERCIAL SPACE EXPLORATION."
-ELON MUSK

Transport presents another major advantage in the field of international aid and relief initiatives. Delivering food and medical supplies to some of the world's most impoverished communities is now achieved more than ever before, thanks to the innovations and efficiencies of modern transport. Some of the world's poorest communities are situated in the most remote and inaccessible locations on Earth. In order to provide relief to them, whether it be education, food, water or medical care, effective modes of transport are critical.

Disaster relief is another life-saving opportunity provided by modern transport. Consider, for example, how helicopters are able to swiftly deliver aid and assistance in times of crisis to isolated, remote communities in jungles, deserts, mountains and on islands. Disaster relief strategies are dependent on sophisticated and effective transport systems. Think of a natural disaster such as a tsunami or tropical cyclone. Thanks to modern technology, such natural disasters can often be predicted. Efficient transport systems then allow people extra time to prepare or evacuate accordingly. In the wake of the disaster, transport allows people to be evacuated, as well as brings aid workers and relief to the affected areas, saving many lives in the process.

Transport played a major role in saving lives after the devastating Indian Ocean tsunami in December 2004. India, for example, deployed 32 naval ships, seven aircraft and 20 helicopters to some of the affected regions to provide relief to the victims. The US deployed 48 helicopters and 10 large navy ships. These ships were able to provide around 340 000 litres of fresh water per day, which was then dispatched and distributed by the helicopters to isolated areas. The US also deployed a 1 000-bed hospital ship that provided medical support to those affected. The relief efforts from one of the worst natural disasters known to man were completely and utterly reliant on modern transportation systems, and without its involvement, tens of thousands more people would have perished in the aftermath of the event.

BUSIEST AIRPORTS (2014) BY NUMBER OF PASSENGERS:

DUBAI 69 MILLION

LONDON 68 MILLION

HONG KONG 63 MILLION

WHAT ARE THE PROBLEMS WITH MODERN DAY TRANSPORT?

It may not seem like it, but the reality is from an environmental and economic point of view, modern transport is a broken system. Without a doubt, the transportation systems available to us today are more reliable and effective than ever before. But there are underlying problems that cause concern to even the most optimistic observers. The rapid increase in urbanisation, otherwise known as urban sprawl, is creating a culture that promotes the adoption of personal vehicle ownership in cities all over the world. The great amounts of pollution that are emitted by motorised transport on a daily basis are of critical concern, as the pollutants are contributing directly to global warming. Our dependence on oil as a fuel source for the majority of our transport systems continues to have a profoundly negative impact on the natural environment. At the same time, the quantity of oil available is heavily

controlled, and limited by global politics. The increasing amount of raw materials needed to provide for the rising demand for motorised transport is also placing enormous strain on the natural environment and its valuable resources.

Motorised transport leads to many problems, especially on the environment that surrounds cities. But as the world's population continues to grow and become more urbanised, transport will play an increasingly bigger role in ensuring our cities function and operate effectively. Projections show that urbanisation combined with the overall growth of the world's population could add another 2.5-billion people to urban populations by 2050. As much as 90% of the increase will be concentrated in Asia and Africa, where the transportation systems are not as advanced as many developed countries.

"THE REALITY IS, GAS PRICES SHOULD BE MUCH MORE EXPENSIVE THAN THEY ARE BECAUSE WE'RE NOT INCORPORATING THE TRUE DAMAGE TO THE ENVIRONMENT AND THE HIDDEN COSTS OF MINING OIL AND TRANSPORTING IT."
–ELON MUSK

DID YOU KNOW?

Traffic congestion represents a major economic problem because of the many working hours lost each day from sitting in traffic jams. The average speed of cars in Mexico City is 4kph in the rush hour.

DID YOU KNOW?

Globally, the transportation industry contributes around 23% of all carbon dioxide emissions per year, second only to electricity generation, which accounts for around 42%.

POLLUTION & GLOBAL WARMING

Global awareness of the severe pollution caused by motorised transportation started growing midway through the 20th century, and as the century drew to a close, transportation was recognised as one of the leading contributors to greenhouse gas emissions. Running our transport systems on oil – in the form of petroleum and diesel – results in large amounts of carbon being released into the atmosphere. It is estimated that vehicles throughout the world burn around 960-billion litres of fuel every year. Most notably these gases lead directly to global warming and climate change. In the US alone, transport is responsible for approximately one-third of all greenhouse gas emissions. It is very clear that reducing the emissions caused by modern transportation is a vital step in reversing the effects of global warming.

The challenge with air pollution caused by transport is that it is made up of primary and secondary pollution – both of which are environmentally problematic. Primary pollutants are substances that are emitted directly into the atmosphere, such as carbon emissions, which are released when petroleum or diesel is burned. Secondary pollution occurs when these pollutants combine with other compounds and particles already present in the air. The best example of this is the process that takes place when carbon pollutants combine with water particles in the air to produce smog. Smog is now a major health concern in many cities around the world. In some areas of cities such as Beijing and Delhi, there are such dangerous levels of smog that people are compelled to wear protective masks to avoid inhaling the polluted air, which contains toxins such as sulphur dioxide and carbon monoxide.

The consequences of global warming pose great damage risks to transport infrastructure, which will create difficulties for transportation systems to operate effectively. The changes in temperature, the increase in intense weather events and rising of sea levels could potentially have major implications upon the operation and maintenance of transport infrastructure. This could lead to the increased risk of disruption, damage and failure of transport systems. It is estimated that developing countries will need to spend somewhere between $200-300-billion per year by 2020 to ensure that transport infrastructure – including roads, bridges and tunnels – are more resilient to the effects of climate change and global warming. In light of these challenges ahead, it will become crucial for us to adapt our transport systems and infrastructure to the inevitable changes we will confront.

VEHICLE MANUFACTURING

Countless numbers of vehicles are manufactured and produced every year in order to provide for the increasing demands of modern society. As populations in Africa, Asia and South America continue to soar and their process of industrialisation continues, the growth of the middle class has the potential to initiate an even greater demand for car ownership. Producing these vehicles requires vast amounts of natural resources and manufacturing materials, such as steel, aluminium, copper, rubber, plastics and glass. The average car alone uses over 1 000 kg's of steel. The iron ore that is used to manufacture the steel needs to first be mined and extracted from the earth. It then proceeds to undergo numerous manufacturing processes before it is converted into a usable material for vehicle production. Consider the amounts of materials needed to produce the countless number of trains, busses, airplanes and ships that are produced every year. In 2014, more than 70-million vehicles were produced and sold worldwide. All the resources used to produce them were sourced from the natural environment.

Every raw material used in manufacturing vehicles is extracted from the earth. They are then engineered and chemically altered into the new materials to create different vehicle parts. Sand is melted and transformed into glass, oil is refined and converted into rubber, and livestock is reared in order to produce leather for seats. All of these material transformation processes require excessive amounts of heat and energy, and emit large quantities of pollution in the process. When these materials are not locally available they must be imported from other countries and transported to the manufacturing plant. Thus, the vehicle manufacturing process has a far wider environmental impact than one would think. Some experts have calculated that the process of producing a new car creates as much carbon pollution as driving it throughout its lifespan.

As we are manufacturing hundreds of thousands of vehicles every day, we are simultaneously disposing of old ones. Thousands of old vehicles are thrown into landfill sites every day, without any of the valuable materials being removed for recycling purposes. Instead of stripping the old vehicles for materials that can undergo recycling processes, we instead dispose of them to landfill sites, where the opportunity to recycle is lost.

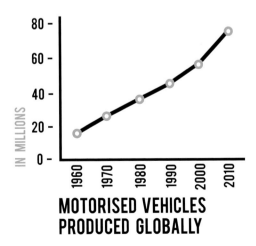

MOTORISED VEHICLES
PRODUCED GLOBALLY

"WE AREN'T ADDICTED TO OIL, BUT OUR CARS ARE."
– JAMES WOOLSEY

DEPENDENCE ON OIL

Oil insecurity, a concept of paramount concern in the global economy and transport industry, ultimately means that modern transport is vulnerable to what are called 'exogenous factors', or factors beyond one's control. No single individual controls or determines the price of oil. One country cannot dictate to another how much oil it can produce, or the selling price. In fact, prices and quantities of oil produced are determined by international supply and demand: if the US demands more oil from Saudi Arabia, for example, the price of petrol will likely increase elsewhere around the world. This is simply due to the economic principle of supply and demand, which states that the less available a product or resource is, or the greater the demand, the higher the price. The unfortunate thing about this situation is that it doesn't just affect a select few, but rather anyone who is involved in, or benefits from, the global transportation system.

Oil is arguably the most important driving force of the global economy, and changes in the price have significant effects on economic growth and welfare around the world. In 1973, shortly before the oil crisis, the price of a barrel of oil was around $19. In 2008, the price reached a peak, where it was sitting at around $145 per barrel. Unfortunately, when oil is in scarce supply, it is the poorer nations that suffer the most, as they are unable to afford the higher prices. Their economies suffer greatly as a result.

We produce and consume approximately 34-billion barrels of oil per year, the large majority of which are used for transportation. As we have already consumed most of the 'easily accessible' oil, mining companies now have to dig even deeper below the surface to extract the valuable resources. Not only are the environmental impacts from this scenario devastating, but so too are the economic consequences. As it becomes harder to find and extract oil, the price increases. This has a great affect on our every day lives as the price of oil affects the price of almost everything else. Oil is not only used as a fuel source for driving vehicles, but is also used to operate machinery in factories and to make petrochemical-based products such as plastics and rubber.

To put it simply, global transportation allows for the improvement of global welfare. But our dependence on oil is hindering our ability to achieve this. That is the biggest problem with modern transport systems. And the problem is worse now that our reliance on fossil fuels to power and maintain the volumes, efficiency and capacity of our transport systems is at an all-time high.

URBAN SPRAWL

Urban sprawl is a major factor contributing to the problems associated with, and demand for, motorised transport, especially in car-oriented cities currently undergoing the process of urbanisation. Essentially a form of urbanisation, urban sprawl is defined as the uncontrolled expansion of cities due to the rapid influx of people from the rural countryside. Cities with a notorious reputation for urban sprawl include Sao Paulo in Brazil, Lagos in Nigeria, Johannesburg in South Africa and Phoenix in the US. Every one of these cities has experienced a dramatic increase in human population, and have often times failed to provide the necessary planning and infrastructure to meet demands.

Cities experiencing rapid economic and population growth generally follow a similar trend that leads to urban sprawl. During the urbanisation process, people flock into the city from rural areas, resulting in a greater density within the city centre. The population of city inhabitants remains heavily concentrated in the city core, with a rapid decline in settlement towards the periphery. Then, as economic growth and public transport networks expand, people begin to move towards the suburbs, gradually softening the population density in the city centre. This generally takes place when the city reaches a certain stage of economic development.

Among the many problems associated with urban sprawl is that it creates a desperate need for increased volumes of motorised vehicles, and in particular, vehicles designed for individual transport. One of the biggest environmental concerns with sprawl is that it leads to increased driving which, in turn, leads to higher levels of carbon emissions and air pollution in cities.

With increasing urban sprawl, many people live greater distances away from the city centre, where the majority of businesses are situated. Because of this, people commute to the city on a daily basis from their suburban homes. However, in most cities, public transport systems are either non-existent or inadequate, and seldom provide services to outlying areas. As a result, an interesting concept arises: transport poverty. In this situation households are forced to pay more for travel than they can reasonably afford. Because of the lack of affordable public transport, they are drawn into personal car ownership. This situation increases the demand for vehicles, which then leads to increased traffic and greater congestion. This situation is occurring all over the world, and so the demand for more vehicles continues to increase globally. Because urbanisation is likely to continue well into the foreseeable future, urban sprawl is quickly becoming an issue of major concern.

The term urban sprawl almost always has negative connotations. It is often criticised for causing severe environmental degradation and intensifying segregation within the city. All in all, urban sprawl contributes to the high numbers of vehicles, road infrastructure, fuel consumption and conversion of rural land into highways – all of which are environmentally damaging.

ARE THERE MORE ECO-FRIENDLY WAYS TO TRAVEL?

Transportation has the ability to improve global welfare and accelerate the development and growth of the economy. This is important as it provides the opportunity to improve the standards of living for billions of people around the world. Although modern transport continues to have a profoundly positive impact on the global population, the reality is that our dependence on oil hinders the potential of transport to achieve this long-term positive growth. In addition, our dependence on oil has increasingly negative impacts on the environment, particularly on the atmosphere, which is leading to degraded air quality and the detrimental transformation of our climate.

While fuel efficiency and material performance continue to improve with each new breakthrough, the truth is the overall volumes of fuel and materials required often outweigh these progressive developments. This is a similar argument to that of increased population growth: although from an individual perspective we are demanding less from the environment – as a result of our improvements in the efficiency and performance of technology – we are, however, collectively placing enormous pressure on Earth. While our transportation systems may be more environmentally friendly today than a few decades ago, the overall negative impact on the environment is at an all-time high. This poses an important question: are there more environmentally friendly ways of travelling that could reduce our carbon footprint?

It is important to understand the term 'environmentally friendly'. There is no

DID YOU KNOW?

In the United States alone, sprawl destroys 2.2 million acres (8900 km²) of farmland & forest every year.

DID YOU KNOW?

Many cities are plagued by traffic conjestion. In densely populated city areas the fastest way of getting around is often by bicycle, which is a highly efficient mode of transport.

DID YOU KNOW?

In the United Kingdom, 5% of carbon emissions are produced by busses, as opposed to 60% from passenger car trips.

form of motorised transport that does not harm the environment, in some way or another. Even today's most efficient vehicles, trains and airplanes require diesel, petrol, or electricity to move. Eco-friendly modes of transport essentially aim to reduce the negative environmental impact of modern transport methods. The less carbon, methane, or nitrous oxide pollution emitted by a particular mode of transport, the more environmentally friendly it becomes. Using public transport such as a train, bus or commercial airplane, still impacts on the environment through carbon emissions. But the pollution attributed to a person using public transport is far lower to those who drive their own cars.

If we truly wish to adopt eco-friendly modes of transport, we should place a greater emphasis on those that do not emit carbon dioxide. Walking is without doubt the most environmentally friendly way of getting around. Absolutely zero carbon dioxide is emitted when walking. Riding a bicycle is much the same, although manufacturing processes have a small carbon footprint. Not only are these methods ideal

from an environmental perspective, but walking or riding a bicycle also contributes positively to human health. The advantages of walking and cycling are endless: they reduce congestion in cities, contribute towards healthier lifestyles, are considerably cheaper than any other form of transport and also carry a radically lower carbon footprint on the Earth.

However, the reality is that we cannot walk far distances in short spaces of time. The use of other forms of transport will therefore still be necessary heading into the future. Public transport offers a great opportunity to increase the movement of people around a city in an efficient manner whilst simultaneously reducing our collective environmental footprint. Railway systems, for example, such as those found in London, New York and Tokyo have proved to be highly effective in moving large amounts of people around a city in a safe and efficient manner, whilst offering a sustainable solution to the problems relating to personal car ownership. With rapid improvements in technology the speed, capacity and efficiency of our public transport systems will continue to improve.

"WHENEVER WE INCREASE ROAD SPACE WE INCREASE TRAFFIC. WE ARE NOT FUNDAMENTALLY SOLVING THE PROBLEM OF CONGESTION."
– GRAHAM CURRY

WHAT ALTERNATIVE FUEL SOURCES ARE AVAILABLE?

Our dependency on oil, coupled with the pollution, natural resource consumption and economic turbulence it creates, cannot continue if we hope to see a sustainable future for the transport industry. The vast majority of motorised transport is powered using fossil fuels, and as a result releases carbon dioxide and other harmful pollutants. Our great and widespread dependency on oil as a fuel source for motorised transport has historically been attributed to their abundance, affordability, accessibility and high-embodied energy. As oil is extremely flammable, it provides the necessary means to effectively power a vehicle's engine. Unfortunately, although oil is highly efficient and reliable to power vehicles, the drawback is the pollution released from its combustion has a tremendously negative effect on our atmosphere and our health.

The environmental damage caused by our oil-dependent vehicles is one of the biggest challenges facing the transport industry. It is clear that the main step in reducing the environmental impact of modern transport is to find alternatives to petroleum-based fuels. Many technologies exist which attempt to substitute traditional oil-based fuels such as petrol and diesel with other sources of energy. These include biodiesel, hybrid fuels and electricity. All three of these alternative fuel sources for transport are available on the market today.

"CARBON FUEL PRICES LOOK SET TO REMAIN HIGH, AND ALTERNATIVE FUELS ARE URGENTLY NEEDED."
– RICHARD BRANSON

DID YOU KNOW?

Brazil has over 40 years experience using sugar cane as a biofuel. In 2008, its cars consumed more ethanol than fossil fuels.

BIODIESEL

Much like other alternative fuels, biodiesel supports some unique features and qualities. Biodiesels can be manufactured from organic materials that have undergone a chemical process, converting them into a fuel source. Such examples include animal waste, vegetable fats, timber and even some forms of trash. Biodiesels are almost identical to petroleum-based fuels in functionality yet are a relatively new fuel to the transport industry. With less than a decade of commercial-scale production, biodiesels are entering the market driven mainly by the perception that they carry less of an environmental impact when compared to petroleum-based fuels. They also have a sense of security attached to them, as they are not as severely affected by oil price spikes and fluctuations. However, the commercial production of biodiesel has caused heated debates, particularly relating to its environmental impact.

On the positive note, biodiesel is safe, biodegradable and produces less air pollution than petroleum-based fuels. Biodiesel can either be used in its pure form, or can combine with normal petroleum-based diesel (between 2-5%) to allow greater efficiency. It is also considered a renewable source of power as it can be produced locally on demand by cultivating crops and animals, or recycling waste. Another positive aspect of biodiesel is that it can be used in existing diesel engines with little or no modification.

From an economic perspective, biodiesels are significantly worse off compared to petroleum-based fuels: they are more than double the price, and there are many variations in biodiesel quality, which influence the consistency in performance and efficiency of biodiesel as a fuel. The best quality biodiesel is about 10% less efficient than normal petroleum-based diesel.

Although biodiesels are regarded as safer for the environment than petroleum-based fuels, it doesn't mean they are necessarily environmentally friendly. The first point of concern is what is referred to as the 'food vs fuel' debate. Biodiesel directly competes with food production and supply measures, as they both essentially compete for available farmland. This is especially the case when considering biodiesel production at a commercial scale. As a result, a major factor to consider in biodiesel production is the food shortages that can be created with increased biodiesel use. Farmland is ultimately used to grow crops for biodiesel manufacturing as opposed to supplying the world with food. Deforestation is a second point of concern. Forests and other fragile ecosystems are often cleared away in order to grow the crops used in biodiesel production.

However, food waste is generally an untapped resource with great potential for generating energy. Around 70% of food waste around the world is sent to landfills. Biodiesel can be produced using food waste such as leftover oil from hotels, restaurants and fast food outlets. As such, there is an incredible opportunity to use this organic waste in the production of biodiesel, thus eliminating the 'food vs fuel' debate.

HYBRID FUELS

Hybrids are vehicles that use more than one form of onboard fuel source to achieve movement. Most hybrid vehicles carry a traditional combustion engine, as well as one or more electric motors with a battery pack. Each of the different power sources – whether petrol, diesel or electricity – has the ability to move the car on its own. Conventional hybrid systems generally work by using electricity, which is stored in batteries, for when the vehicle is moving slowly, and then when greater speed is required both power sources work together in conjunction. At stages in between, any excess power that is generated by the engine is used to recharge the batteries.

There are some great advantages to using hybrid vehicles, one of them being their environmental and economic benefits. Hybrids produce considerably less pollution compared to petroleum-based vehicles. They are also more economical than conventional engines, as they are more fuel-efficient. Thanks to the financial incentives and allowances from many governments around the world, the price of hybrids has dropped drastically in recent times, making them more affordable and desirable in the public eye.

But hybrids also have their challenges. Historically, they have carried lower power output, higher maintenance costs and poorer handling when compared to traditional, petroleum-based vehicles. In the past, hybrids were generally perceived as being inferior to petroleum-based cars in terms of performance. However, this situation seems to be changing for the better, with the recent release of revolutionary hybrids, such as the BMW i8 and the Toyota Prius, which are proving to be highly efficient.

Many skeptics of hybrid vehicles argue that when manufactured they produce more pollution than traditional vehicles, and the environmental benefits of hybrids are therefore skewed and obsolete. But one cannot deny the potential of hybrid technology, and the concept of reduced petroleum reliance holds great promise for a more sustainable future for transportation.

"FOR ANY ALTERNATIVE LIQUID FUELS TO BE A VIABLE OPTION, WE NEED MASSIVE AMOUNTS OF FEEDSTOCK- THE RAW MATERIAL TO MAKE THE ENERGY- AND IT HAS TO BE CHEAPER THAN- OR AT LEAST COMPARABLE TO- TRADITIONAL FUELS."
– RICHARD BRANSON

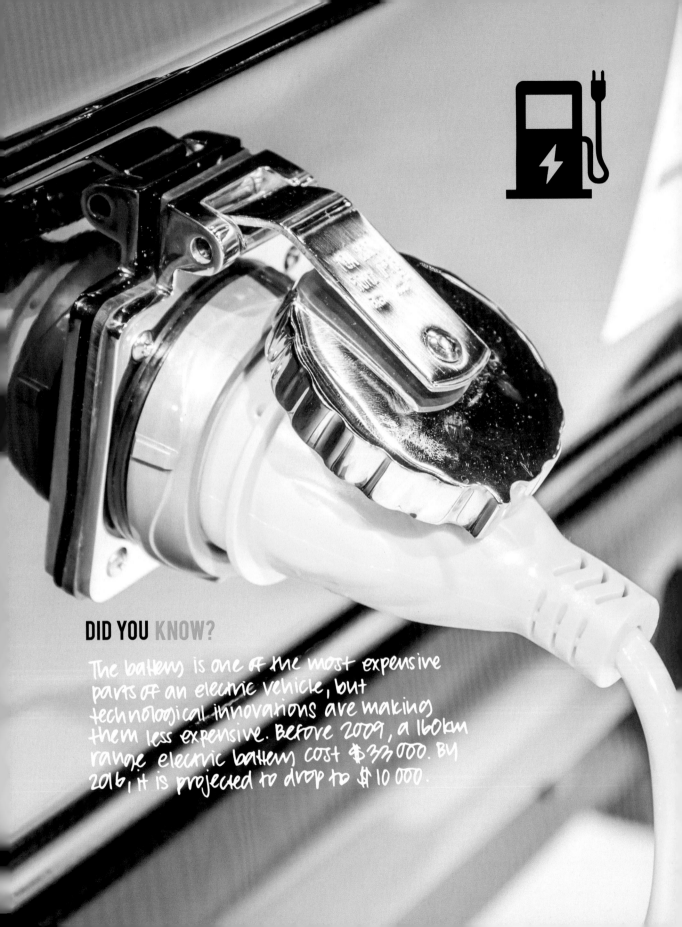

DID YOU KNOW?

The battery is one of the most expensive parts of an electric vehicle, but technological innovations are making them less expensive. Before 2009, a 160km range electric battery cost $33 000. By 2016, it is projected to drop to $10 000.

ELECTRIC POWER

Although fully electric vehicles are not a new concept in the automotive industry, they have only recently become a mainstream product. They can now be purchased easily due to their widespread distribution. Electric vehicles run on rechargeable batteries installed in the car. These batteries not only power the vehicle, but also provide power for the lights, radio, air-conditioning and door locking system – that is, anything that requires power. The batteries can be recharged at charging stations, similar to petrol or gas stations. In terms of pollution generated by the vehicles themselves, electric vehicles are certainly a step in the right direction: once production and distribution have taken place, the vehicles are 100% eco-friendly, as they do not emit any toxic gases or polluting substances.

Electric vehicles are also a highly effective mode of transport. Up to 80% of the energy in the battery is transferred directly to power the vehicle. This proves far more efficient when compared to petroleum-based vehicles, where only 14-26% of the energy is harnessed.

Producing and using electricity to power vehicles has caused concern in the past. Historically, the processes involved in generating the electricity have been produced through unsustainable methods, such as coal-fired power plants. It must be noted that although running vehicles from coal-powered electricity is environmentally harmful, it is still less damaging to the environment than using oil. But this situation is quickly changing with the recent emergence of renewable energy storage technology. Innovative battery systems have been developed that can store electricity generated from renewable sources, mostly solar energy, and then use the stored energy to recharge the cars' battery.

The 'Powerwall'– a revolutionary new battery technology developed by Tesla Motors in the US – can effectively generate and efficiently store solar energy harnessed from solar PV panels. This stored energy can be used either to electrify a home or to recharge an electric car overnight. This advancement has the potential to transform the transport industry into a sustainable entity, as the very principle of powering vehicles with renewable energy has the potential to be applied across many modes of transportation. Without a doubt, the successful integration of renewable energy into motorised transport could revolutionise the industry and propel us all into a new era. This step could be compared with the invention of the wheel, as a pivotal invention in human history.

CAN TRANSPORT BECOME MORE SUSTAINABLE?

There is no denying that significant changes in modern transport technology are necessary. If we want our transport systems to continue providing the safe, reliable and affordable movement of people and goods whilst reducing their environmental impact, we need to transform modern transportation into a far more sustainable and environmentally sensitive system.

The second half of the 20th century was characterised by the popular trend of individual car ownership. From the 1950s onwards, the vehicle production industry boomed, particularly in the US, with the rising desire for vehicle ownership from the growing middle class. This had huge implications for transport as it saw the move away from more sustainable transportation like bicycles and public transport towards a car-dominated society. This trend has gained incredible traction and has now led to a culture of car ownership in many countries like the US, Australia, China, Brazil, Mexico and South Africa. Adding to this, as the global middle class is set to increase by nearly three-billion people by 2050, more and more people are set to become dependent on personal vehicles to get around.

Many cities around the world have traditionally attempted to solve some of the problems associated with transportation, such as traffic congestion, by simply building more roads and wider streets. They have done this to allow for a greater number of vehicles to make use of the roads, thereby increasing and accelerating movement within the city. However, this outdated way of thinking by no means solves the car dependency problem that plagues so many cities today. Building more roads and wider streets have proven to only temporarily solve the issue of traffic and congestion within a city. Once the city expands and becomes more populated, more cars enter the roads, repeating the problem all over again. In addition, the widening of the roads destroys the fabric of community and pedestrian life within the city.

Fortunately, at the turn of the century, people started to become aware of the negative implications of our transportation systems. The longevity of global transport is at a huge risk unless major transformations can take place. Important steps need to be taken if we are to reverse the unsustainable realities of modern transport.

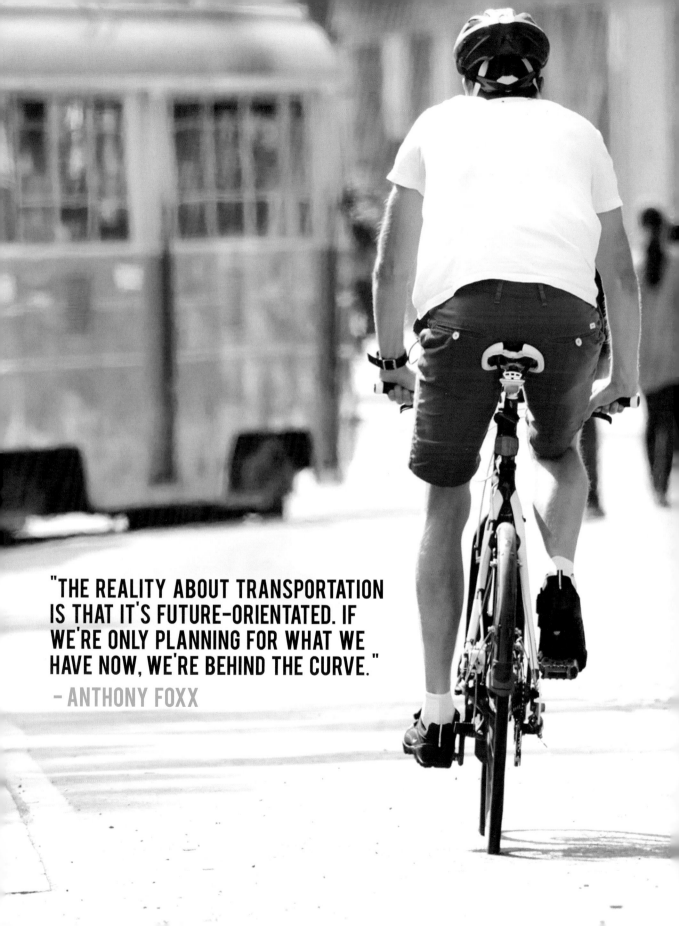

"THE REALITY ABOUT TRANSPORTATION IS THAT IT'S FUTURE-ORIENTATED. IF WE'RE ONLY PLANNING FOR WHAT WE HAVE NOW, WE'RE BEHIND THE CURVE."
- ANTHONY FOXX

DID YOU KNOW?

London's underground train system was built in the 19th century, yet it is widely acknowledged as one of the best in the world.

PUBLIC TRANSPORT

Public transport will play a key role in reducing carbon emissions linked to the industry. Most forms of public transport, such as busses, trains, trams and ferries still produce a certain level of pollution, but compared to individual modes of transport such as cars, they have far less impact per person travelling. There are numerous advantages in adopting and expanding public transport; it reduces congestion in cities, saves money spent on fuel and other means of travel, drives community growth and revitalisation, reduces overall oil consumption, air pollution and carbon emissions, and provides economic opportunities in the form of jobs. When a bus moves 50 people from point A to point B, the environmental impacts are considerably less than if all 50 people drove their own cars. Public transport also reduces the congestion of roads significantly in cities, and allows for a more efficient movement of people. Therefore, the widespread and increased adoption of safe, reliable and convenient public transport is an absolute necessity in ensuring a sustainable future for humanity.

The challenges ahead for public transport cannot be overlooked or ignored. Because of the rapid, uncontrolled development of urban sprawl, public transport cannot exist as an entirely convenient alternative to individual car ownership. Since cities are expanding faster than the rate of public transport infrastructure, many people continue to rely on individual modes of transport for commuting, or resort to unregulated and less safe forms of public transport. Urban planners need to ensure that public transport keeps up with the urbanisation process as much as possible.

In cities around the world that are currently undergoing rapid urbanisation, especially those in less developed nations, certain types of public transport systems that are inflexible, such as rail networks, may not necessarily be the best option moving forward. As city centres continues to shift and urban boundaries spread outwards, the ability of inflexible transport systems to adjust to the change is slow. Transport infrastructure that is inflexible is often expensive and timely in construction and therefore not always the best solution when the need is urgent. Other public transportation systems that are more flexible and adaptable to change, such as bus systems, will provide a greater long-term solution. Busses and bus lanes are often cheaper to implement, operate and maintain, and can adapt more readily to the city's changing needs. As the dynamics of cities are changing all over the world, special focus needs to be placed on the type of public transport systems that are used.

FUEL-EFFICIENT TECHNOLOGIES

A number of fuel-efficient technologies are already available on the market. These include biodiesel, hybrid and electric-powered vehicles. Similar to developments in transportation in the past, these will continue to evolve and become more efficient, reliable, affordable and widespread as demand and technology progresses. It is important that these technologies continue the momentum and become even more environmentally friendly, especially in their manufacturing processes. A movement away from petroleum-based fuels is crucial if the transport industry is to become sustainable.

While fuel-efficient vehicles are currently more expensive than petroleum-based vehicles, history shows that prices will drop as time passes. It will become essential for fuel-efficient technologies to become mainstream and commercially viable, and outperform and replace petroleum-based vehicles. Although some available fuel-efficient technologies still require an element of petroleum, such as biodiesel and hybrid vehicles, they are still significantly more environmentally friendly than traditional petroleum-based vehicles. The ideal situation will be to generate fuels that are carbon-free and emit zero pollution during consumption. Fortunately, thanks to advances in technology, electric vehicles powered by renewable energy are starting to show promise, as the storage of renewable energy becomes more reliable and effective.

Major breakthroughs in alternative fuel technology is imminent, as many companies continue to research and discover new ways of producing fuels and increasing their efficiency and performance. The Toyota Prius and BMW i8 models both run on efficient hybrid technology. They contain both combustion engines and electric motors that switch depending on the vehicles speed. The Nissan 'Leaf' and Tesla Model S run purely on electricity and can be charged overnight. Such vehicles have proven to perform to the same if not higher standard of traditional vehicles. Adding to this, the widespread implementation of fuelling and charging stations for such vehicles are well underway. This will allow such fuel sources to become more convenient. The only downside to such vehicles has been the price tag, but as their production and adoption ramps up, the cost of such vehicles will decline. In terms of biofuel, Virgin Atlantic has announced the development of a world-first low-carbon aviation fuel with half the carbon footprint of conventional airline fuel. The airline believes that the new fuel source will save around 50% on lifecycle carbon emissions, and can reduce the carbon per passenger km by 30% by 2020.

URBAN DESIGN & DENSIFICATION

Cities of the future need to take into consideration the environmental, economic and social challenges of transportation. The urban design principle of densification – which is based on the notion of increasing the number of people living on a piece of land – is one strategy that takes these considerations into account. Densification in cities has two major advantages, both of which impact positively on transportation systems. The first is that densification hinders and prevents urban sprawl from occurring. Preventing urban sprawl will reduce travel distances between where people live and where they work. Secondly, densification in cities leads to tight-knit communities that can live, play, shop, exercise and learn within convenient walking or transit distance from their homes. Well designed, dense cities makes public transport more viable, whilst simultaneously reducing the need for it.

Cities of the future need to be designed in ways that provide as many alternatives to the personal car ownership as possible. Such designs include planning for public transport systems and the allocation of sufficient cycle lanes. Non-carbon emitting modes of transport need to be given top priority, and only sustainable urban design can provide for this.

However, the promotion of carbon-free methods of transport will not be adopted sufficiently without proper infrastructure in cities. In many cities throughout the world, entire lanes have been dedicated solely for cyclists. Yet many people in these cities still choose to drive cars and willingly sit in heavily congested roads every day. This is because cycle lanes are often unsafe, or at least perceived to be. However, through considerate and effective design, this challenge can be overcome. Copenhagen in Denmark, for example, has come up with an extremely simple yet innovative solution. Vehicles do not park on the side of the pavement, but rather about 2m from it. The cycle lane is then allocated in place of where the vehicles would have parked. By doing so, the vehicles create a protective barrier to the cycle lane.

Many cities today are plagued by traffic congestion, and in many cases, the fastest way of getting around a densely populated city areas is often by bicycle. Due to massive traffic congestion in Mexico City, the average speed of a car is a mere 4km/h in the rush hour. Bicycles during traffic hours in Mexico City, on the other hand, have a comparative average speed of 10km/h. In Amsterdam, over 60% of trips are made by bicycle, whilst 31% of city inhabitants list a bicycle as their main mode of transport for daily activities. This is due to the fact that the city is dense, and the infrastructure allows for a diverse range of transportation to safely and effectively take place.

DID YOU KNOW?

Urban environments are most effective when a number of elements come together in the form of mixed use, density & connectivity.

DID YOU KNOW?

Buying locally produced & manufactured goods helps cut down on processing, packaging & transportation waste, leading to less pollution.

CONSUMING IN LOCALITY

In simple terms, locality means consuming resources and materials that are locally available. The most basic environmental benefit of locality is that it reduces the need for transport. A fruit or vegetable, for example, that has been grown and consumed within close proximity of a community has a significantly less environmental impact when compared to one that has been harvested in a foreign country and then transported across the globe to the same community. Any consumer good that has been grown, extracted, assembled or manufactured in a foreign country has created the need for international transportation.

Because the global transportation network is so advanced, it has become increasingly easy and affordable to transport goods across great distances. When products are locally sourced, the transportation and delivery costs can be reduced considerably. As a result, less energy and natural resources are needed to get the product into the hands of the consumer. A concept such as this, when implemented, goes a long way to reducing the environmental impact of every product and service we use.

Consider also, the important effect of locally produced goods not only in reducing the impacts of transportation, but also in promoting local economic development. In an ever-globalising world, local communities are finding it increasingly difficult to compete with international markets and manufacturers. Purchasing and consuming locally produced goods and services allows for the strengthening of the local economy, both from a financial and social aspect.

There are situations of course, where there is no alternative but to purchase internationally produced products, as there may be no competitive or quality product available that is locally produced. Whenever possible though, it is of utmost importance to promote locality as it has a less negative impact on the environment, boosts the local economy, and improves the resilience and well-being of that particular community.

"LOCALLY PRODUCED FOODS - DEFINED AS THOSE HARVESTED WITHIN A 100-MILE RADIUS OF ONE'S HOME - HAVE LESS IMPACT ON THE ENVIRONMENT BECAUSE OF THE DECREASED NEED FOR TRANSPORTATION FROM SOURCE TO CONSUMER."

– TYLER FLORENCE

BEHAVIORAL CHANGE

We all face the same choices with regards to transport every day: do we walk or cycle to work and thus emit zero carbon in the process, or do we drive a car and emit considerable pollution? Do we decide to drive alone to work or school, or do we share lifts with work colleagues and friends who live close by, or use public transport, and in the process reduce the number of vehicles on the road? Do we choose to purchase food grown in another country and transported across the world, or do we opt instead for that which is locally produced? These are the types of questions we need to start thinking about. The conveniences provided by modern transport has made these decisions easy to ignore and neglect, but this very way of thinking urgently needs to change.

Each of us has the capacity to help transform the transport industry into a sustainable one. What is required is a shift in mindset that leads to a change in behaviour. Unfortunately, not many people are willing to change their habits and take more sustainable ways of moving around. Even when safe, efficient, cheap and reliable public transport services are available and easily accessible, many people still prefer to drive their own vehicles over public transport. This is a result of habit, cultural values and perceived convenience.

It is important that everyone understands the negative impacts of our modern-day transportation systems, especially on the environment. Cities that become people friendly – that is, one that accounts for pedestrians and cycling – will have far lower environmental footprints than those where the motor vehicle is the dominant method of travel around a city. Cities such as Copenhagen and Amsterdam are amongst the most pedestrian-friendly cities in the world. The inhabitants of these cities have realised that carbon-free ways of travel indeed contribute greatly to their health and lifestyles. These people choose to ride bicycles or walk to work as opposed to driving cars. Even those who work great distances from their home make use of sustainable forms of transport. For these people, daily transport is contributing positively to their health and allowing them to live a more active lifestyle. This example shows that if transport is to become sustainable, it is as much about a mindset change than anything else.

It is understandable that in some cases sustainable forms of transport cannot be taken, whether it is because of the lack of infrastructure, weather conditions or travel distances. However, a special effort should be made by individuals whenever movement can be done in environmentally friendly ways. The infrastructure can be put in place, but it is ultimately up to the people to use them.

DENMARK
NETHERLANDS
SWEDEN

THE MOST BICYCLE-FRIENDLY COUNTRIES IN EUROPE

CONSUMER
GOODS

WHAT ARE CONSUMER GOODS? HOW ARE CONSUMER GOODS PRODUCED? WHERE DOES ALL OUR WASTE GO? WHAT ARE THE ENVIRONMENTAL EFFECTS OF ALL OUR WASTE?

HOW DOES THE RECYCLING PROCESS WORK? WHAT IS THE FUTURE OF THE RECYCLING INDUSTRY? ARE WE DESIGNING PRODUCTS BETTER THAN WE DID IN THE PAST? ARE THERE BETTER WAYS TO DESIGN, MANUFACTURE AND USE PRODUCTS?

WHAT ARE CONSUMER GOODS?

AND HOW DO THEY BENEFIT OUR LIVES?

As a modern society we produce, consume and dispose of a variety of goods on a daily basis. Practically anything that can be purchased at a store can be considered a consumer good: cars, clothing, jewellery, furniture, computers, cutlery and stationery.

Consumer goods are essentially physical products that have been produced and then purchased by someone to satisfy their needs and wants. Also called final goods, each consumer good is the end result of a distinct set of production and manufacturing processes. There are generally two categories of consumer goods: durable and non-durable goods. A durable good is a consumer good that has an extended life expectancy, such as a house or vehicle, which is intended to last many years. Products are generally deemed durable if they are designed to last beyond three years. Non-durable goods, on the other hand, are products that are purchased for immediate or short-term consumption. Food, washing powder and petrol are examples of non-durable consumer goods as they are consumed immediately and cannot be reused.

The vast amount of consumer goods available to us today has influenced our lives tremendously. Consider how different our lives would be without many of the goods we enjoy today: cars, cell-phones, shoes, clothes and computers. Over the past few centuries, the range and diversity of consumer goods has increased dramatically as a result of rapid improvements in technology and production techniques. The breakthroughs in science and engineering since the start of the Industrial era has made it possible to manufacture millions of products in an efficient, inexpensive and consistent manner. Consumer goods have become increasingly affordable thanks to mass production processes, which have decreased production times and ensured greater quality control.

"A GREAT PRODUCT ISN'T JUST A COLLECTION OF FEATURES. IT'S HOW IT ALL WORKS TOGETHER."
– TIM COOK

Breakthroughs in transportation and communication have accelerated this further with inventions such as the internet and large transport vehicles such as cargo ships. This has provided for greater opportunities for international trade, as products can now be purchased from all corners of the globe and transported to one's doorstep within a matter of days. Global competition between brands has made products more available, diverse and affordable, often resulting in greater value for customers. Because of the wide selection of cellphones, computers, clothing, gadgets, books and medicine available to us today we are able to enjoy a far higher standard of living than civilisations and societies of the past.

Many companies that design and manufacture useful products seek to innovate and provide greater service and value for customers. These companies are often held in high esteem as they contribute positively to our lives. Companies such as Volkswagen, Apple, Nike, Microsoft and Boeing have changed the world for the better through the innovative products they have created. These products have contributed to the betterment of business, communication, healthcare, education and transportation.

Most consumer goods exist in competitive markets, whereby competitors make similar products to one another and market these products to the same customers. This increased competitiveness to win over customers has given rise to a culture of innovation and increased quality. We can see this trend across a variety of product markets. Cell phones, for instance, are becoming thinner, lighter and more affordable. They often have more features than previous models and have longer-lasting batteries and greater storage space. The technology of sports footwear is also improving dramatically, leading to greater durability, comfort and performance for athletes. Overall, many consumer goods companies are using their creativity and resources to create products that inspire us, motivate us and bring greater convenience to our lives.

"WHEN YOU TAKE TECHNOLOGY AND MIX IT WITH ART, YOU ALWAYS COME UP WITH SOMETHING INNOVATIVE."
– ROBERT RODRIGUEZ

HOW ARE CONSUMER GOODS PRODUCED?

We often fail to appreciate and consider the vast amounts of energy, fuel, technology, research, organisation and logistics that goes into both creating products and having them transported across great distances to our local store or even our doorstep.

Manufacturing is the process of managing the flow of information and materials needed to convert raw material into manufactured materials and then finished products. All consumer goods undergo processes that transform them into the useful products we use everyday. No matter how small, simple or lightweight a consumer good may be, every single man-made product we purchase has gone through a long and intricate process of transformation to become the final product. The processes and procedures that take place to manufacture a pair of shoes, for example, will differ to those needed in the manufacturing of a cellphone, a water bottle or a magazine, despite the differences in use and materials.

Almost all consumer goods undergo the same three stages in their production. These manufacturing processes can be organised as raw material extraction, material processing and final assembly. It is important to understand these stages, as the various processes can have a significant impact on both mankind and the natural environment.

DID YOU KNOW?

Every year we extract 55 billion tonnes of bio-mass, fossil energy, metal & minerals from the earth. This is almost 10 tonnes for every person in the world. And for people in the western world this number is much higher.

"RAINFOREST LAND IS MISTAKENLY VALUED SOLELY FOR THE WORTH OF ITS TIMBER, MINING AND OIL RESOURCES BY SHORT-SIGHTED CORPORATIONS AND GOVERNMENTS."
– CHRIS KILHAM

RAW MATERIAL EXTRACTION

The very first stage in the production of any consumer good inevitably involves the extraction of raw materials from the earth. Depending on the type of consumer good to be manufactured, different minerals and resources are required. Energy and fuel are always needed in order to extract the natural resources from the earth. These processes include mining, logging and water capture. In order to produce paper or timber products, trees must be cut down before being sent to a paper mill or sawmill. To produce plastic, oil and natural gas must be extracted from the environment, whereafter they will be refined at a chemical factory. The reality is every consumer good is made from raw materials as the starting point of their creation.

Raw material such as gold, platinum, diamonds, uranium, coal, oil, timber, iron ore, marble, granite and clay are common ingredients in many of our consumer goods. These natural resources need to be extracted from the earth through numerous

mining operations. They are often dug out from deep beneath the earth or even on its surface, and the processes are often extremely energy intensive and carry a heavy environmental impact. The deepest mines in the world can be found in South Africa, where gold mines extend more than four kilometres below the surface of the earth. Mines such as these call for excessively energy-intensive technologies which often cause devastation on parts of the natural environment, especially fertile soil and underground water supplies.

In addition, most consumer goods are composed of a large number of raw materials. There are very few consumer goods in today's world that consist solely of one raw material. A vehicle, for example, has its frame made from steel, wheels from rubber, seats from leather, petrol from refined oil, dashboard from plastic or rubber and parts of its engine from aluminium and platinum. Each of these materials are extracted separately, almost always from different locations.

"MINING IS LIKE A SEARCH-AND-DESTROY MISSION."
– STEWART UDALL

MATERIAL PROCESSING

Once we have extracted raw materials such as iron ore, timber, oil, gold and platinum from the earth through mining and logging operations, we are able to deliver these resources to factories and other facilities where they can be refined and converted into useful materials, otherwise known as producer goods. This is known as the material processing stage, and is testimony to our ability to shape and transform the resources the earth provides into useful and exciting materials. Over the past few centuries, our industrial and technological advancements have made it possible for us to create an incredibly diverse and useful range of materials, all with different strengths, flexibilities, shapes and sizes.

In times gone by we were only capable of using the raw materials themselves to create products and goods. Nowadays, we are able to create completely new materials from these raw materials that are far better suited to providing for our needs. In the past, people were only able to construct buildings from raw materials. Houses were made out of timber from trees, and castles were built out of stone

cut from rock. Through great leaps in technology and material processing, we are now able to create new materials from what the earth provides. Instead of timber and stone, we are now able to create buildings out of steel and concrete. Every year, people are finding new ways to make materials such as concrete, steel, plastic and glass more efficient, higher performing and durable. Oftentimes we are able to reduce the environmental impact of these materials by lowering the amount of energy, fuel and water required to produce them. This is vitally important, as the material processing stage requires vast amounts of water, energy and fuel in order to transform natural resources into manufactured materials.

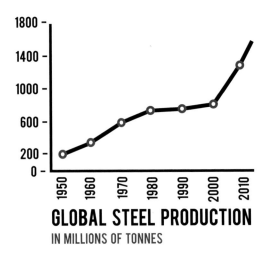

GLOBAL STEEL PRODUCTION
IN MILLIONS OF TONNES

ASSEMBLY

The final stage in the manufacturing of any product involves the assembling of the different manufactured materials. In production lines and factories, all the components that have been specifically manufactured come together to be assembled into the final product. For any product designer, this is the most critical and exciting part of the manufacturing process, as all the individual parts come together to create the final product envisioned from the start.

It is usually within a factory environment that the final assembly comes together. An assembly line is an effective and efficient way of putting all the different parts together, and is essentially made up of workers and machines that progressively assemble a succession of identical items. First invented by Henry Ford, this Industrial era invention created a process whereby a product is moved through the various stages of assembly over a conveyor belt until completion.

The advantage of an assembly line is that it is able to repeat the same process repeatedly with perfect timing and precision, ensuring quality and consistency with the manufacturing and assembly of each repeated item. This is ideal for when great amounts of a single product need to be created. A cellphone is a perfect example of a product that undergoes this process. It is made up of many different materials including copper, glass, rubber, plastic and aluminium – all of which have been sourced from around the globe. The materials that make up the glass screen and speakers come from Mongolia, the software is developed in the US and the final assembly takes place in enormous assembly line factories in China. Assembly lines are the common method of assembling mass produced goods such as cars, computers and household appliances.

DID YOU KNOW?

Although General Motors began using robots on the assembly line in the 1960s, it was not until the 1980s that robots were extensively used on the industrial assembly line.

DID YOU KNOW?

The Payata's dump is Manila's largest garbage disposal site, receiving about 5000 tons of garbage everyday. Six mountains of garbage up to 15 metres high have been created.

WHERE DOES ALL OUR WASTE GO?

Considering the sheer amount of products we use on a daily basis, a significant amounts of waste is produced. It is estimated that globally, we generate 1.1-trillion kg's of garbage every year – the weight of about 7 000 Empire State Buildings. This garbage of ours that we call 'waste', comes in many forms such as chemical, household, industrial, medical and organic waste. These streams of waste are produced in enormously large quantities worldwide. Unfortunately, many individuals, communities, industries and local governments are ignorant of the fact that their waste has to end up somewhere. Very few of us know exactly where it goes, or what effects it ultimately has on us or the environment.

Organic waste, mostly made up of the leftover food we throw away, makes up around half of the garbage we produce as a global society. This currently sits at around 45% of the total waste generated, followed by paper (17%), plastic (10%), glass (5%) and metal (4%). The various forms of waste we produce end up in different locations after their disposal. Before reaching its final location, all garbage taken by the city or government waste disposal system first goes to a place called a transfer station. This is where local trash is taken and temporarily stored before being transferred to its final location. Most of the waste gathered in transfer stations is sent off to one of three end locations: landfill sites, incinerators, or recycling centres.

A landfill site, also known as a dumping ground, is essentially a site where waste materials are disposed of by being buried in a large excavated area of earth. This is the oldest form of waste treatment. In both developed and developing countries, the majority of solid waste goes into landfills where it's generally covered up and left to decompose or erode away – processes that can take thousands of years to complete. As more waste gets deposited in

"38 THOUSANDS TONS OF TRASH ARE PRODUCED EVERY DAY IN NEW YORK CITY. IN ONE HOUR, NEW YORK PRODUCES ENOUGH TRASH TO FILL THE STATUE OF LIBERTY!"
– MICHELL JOACHIM

the landfill, the existing waste is compacted and buried beneath the newly deposited waste. This process is ongoing and continues until the landfill is completely filled. When organic matter is involved, this compaction and burial process removes the oxygen and causes the organic matter to break down in a process called anaerobic decomposition. Methane gas, a greenhouse gas that is 21 times more potent than carbon dioxide, is produced as a result. This has a drastic effect on the health and condition of the atmosphere.

Landfill sites are also extremely damaging to the surrounding environment. Oftentimes much of the waste (especially hazardous and toxic waste) has the ability to seep into the soil where it can enter groundwater systems and contaminate areas both local and further afield. Combining certain chemicals and gases within a landfill site also poses health and environmental dangers, as spontaneous combustion of liquids and gases is a regular occurrence that result in uncontrolled fires. From an environmental perspective, landfill sites are nothing short of disastrous, and flooding them with more and more waste increases the problem.

Due to increasing consumer habits and the resulting accumulation of waste, landfill sites are being filled up faster than we expected, creating a need for more landfills. It is estimated that at the current rate, the United Kingdom could run out of landfill space in eight years. Dubai too has challenges ahead. One of Dubai's two landfill sites are already filled to capacity, with the other estimated to reach full capacity in seven years. It may sound strange, as many people automatically assume that landfills can be located anywhere. Truth is, landfills require particular soil and rock conditions in order to sufficiently contain waste. They also need to be located within close proximity to the source of waste – cities. With our increasing production of waste, finding suitable locations to create landfills within a close enough proximity to the sources of the waste (such as industrial zones and cities) is becoming increasingly difficult and costly.

The second location for end waste disposal is an incinerator. These are large, incredibly hot furnaces that are used to burn the waste and convert it into ash, gas and ultimately heat. Incineration processes

DID YOU KNOW?

Municipal solid wastes (MSW) in general constitute about 14-20% of all wastes generated worldwide, with other types of waste including construction & demolition wastes (30%) manufacturing (20%) & mining & quarrying (23%).

reduce the mass of the waste by up to 95% – depending on the type of material being burned. This reduction in mass significantly reduces the amount of leftover waste sent to landfills. Ultimately, incineration does not replace the need for landfill sites, it rather reduces the amount of waste that needs to be sent there.

In the past, incineration was generally conducted without separating materials, whereby everything would be burned together in a giant furnace. This caused significant damage to the atmosphere and the surrounding air quality, as this method of waste disposal often released high amounts of poisonous gases and pollutants into the air. However, strict regulations in many countries now require that the different types of waste be separated before being treated. Ideally, the gases should first be treated, so as to eradicate the pollutants in the incinerator before they enter the atmosphere. A major opportunity that has recently emerged has been the ability to generate electricity from the heat created when burning the waste. This is a promising form of electricity generation and is called waste-to-energy.

The third possible location of waste disposal is recycling centres. Recycling is acceptably defined as the process of converting waste products into reusable materials. By making or manufacturing new products from old ones we are able to engage in a sustainable activity that reduces our environmental impact on Earth. Different types of waste, including glass, plastic, timber, rubber, metals and chemicals, all undergo different recycling processes. The sheer value of recycling from an environmental point of view has grown enormously in recent times. The recycling of used materials and products has great economic value as well. When recycled, these materials can often be sold at around 30% of their original value. This gives companies the opportunity to make a profit whilst reducing material consumption and waste.

"THE CONCEPT OF THROWING AWAY FOOD TO LANDFILLS IS EQUIVALENT TO AIR-CONDITIONING EMPTY BUILDINGS."
– PETER LENHER

"HISTORICALLY, INDUSTRIES, COMMUNITIES, BUSINESSES AND INSTITUTIONS ALL DID THEIR OWN THING WITH WASTE. SOME RECYCLED A BIT, SOME COMPOSTED A BIT. AND SOME DID NOTHING. BASICALLY THEY WERE INEFFICIENT AND THE MAJORITY OF THEIR WASTE WAS ENDING UP AT LANDFILLS, RESULTING IN GREENHOUSE GASES."

– KEVIN SCOBLE

WHAT ARE THE ENVIRONMENTAL EFFECTS OF ALL OUR WASTE?

Many people are completely unaware of the environmental impacts that arise from the manufacturing and disposal of consumer goods. With a product such as a vehicle, for example, any natural resources, such as iron ore, platinum, oil and aluminium that is used in vehicle production need to first be extracted from the earth. These mining processes have devastating impacts to ecosystems, as they are often cleared away and destroyed in order for mining activities to effectively take place.

There are many cases in which the resources are found deep in the heart of thriving and diverse ecosystems, which are then damaged, disrupted or destroyed in order for the desired resources to be found and extracted. Examples of these include the flourishing ecosystems of the Amazon rainforest where timber is logged, or the outback of Australia where coal is mined. Although sometimes the operations take place far from fragile ecosystems, the effects of the activity can have a ripple effect that impacts on surrounding ecosystems or even human settlements.

Following the extraction of raw materials, the manufacturing processes use extremely high temperatures to convert these resources into usable producer goods, which in turn creates high energy demands. Iron ore is converted into steel, sand into glass. When a vehicle is finally assembled and purchased by the buyer, it further emits carbon dioxide through the consumption of fuel. And finally, when the vehicle has served its purpose and its lifespan has come to an end, the materials are often sent to a landfill site instead of being recycled. Most stages of a product's lifecycle carry an environmental footprint. The waste and pollution produced by our consumer goods can be broken down into three categories: hard trash, hazardous waste and air pollution.

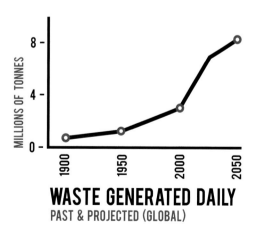

WASTE GENERATED DAILY
PAST & PROJECTED (GLOBAL)

HARD TRASH

Hard trash can drastically affect the environment, and the consequences can be felt for hundreds of years, often far from the source of disposal. Hard trash can be any solid form of garbage that people dispose of, such as plastic bottles, newspapers, old furniture, electronic equipment or leftover food. With an increasing number of consumer goods being produced and consumed around the world on a daily basis, hard trash becomes an important environmental concern.

One of the biggest environmental challenges facing the disposal of hard trash is the degradability of the materials, or lack thereof. The average plastic bottle, for example, will take somewhere around 450 years to completely degrade. Sometimes it can even take over 1 000 years, depending on the type of plastics used to produce the bottle. The scope of the problem increases heavily when taking into account that about 1.5-million barrels of oil are used everyday to make plastic bottles, and even more oil, in the form of petroleum, is used to transport it. In isolation, a single plastic bottle has minimal effects, but as we consider the sheer mass of plastic bottles thrown away every day, it becomes clear that the way we deal with our hard trash is extremely important.

Some of the products that we consider to be hard trash are made up of chemicals that, under certain conditions, can be harmful to humans, animals and plant life. When these products are disposed of irresponsibly, the chemicals that make up the product can slowly begin to seep into the earth below. When rainfall occurs, the chemicals dissolve off the products and enter nearby groundwater streams. An example would be hard trash disposed of in landfill sites or municipal septic systems. Groundwater contamination is extremely difficult, and sometimes even impossible to clean up.

Hard trash can cause devastation on both marine and land ecosystems. When tossed into the ocean, it can travel great distances with currents and winds. Plastics in particular are not a naturally occurring substance; they are highly engineered materials. As they are often extremely strong, durable, non-biodegradable and poisonous if consumed, any animal that gets tangled in, trapped in, or swallows plastic products can suffer serious harm or even death. Birds, turtles and dolphins are common victims to garbage found in the ocean, and often mistake it for food. It is estimated that at least 6.4-million tonnes of plastic litter enter the oceans every year, causing severe damage to precious marine ecosystems and killing thousands of marine animals in the process.

"SOLID WASTES' ARE THE DISCARDED LEFTOVERS OF OUR ADVANCED CONSUMER SOCIETY. THIS GROWING MOUNTAIN OF GARBAGE AND TRASH REPRESENTS NOT ONLY AN ATTITUDE OF INDIFFERENCE TOWARD VALUABLE NATURAL RESOURCES, BUT ALSO A SERIOUS ECONOMIC AND PUBLIC HEALTH PROBLEM."

– JIMMY CARTER

400 MILLION TONNES

THE AMOUNT OF HAZARDOUS WASTE WE PRODUCE EACH YEAR

HAZARDOUS WASTE

Hazardous wastes are poisonous chemicals and are often the byproducts of various manufacturing processes, farming methods, city sewerage systems, construction activities and laboratory chemicals. This form of waste may be in liquid, solid or sludge form and may contain chemicals, heavy metals, radiation or other deadly toxins. Even households dispose of hazardous forms of waste when discarding items such as dead batteries, cleaning equipment, paint or pesticides.

Most hazardous waste is identified by one or more of its dangerous properties or characteristics, including corrosiveness, flammable nature or toxicity. From an environmental point of view, the processes of disposing hazardous waste need to be done appropriately or severe damage can occur, most notably water or soil contamination. Ideally, hazardous waste should be safely contained while it is stored, transported and properly disposed of in order to prevent accidental release into the environment. While advances in technology have greatly improved our ability to treat or dispose of hazardous waste in ways that prevent environmental harm, the reality is accidents or unregulated treatment still occurs.

A byproduct generated from incineration activities – fly ash, is one of the most common forms of hazardous waste. Fly ash is considered a highly hazardous substance that must be disposed of in a specially-designed facility. One of the most environmentally disastrous hazardous waste accidents occurred at the TVA Kingston Fossil Plant in the US in 2008, when a large rupture to a container released approximately 4-billion litres of coal fly ash slurry – a byproduct of the coal combustion process. Pollutants such as arsenic, chromium, copper, lead, mercury and zinc entered a nearby river and caused devastation to both local homes and the surrounding environment. The hazardous waste entered several river networks, including the Tennessee River. Around 65 000 kg's of arsenic, a deadly pollutant, was released into the rivers. In fact, twice as much arsenic was released in that one accident than the amount discharged into waterways from all coal plants in the US the same year.

Hazardous waste particles can be small enough to attach to water particles, which can lead to acid rain. Many ecosystems simply cannot protect themselves from this toxic rainfall, and often perish or deteriorate as a result. Acid rain was first observed in the mid 19th century, when some people noticed that forests located downwind of large industrial areas showed signs of rapid deterioration.

AIR POLLUTION

Air pollution in the form of hazardous gases occurs predominately in two specific stages of a product's life cycle. The first occurs during the manufacturing stage, whereby the excessive heat needed for manufacturing activities to transform and shape materials emit significant amounts of carbon dioxide into the atmosphere. Limestone, for example, must be heated to 1 450°C before it can be turned into cement. Due to the heavy reliance on fossil fuels for electricity, fuel and heat, the manufacturing industry is the main producer of greenhouse gas emissions within the entire industrial sector. The industrial sector itself, which covers manufacturing, mining, construction and agriculture contributes to over 20% of all fossil fuel related carbon dioxide emissions. Other harmful gases that are emitted during manufacturing processes include sulphur dioxide, nitrogen dioxide and carbon monoxide – all greenhouse gases.

The second stage in the production of air pollution occurs in the disposal stage of a product's lifecycle. Due to the diverse range of materials used in consumer products today, not all products emit harmful gases when disposed of, but for those that do, various problems can arise. The manner in which something is disposed of, whether sent to a dumping ground or burned in a furnace, determines whether or not a material will in fact produce harmful gases. When organics are sent to landfill sites, the compaction of waste eliminates most of the oxygen, which results in the production of methane gas from the decaying matter. If left untreated, methane gas contributes directly to global warming.

Although many countries around the globe have put in place strict regulations for the burning of waste, the reality is that unregulated or illegal outdoor burning in garbage dumps continue to take place. These fires are producing far more pollution into the atmosphere than what is shown on official records. It is estimated that more than 1.1-billion tonnes, or 40%, of the world's waste is burned in such unregulated fires, meaning the greenhouse gas emissions from waste disposal is significantly underestimated. Most greenhouse gases, including carbon dioxide, methane, carbon monoxide and sulphur dioxide are released into the atmosphere when waste is burned illegally. The challenge is that these unregulated fires are near impossible to account for, making the resultant pollutants extremely difficult to quantify or prevent. In contrast, when waste is burned at conventional incineration plants that are regulated, the gases released can be captured and used for other purposes, such as electricity generation, heating and fuel sources.

"LANDFILLS ARE NOT ONLY ENVIRONMENTALLY PROBLEMATIC BECAUSE OF THE LAND THEY EAT UP, THEY ARE SIGNIFICANT CONTRIBUTORS TO CLIMATE CHANGE. THE METHANE RELEASED FROM LANDFILLS IS 20 TIMES WORSE FOR THE ATMOSPHERE THAN CARBON DIOXIDE."

– KEVIN SCOBLE

240 KG'S
OF FOSSIL FUELS

22 KG'S
OF CHEMICALS

1500 KG'S
OF WATER

THE AMOUNT NEEDED
TO MANUFACTURE

ONE COMPUTER

HOW DOES THE RECYCLING PROCESS WORK?

Recycling is an important part of sustainable development. By definition, it is the act of converting used, expired, depleted and unwanted materials and products into something new, whether for the same or different use. Interest in recycling has increased dramatically throughout the industrialised world over the past two decades. This is due to a variety of factors, including the problem of our increasing waste generation and dwindling capacity of our landfills, air pollution from the incineration of garbage as an alternative to landfilling, increasing resource consumption, and a general awareness and appreciation for environmental protection.

As a response to this increased awareness and concern, many governmental policies, regulations and programs have been created to increase recycling practices across the residential, commercial and industrial sectors, and reduce the amount of waste sent to landfill sites and furnaces. Some policies have been created to increase the amount of recyclable materials collected from waste, while others have been created to stimulate the demand for recycled materials in order to create new products.

Recycled materials play an important role in reducing both air and water pollution that is usually created through mining and manufacturing processes that rely solely on creating unprocessed, virgin raw materials. Because the recycling process reduces the need to extract, process, refine and transport materials such as timber, petroleum and iron ore to create new goods, less energy and materials are required. By reducing the amount of waste to landfills through recycling processes, fewer resources are wasted and the lifespan of existing landfills can be extended, reducing the need for more land to be destroyed in the process of creating new ones.

It is undeniable that creating products from recyclables instead of virgin raw materials creates less pollution and imposes less pressure on Earth's natural resources. By creating paper out of old newspapers instead of new pulp, making compost from old organic waste, or making aluminium soda cans from discarded aluminium scraps, we can effectively reduce the vast amounts of energy, water and material we consume.

"RECYCLING SAVES MONEY AND REDUCES POLLUTION. IT CREATES MORE JOBS THAN LANDFILLING OR INCINERATION. AND A LARGELY IGNORED BUT VERY IMPORTANT CONSIDERATION: RECYCLING REDUCES OUR NEED TO DUMP OUR GARBAGE IN SOMEONE ELSE'S BACKYARD."

- DAVID MORRIS

METALS

Steel, aluminium, zinc, copper and iron are among the most commonly used metals in industry today. All metals must be refined before they can be used. The process of mining, extracting, shipping and refining these metal ores into various types of metals, with different weights, shapes and applications, takes up a vast amount of energy and environmentally damaging processes to produce. The recycling of metals is extremely important, as the energy requirements to recycle metals are significantly less than the manufacturing of a virgin product. The recycling benefits of metals not only hold environmental benefits but huge financial returns as well. Metal deposits, much like fossil fuels, are a non-renewable resource and will inevitably run out unless we find ways of both increasing their efficiency and performance, and reducing our need to extract them.

Steel is probably the most well-known form of metal on the market. Because of its strength and durability, steel is often used as the main component in heavy-duty machinery and building structures. It can be used over and over again without a loss of quality. To make steel, iron ore is first mined from the ground, then melted down in a furnace of high heat to remove all impurities before carbon is added. The recycling of 1 metric tonne (1 000 kg's) of steel saves 1.1 metric tonnes of iron ore, 630 kg's of coal and 55 kg's of limestone.

The metal we know as aluminium is amongst our greatest recycling success stories. Aluminium is a light, thin, metal, used mostly to produce food and soda cans, but it's also used in industry to produce window and door frames, car parts, gutters, aluminium foil, cookware and airplane parts. Aluminium is very expensive compared to other metals and takes enormous amounts of energy to be produced. Remarkably though, well over 95% of aluminium products can be recycled, and an aluminium can that is recycled can be back on the store shelves within two months.

Recycling metals is extremely important as many of the goods we purchase and use today contain significant amounts of metal. A typical appliance such as a fridge or microwave is about 75% steel in weight, and automobiles are about 65% steel and iron. The environmental advantage of using recycled scrap metal to make new metal-based products is enormous. Carbon emissions are cut by around 60%, as compared to the process of creating products from virgin metals.

DID YOU KNOW?

Recycling one metric ton (1,000 kg) of steel saves 1.1 metric tons of iron ore, 630kg of coal, & 55kg of limestone.

DID YOU KNOW?

In 2013, global production of plastics reached nearly 300 million metric tons, with 57 million metric tons in Europe alone. China is one of the largest producers of plastics in the world, accomodating almost 25% of the global share in 2013.

PLASTICS

Due to the fact that plastics are used in so many aspects of our lives, they represent a significant and ever-growing part of the modern world's waste stream. Plastics form part of a group of materials known as polymers. They are created using chemical engineering processes, and are usually made up of petrochemicals. Because of their light weight, low cost and incredible durability and strength, plastics are used for countless purposes, and are replacing many other materials such as glass and metals. The increased production and use of plastics poses great concern due to their consumption of natural resources, the toxicity linked to their manufacture and use, as well as the environmental impact arising from their disposal.

As plastics (or polymers) are made using chemical processes, their production and disposal poses a serious threat to the environment. Plastics do not degrade easily, and therefore create problems for landfills. The production of plastics also uses significant amounts of oil and energy.

There are many forms of plastic. They all have different strengths, thicknesses, applications and even resistances to heat. Much of what we use today is made from one or another form of plastic. Polyethylene terephthalate (PET), Polyvinyl Chloride (PVC) and Low Density Polyethylene (LDPE) plastics are just some of the many types we use today. Their environmental effects differ as a result of their density, strength, flexibility and use.

Unfortunately, the production and engineering of the various forms of plastics produce some of the most substantial public health threats within industrial processes. This includes lethal gases such as chlorine and phosgene. The plastics industry is second only to the chemical industry in generating gases that damage the ozone layer.

Thanks to continued innovation in the industry, plastics are often quite durable against water, oil and dirt. As a result, they can often be reused without even needing to be recycled.

Most forms of plastic can be recycled. Because of chemical-engineering innovations, used plastic products can be shredded and separated by machines and reprocessed without significant material breakdown. This enables us to use the same materials in new ways, which reduces the materials and energy used to make the virgin material and increases their longevity in the form of recycled products. Countless plastic products, including bottles, containers, sealants, packaging, toys, pipes, bags and decorations, can be recycled and given new forms of life.

The financial and environmental benefits of recycling plastics are enormous. Once the plastic strips are melted down they are recycled into small pellets for easy transportation. They can then be remelted and cast into new shapes, colours and sizes for the creation of new products. Recyclable plastics lack the quality and durability of virgin plastics, yet have a significant use for industries around the globe.

CHEMICALS

Chemicals, in scientific terms, relate to pretty much every pure substance that exists on Earth, including gold, water, platinum and oxygen. Chemical compounds are made up of a number of these pure substances. These include water, carbon dioxide and salt. In everyday consumer and industry terms though, the term 'chemical' is generally used to refer to artificially created substances that can often be harmful to human health and the natural environment. Chemical products, for that matter, range extensively in scope to include soaps and shampoos, pesticides, cleaning liquids, medications, paints/varnishes, garden chemicals and automotive products.

The correct disposal and recycling of such chemicals is extremely important, as the exposure of such chemical products to our oceans, lakes, rivers, soils and our animal life can cause major harm. There are often incidents when chemicals are not correctly and responsibly disposed of and as a result cause major environmental damage. Oceanic oil spills, for example, are extremely destructive to the marine environment, as the oil released contaminates the ocean, killing plants and animal species in the process. Chemicals from factories seep into rivers or groundwater, contaminating the food and water supply for plant and animal life, altering the environment into a state from which it may never recover. When hazardous household waste ends up in landfills, it has the potential to contaminate the soil and groundwater in equal measures. Such chemicals also pose a threat to waste workers, who,

through inhalation or physical exposure could be severely harmed by the substances. Pouring such chemicals down the drain, on the ground, or disposing of them in the regular garbage could lead to these situations.

The most dangerous of such products include batteries, fluorescent light bulbs, household cleaners, garden and swimming pool chemicals, paint products and automotive products. Such hazardous waste should never be disposed in landfills, dumped in sewers, drains or bodies of water, mixed with regular garbage, swallowed, or burned.

The solution to dealing with hazardous household chemical waste is to set up chemical waste treatment programs to prevent such chemicals from harming both humans and the environment. Perhaps more importantly, industries should adopt methods of chemical waste disposal that do not pose a threat to the environment. When disposed of correctly, via a hazardous waste treatment program, such chemical products are treated and discarded in such a way as to reduce their environmental impact.

The importance of buying and using products that are biodegradable and non-harmful to the environment when manufactured, transported or disposed of is extremely important, as it protects our ecosystems from harm. Such products are growing in popularity, as more and more people become aware of both the environmental and health risks associated with them.

ORGANICS

Anything derived from living matter is organic. Organic waste generally relates to the vast amount of leftover organic materials we create, in the form of food, grass and plant clippings. Roughly half the amount of matter that goes to landfills is organic, and this poses various problems. The first is that organic waste dumped in landfill sites undergoes a process called anaerobic decomposition. This is a biological process whereby bacteria decompose organic matter in the absence of oxygen in the landfill. This results in huge amounts of methane gas and carbon dioxide being released into the atmosphere. If we are to harness value from this decomposition process, it won't be from current disposal methods in landfill sites. The methane released from organic waste in the anaerobic decomposition process holds the potential for biogas generation. For the natural gas industry, this provides the opportunity to supply the world with a gas resource without having to waste extreme amounts of water in the gas mining process, or cause irreversible land damage from the mining sites.

The second problem is that by mixing our organic trash with non-organic trash, we effectively lose the opportunity to use the organic matter in new and sustainable ways. As organic waste is natural, biodegradable and rich in nutrients, it has the potential to be recycled as fertiliser or compost. All the nutrients and minerals that plants use to grow, originate from organic matter in the earth. By separating our organic waste from our non-organic waste, we effectively hold the potential to reduce the amount of waste in landfill sites, reduce carbon and methane emissions, and create nutrient rich fertiliser to grow plants and crops. Fertiliser and compost can be created by mixing food waste, grass clippings and dead plant matter with soil. This can be done on a large industrial scale or even in your backyard. After mixing it in a large bag or heap of soil with some water, it can be left in the sun to decompose and transform into a nutrient rich fertiliser.

If the correct recycling processes and systems for organic waste can be put in place and carried out by individuals in the households, as well as large scale enterprises such as restaurants, hotels, factories and shopping malls, then the potential for reducing environmental damage and creating new resources for energy and fertiliser increases dramatically.

DID YOU KNOW?

The food wasted by the United States & Europe alone could feed the world 3 times over.

PAPER & TIMBER

Some trees are rare or take decades to grow and reach maturity, whilst others are plentiful and can be grown very quickly and without much effort. While all forms of wood can be considered a renewable resource, the reality is many tree species take long periods of time to grow. In light of this, some trees must therefore be considered non-renewable, as they cannot be replaced and regrown at the same rate they are being taken down. It is for this reason that our rainforests are endangered. These mature ecosystems have taken hundreds, if not thousands, of years to grow, and cannot replenish or rejuvenate easily. On the other hand, other forms of wood can be considered sustainable if grown and farmed under the right conditions and within the right geographical area.

When purchasing or making products, it is important to know what type of timber you are buying, and whether or not it is forested in a sustainable manner. Timber is commonly used to make furniture and building material, and is sourced by chopping down trees, clean cutting the wood to various sizes, and occasionally stained or varnished for waterproofing purposes and visual effect. Paper is made from wood pulp combined with recycled paper or cotton pulp. Not only are large amounts of timber used in the manufacturing process of paper, but an extremely large quantity of water is used as well.

Paper and timber have massive recycling potential. Paper and wood that is recycled not only makes the best use of what is sourced from a tree, but also extends the lifespan and use of its fibres. There will always be a demand for virgin timber and pulp, and the lifespan and quality of recycled fibres is lower, and demand for the quality that virgin products can provide remains high.

From an environmental perspective, the process of manufacturing recycled paper uses half the amount of energy and half the amount of water. Recycled paper products create around 75% less air pollution, 35% less water pollution, and save 15% on tree pulp. It also reduces the amount of solid waste needed to go to landfill sites. Timber itself has many second life possibilities. When the lifespan or use of various timber products runs dry they can be recycled for use in new buildings, new forms of furniture, animal bedding, compost and biomass energy to generate heat and electricity.

Most paper and timber products are biodegradable, meaning that discarding them to the earth poses little or no environmental threats. Not all forms of paper and timber can be recycled easily though. When tainted by oils and grease, they must go through difficult processes to remove the contaminants or else be discarded to landfill sites.

GLASS

Glass is an incredible product, not only because it is one of the oldest and most versatile man-made materials, but it can also be recycled with incredible efficiency. Glass is hard enough to protect and shelter us form the elements, yet shatters and breaks with ease. Glass is perceived as a strange material to many, as it behaves like a solid, yet is also considered to be a type of liquid. Glass can be seen everywhere – in windows, mirrors, bottles and light bulbs.

Believe it or not, glass is made from liquid sand. It is made by heating ordinary sand at incredibly high temperatures (1700°C) until it turns into a liquid. When molten sand cools down, instead of retuning into its previous state, it gains a completely different structure. The new substance is never able to return to a solid state, despite how much it may be cooled. This new substance is a cross between a solid and a liquid – a 'frozen liquid', otherwise known as an amorphous solid. Glass is transparent, resistant to chemical change, inexpensive to make and easy to shape in its molten state. Glass can be recycled over and over again, making it a sustainable and useful material. In fact, it is 100% recyclable, and unlike other materials, experiences no loss of purity or quality when recycled.

In an industrial glass manufacturing plant, sand is mixed with old glass, soda ash and limestone. These ingredients are heated in an extremely hot furnace and melted. The soda ash helps to save energy as it lowers the melting point of the sand, saving electricity. The unfortunate drawback is that is produces an undesirable characteristic: the newly created material is not water resistance and would dissolve if it became wet. To reverse this effect, limestone is added. This is the most common way of producing glass.

The process of making recycled glass, as opposed to new glass, uses 40% less energy. Every kilogram of glass that is recycled saves more than a kilogram of the raw materials otherwise needed to create new glass. These materials include sand, soda ash and limestone. The respective amounts saved are 600 kg's, 180 kg's, and 170 kg's. The process of creating recycled glass starts with the crushing of old or unwanted glass into a product called 'cullet'. Cullet burns at a much lower temperature to sand, and therefore reduces the heating requirements. It is incredibly important that we recycle glass. If sent to a landfill site the material can take up to one-million years to break down.

RUBBER

When we think of rubber, we usually think of elastic bands, car tires, or even pencil erasers. But rubber has many more uses and comes in many forms. Rubber is used in latex gloves, waterproof shoes, swimming caps, hose pipes and wetsuits. Rubber was used over 1 000 years ago, where it was traditionally taken from natural sources. Natural rubber is sourced from certain trees, where latex, a sticky, milky liquid is removed. The latex is then refined into one of the common forms of rubber we use today.

Synthetic rubber is an artificial rubber that is made in a chemical plant from petrochemicals. Approximately 70% of rubber today is synthetically produced. Although there is only one type of natural rubber that can be created, synthetic rubbers come in all different types, each with their own properties and advantages. All synthetic rubbers have a different melting point, elasticity, durability and strength.

One of the most highly manufactured and produced rubber products today is a vehicle tyre. Tyres are made from strong, durable and dense rubber, and are used on the wheels of cars, motorcycles, airplanes and busses. Tyres are a synthetic rubber and require a huge amount of oil to be made. It takes about 27 litres of oil to produce one car tire. Every vehicle uses tyres, and the more vehicles produced, the more rubber tyres need to be produced as well. As it stands, rubber tyres, and other rubber products have little recycling potential. Tyres and other rubber products are also not biodegradable. The most common second life use for rubber tyres has been in the waste-to-energy sector. As tyres are made predominantly from oil, they can effectively be burned for energy. Although this gives an extended use to old tyres, their role as a fuel source is questionable from an environmental perspective. When burned, tyres produce the same amount of carbon dioxide as oil. Although burning tyres for fuel reduces mining operations for fossil fuels and keeps tyres from filling up landfill sites, they are far from environmentally friendly.

There are, however, other ways that tyres can be recycled. One use is in creating rubberised asphalt for highways. This helps to lower the cost and mining of materials for highway construction and extends the material use of tyres. Tyres can also be recycled to make basketball courts, backfill to construction activities, soil erosion control barriers or drainage foundations around buildings. Ideally, used tyres should be retreaded wherever possible to be made roadworthy again, reducing the need to produce more tyres and discard old ones. Artificial reefs in the Caribbean and other areas are being created with used tyres, in order to encourage underwater sea life. Unfortunately none of these applications are currently sufficient enough to reduce the high quantity of discarded tyres we are producing.

250 MILLION

THE NUMBER OF CAR TIRES DISCARDED EVERY YEAR

DID YOU KNOW?

Today more than 90% of the natural rubber supply comes from southeast Asia. As rubber trees require a hot, damp climate, they grow only in the "Rubber Belt" - an equatorial zone that stretches around the world.

WHAT IS THE FUTURE OF THE RECYCLING INDUSTRY?

If we are to truly lead the product manufacturing industry into a sustainable future, it becomes of utmost importance that we take full advantage of the opportunities that waste provides. Traditionally, waste has been viewed solely in negative terms – regarded as nothing more than a liability to both man and Earth, an inconvenient byproduct of consumerism. This perception of waste needs to change.

As more and more previously impoverished nations in Africa, South America and Asia undergo the transformative processes of industrialisation and modernisation, the wealth of such nations will increase, and along with it, the purchasing power of its citizens. Together with the ongoing rise in global population, the overall level of humanities' consumption will continue to increase and expand. The Industrial era was effective in teaching us how to efficiently extract resources, turn them into products, use them and then dispose of them. But if we are to see any real, tangible transformation in the consumer goods sector, it becomes critical that we adopt new ways of thinking and behaving that are relevant to the way we deal with all our waste.

Until recently, what we have failed to acknowledge and take advantage of is that waste is a resource. The sheer amount of energy and materials that went into creating these products still remain locked within them. Through creative and innovate thinking we can extend their value and potential far beyond their primary use, whether it be to create new products, new materials or convert them into fuel or energy resources.

By viewing waste as an opportunity rather than an inconvenience, and as an asset instead of a liability, we can extend the life of discarded products and materials and circulate them back into the global economy. Instead of sending organic waste to landfills and dump sites, where it will decay and produce environmentally harmful methane gas, we can send them to waste-to-energy plants where the methane can be captured and harnessed as a fuel or energy source. Instead of mining for more iron ore and limestone to create steel and concrete for buildings, we can recycle and reuse the same materials from old buildings and bridges that are to be demolished.

A world of opportunity exists to recycle, reuse and harness the energy potential of waste products. One of the most exciting developments in the recycling industry – low-temperature gasification – has proven that all landfill waste can effectively be recycled. Conventional methods of gasification burn waste in furnaces at extremely high temperatures in order to produce energy from waste. The downfall of this method is that due to the extremely high temperatures within the furnace, the non-fuel generating materials (mostly metals) are melted down with the all the other materials such as paper, organics, plastic and rubber that provide fuel for the furnace. When all the waste materials are burned in the intensive heat the metallic objects are melted down and ultimately mix together to become a metal liquid. When cooled, the metals from the furnace harden into an unusable mixed solid mass that has to be sent to a landfill site. In contrast to this, the process of low-heat gasification prevents this problem from occurring. The furnace is set to a temperature hot enough to melt all the fuel generating elements, yet low enough to leave the metals in their solid state. As the fuel generating materials burn up, the metals remain unchanged, and afterwards can be easily recycled back into industry.

Another major breakthrough with low-temperature gasification is the technology can be portable. Traditionally, waste-to-energy facilities have mainly been large, fixed facilities. In contrast, the exciting thing about these waste plants is that they are uniquely portable and can scale up or down, depending on the amount of waste to be burned. These portable waste plants then conduct the low-temperature gasification process. But this method has another advantage. When the waste is burned in the gasifier, synthetic gasses are released. These gases can be captured and combined with biodiesel, which can then be used for electricity, fuel or heat purposes, depending on the gases mixed. This technology allows us to recycle usable materials, dramatically reduce the amount of waste sent in landfill sites and make electricity and biodiesel from our unwanted garbage.

These systems of waste disposal can go one step further and offer a host of other opportunities. For instance, we can make use of the electricity and heat generated through the recycling processes to power greenhouses to grow crops. The carbon dioxide emitted from the exhausts of the heat transfer devices can feed back into the greenhouse. Exposing crops to small

"POLLUTION IS NOTHING BUT THE RESOURCES WE ARE NOT HARVESTING. WE ALLOW THEM TO DISPERSE BECAUSE WE'VE BEEN IGNORANT OF THEIR VALUE."
– R. BUCKMINSTER FULLER

"YEARS AGO, WE ALL TALKED ABOUT RECYCLING AND NOT DUMPING THINGS DOWN YOUR DRAIN AND ALL OF THAT, BUT TALKING DOESN'T HELP MUCH. BASICALLY, IT'S GOING TO HAVE TO BE LEGISLATION, BECAUSE THE IMPACT IS SO HUGE AND DIVERSIFIED."

– TED DANSON

levels of extra carbon dioxide can increase their productivity by as much as 30%. Instead of releasing the carbon into the atmosphere, where it will cause excessive damage, we can instead use it to solve other problems – food supply. This also reduces the need to import certain foods across the world. It effectively creates a closed-loop system, where discarded consumer goods are able to produce value over and over again beyond their intended lifecycle, with minimal damage to the environment.

Some of the most exciting ideas and opportunities on how to deal with waste have come from industry and government-funded research centres. New experiments and on-going studies are revealing incredible opportunities for converting waste into valuable and sustainable resources. Through innovative technology and well-executed programs, we can take hold of these opportunities and turn them into everyday realities.

Through effective government planning at both local and global levels we can implement policies and regulations that create tax penalties for companies and industries that send their recyclable waste to landfills instead of existing recycling centres. Financial incentives can be created for companies and industries that choose to use recycled materials instead of virgin materials in the manufacturing processes. Valuable funding and resources can be given to recycling initiatives and research departments that seek to create and implement new technologies and ideas that harness the value of waste in economical and environmentally friendly ways.

Through effective government policies and programs, coupled with the right technology and infrastructure, we can steer the waste recycling industry into something that is sustainable for our planet and our economies.

30% **CONSTRUCTION & DEMOLITION**

20% **MANUFACTURING**

23% **MINING & QUARRY**

20% **MUNICIPLE**

WASTE GENERATED WORLDWIDE

ARE WE DESIGNING PRODUCTS BETTER THAN WE DID IN THE PAST?

Almost every product we manufacture today carries a lower carbon footprint than the same products produced 50 years ago, whilst at the same time carries a higher efficiency and performance. We have taken decades to learn how to produce the same materials and products in the most efficient manners possible. And whenever we begin to believe that we have reached the pinnacle of product design and manufacturing potential, newer innovations and technologies emerge that completely outshine anything else from the past. From cars to airplanes and plastic bottles to computers, almost all of our products are continuously being improved year after year thanks to creative thinking and visionary leadership.

Most of these improvements in product design and performance have a lot to do with improvements in material efficiency and performance, which reduce the natural resource and energy amounts needed to create these products. Steel, aluminium, concrete and plastic are examples of materials that have undergone drastic improvements over the decades. A material such as steel is essential for the manufacturing of many industrial products such as cars, planes, bridges and buildings. Thanks to the incredible breakthroughs in material technology over the past few decades, we are now able to make industrial products like steel more efficiently than ever. On average, making a kilogram of steel today takes one third as much energy as it did in 1950, and produces as much as 10% less carbon in the process. It is also lighter, more durable, less corrosive and has far fewer contaminants. The improvements in the performance and efficiency of modern manufacturing processes continue to increase annually, while at the same time the efficiency of the products improves. From an environmental perspective, this is where we need to be heading.

DID YOU KNOW?

The amount of energy required to produce a tonne of steel has been reduced by 60% in the past 50 years.

"THERE APPEARS TO BE A DEEPLY EMBEDDED UNEASINESS IN OUR CULTURE ABOUT THROWING AWAY JUNK THAT CAN BE REUSED. PERHAPS, IN PART, IT IS GUILT ABOUT CONSUMPTION. PERHAPS IT ALSO FEELS UNNATURAL."

– WILLIAM BOOTH

Concrete is perhaps the most important material man has ever created, both in terms of the amount we produce every day as well as the total amount we have already laid down. Concrete has been the foundation for the massive expansion of urban areas of the past several decades, and will continue to perform a central role in the future in light of the rapid industrialisation and urbanisation that is expected to take place. If you look at almost any modern city today, the predominant material you will see will be concrete, followed by glass, steel and masonry. But concrete has come a long way since it was first invented in 1849. In the last 60 years, the production of concrete has increased 25-fold. This is significant when compared to the smaller increase of another key manufacturing material - steel - which has only increased 8-fold. Fortunately, coupled with the increased demand for concrete, there has been a dramatic improvement in concrete innovation.

For example, concrete is now being developed to repair itself. With the addition of certain polymers, chemicals and other advanced materials to the concrete mixture, concrete columns and slabs are gaining the ability to self-repair. When cracks and weak points in the concrete begin to occur, a microcapsule breaks, causing a chemical reaction that fills the damaged area. Other innovations in concrete technology are allowing the material to act as a pollution-reducing agent.

Aluminium too is a material that has benefitted significantly thanks to technological advances of late. The weight of aluminium has decreased significantly in the past three decades, especially soda cans. It is estimated that if the total amount of aluminium cans that were made in 2010 were produced as they were in 1970, production would have required an additional 680-million kg's of aluminium. This is equivalent to 3 400 Boeing 747 airplanes.

The materials used in products are not the only things that have improved in efficiency. Many products themselves have also improved significantly in efficiency. The production of vehicles, for instance, has drastically improved over the years. Vehicles today drive faster, get better mileage and are significantly lighter than vehicles manufactured 50 years ago. Also consider a computer. In the last few decades alone, computers have become one-third of the size whilst offering double the services.

The major breakthrough in material manufacturing and product design is that we use less fuel, energy, labour and time when producing these goods. Such efficiency will be of utmost importance for the future, as it can offset the predicted increases in consumption created by rapid population growth, industrialisation and the increasing purchasing power of the world's population.

"I'VE BEEN AMAZED AT HOW OFTEN THOSE OUTSIDE THE DISCIPLINE OF DESIGN ASSUME THAT WHAT DESIGNERS DO IS DECORATION. GOOD DESIGN IS PROBLEM SOLVING."
- JEFFERY VEEN

ARE THERE BETTER WAYS TO DESIGN, MANUFACTURE AND USE PRODUCTS?

One of the fundamental challenges we are facing on a global level is that we are inevitably going to run out of resources to mine and places to throw our trash. For the sake of both humanity and the environment, we need to start investing in new and creative ways of making use of what we have already extracted from the earth, and reducing our need for what remains.

Conventional approaches to sustainability make the efficient use of energy and materials their ultimate goal. While this can be a useful transitional strategy, it doesn't really provide a solution to the problem, but only lessens the impact. One way to achieve a greater level of sustainability within the consumer goods sector would be to explore the idea of upcycling products as opposed to downcycling them. Downcycling is a conventional yet short-sighted approach whereby materials are converted into products of lower value after their primary use has expired. The concept of upcycling, on the other hand, promotes the design of products whereby their materials can be used to create another product of the same, or even better quality, after its primary use has expired. Upcycling offers an incredibly value-driven and immensely innovative way of designing, manufacturing and using products, ultimately extending their value and lifespan. Instead of sending an old ladder to a landfill site, we can convert it into a bookshelf. Old wrenches can be used as wall hooks instead of being sent to a landfill site. The fundamental principle of upcycling is every product can be reused in new and exciting ways, whether through the design of the product itself by the manufacturer, or the creative resourcefulness of the consumer.

The biodegradability of materials becomes increasingly important as well. We urgently need to start designing products that enhance biodegradability. The term 'biodegradable' essentially refers to a material that breaks down naturally into organic matter as a result of exposure to moisture, heat and micro-organisms. Instead of

"THAT'S THE INTERESTING THING ABOUT AN OBJECT. ONE OBJECT SPEAKS VOLUMES ABOUT THE COMPANY THAT PRODUCED IT AND IT'S VALUES AND PRIORITIES."
– JONY IVES

"YOU HAVE TO DEEPLY UNDERSTAND THE ESSENCE OF A PRODUCT IN ORDER TO BE ABLE TO GET RID OF THE PARTS THAT ARE NOT ESSENTIAL."

– JONY IVES

DID YOU KNOW?

While 40% of consumers say they are willing to purchase 'green' products, only 4% of consumers actually do when given the choice.

designing and manufacturing products in ways that take hundreds of years to decompose, we can rather look to design products that can actually add value to the soil. Products that are designed and engineered with materials that are biodegradable can reduce the time taken for products to decompose naturally. We have already seen this, as some plastics are able to decompose in less than 50 years, compared to other plastics that can take over 1 000 years. Products that make use of paper, cardboard and certain types of plastics can carry nutrients or seeds in them, so that when they are disposed they can be a beneficial ingredient to soil.

The very idea and perception of a sustainable product needs to be rebranded. There is a large public misconception of what a sustainable or 'green' product really is. Too many people tend to think of a sustainable product as a compromise; something that is more environmentally conscious, yet holds less value, performance or beauty than a conventional product. We tend to think that if a product is 'natural', then it is automatically sustainable. This trend of 'green washing' is highly prevalent in society as customers who are eager to take part in the sustainability movement are often naive or oblivious to what 'eco-friendly' or 'sustainable' really entails.

Thankfully, misconceptions about sustainable products, including the idea that green products are too expensive, underperforming or less appealing in comparison to regular products, are steadily dissolving in light of recent breakthroughs in technology, material and design. Many innovative and cutting edge companies are bringing out revolutionary products that prove to be superior in performance to its conventional counterparts and defy all negative misconceptions about 'green' products. Tesla Motors is an electric car manufacturing company that has single-handedly demonstrated that the electric vehicle can be a safe, reliable, efficient, and most of all, environmentally friendly, alternative to petroleum-based cars. Tesla motors, under the vision of creative entrepreneur Elon Musk, is creating cars that are widely acknowledged for their ability to outperform competitors in essential features such as handling, speed, safety, reliability, as well as design aesthetic and comfort. Tesla motors aims that by creating a vehicle that is just as good, if not better than any other car on the road, it can position the electric car as the car of choice for the future.

Due to irresponsible design, we go through a tremendous amount of unnecessary and avoidable waste. Consider the

"EVERY BUSINESS AROUND THE WORLD MUST NOW RADICALLY CHANGE ITS THINKING. IN EVERY ASPECT OF ITS OPERATION, IT MUST DO MUCH MORE TO REDUCE THE AMOUNT OF CARBON DIOXIDE IT RELEASES INTO THE AIR."
– RICHARD BRANSON

waste produced when purchasing something as simple as a pair of shoes. When we buy the shoes, they are packaged for us in a cardboard box, which is then often given to us in a plastic bag to carry. Once we get home, both the box and bag are usually thrown away. This contributes to more unnecessary waste. But through smart and thoughtful design, we can reduce such unnecessary waste dramatically. Puma, the world renowned sports brand, has recently designed and brought to market a 'Smart Little Bag' that initially serves the purpose of a shoebox to transport the footwear from the manufacturer to the store, and then from the store to the customer's home. Later on, instead of being thrown away like so many other shoeboxes, the smartly designed bag becomes a durable and stylish carry bag that can be used indefinitely for multiple purposes. The impressive design is made from recycled materials and uses significantly less cardboard than conventional boxes.

If any of these ideas are to be achieved and adopted, it becomes fundamentally important to reshape both the way we view products and the way we consume them. Approaching the design of sustainable products with words like 'resourceful', 'eco-superior' or 'infinite' can help us rethink the value of sustainably designed products and the impact they can have. At the end of the day, it comes down to creating products that hold real, tangible value by contributing positively to people's lives whilst simultaneously reducing humanities' carbon footprint and impact on the environment. Product designers and manufacturers need to consider the environmental effects of the entire products life cycle, and seek sustainable, environmentally friendly solutions to every phase of a products creation, use and disposal. To achieve this, intelligent and creative design strategies, concepts and ideas need to be encouraged, nurtured and sustained across the consumer goods industry in order to create products that make a positive difference in the world.

"OUR WAR ON CARBON DIOXIDE NEEDS TO BE EXPANDED BY GOVERNMENTS AND BY BUSINESSES INTO EVERY PRODUCT, EVERY APPLICATION AND EVERY DESIGN."
– RICHARD BRANSON

"THE WORLD WE HAVE CREATED TODAY HAS PROBLEMS WHICH CANNOT BE SOLVED BY THINKING THE WAY WE THOUGHT WHEN WE CREATED THEM."
– ALBERT EINSTEIN

DID YOU KNOW?

Global consumption of resources will nearly triple to 140 billion tons per year by 2050.

BUILDINGS & CITIES

WHY DO WE BUILD SO MUCH? WHAT ARE CITIES AND WHY ARE THEY IMPORTANT? **WHAT IS A BUILDING LIFE CYCLE?** WHAT EFFECT DO BUILDINGS AND CITIES HAVE ON THE ENVIRONMENT? **WHAT ARE THE PROBLEMS WITH OUR BUILDING METHODS TODAY?** HOW CAN WE MAKE BUILDINGS SUSTAINABLE? **WHAT SHOULD CITIES OF THE FUTURE LOOK LIKE?** DO CITIES HOLD THE KEY TO SUSTAINABILITY?

"ARCHITECTURE IS A VERY DANGEROUS JOB. IF A
WRITER MAKES A BAD BOOK, EH, PEOPLE DON'T READ
IT. BUT IF YOU MAKE BAD ARCHITECTURE, YOU IMPOSE
UGLINESS ON A PLACE FOR A HUNDRED YEARS."
-RENZO PIANO

WHY DO WE BUILD SO MUCH?

It is estimated the we spend on average 90% of all our time indoors. As such, buildings are exceptionally valuable to humans as they provide for one of our most fundamental needs in life: shelter. In a sense, buildings protect us by offering adequate and reliable shelter from natural elements, including the rain, snow, wind and sun. They provide places of safety and security, rest and solitude, as well as warmth and comfort. It is within buildings that we are able to perform a wide range of human activities, no matter the time of day or outdoor weather conditions.

It is within the sheltered spaces of buildings that almost every significant human activity takes place: living, learning, working, socialising, praying and exercising. Buildings are the vessels where the majority of human productivity, engagement and recovery take place. From schools to office blocks, factories to theatres and homes to hospitals, many of the activities essential to human progress, entertainment and wellbeing takes place within the protected, organised and sheltered spaces of the built environment.

As the human population continues to grow at the rapid scale it is currently experiencing, the need for more housing, hospitals, schools, offices and transport facilities becomes increasingly important. It is not only necessary to provide for the sheer amount of facilities and structures needed to meet the increasing demand of today's world, but also to design, construct and maintain such buildings in ways that are sustainable and carry value for many generations to come.

In order to create and maintain buildings that carry relevance and worth long into the future, it is essential that we are able to correctly manage, facilitate and nurture the creative and intellectual skills necessary to create such environments. This is only possible through a careful consideration of the building's entire life cycle, the needs of those who will use it, as well as the surrounding cultural, social and environmental conditions in which the building lies. Buildings and urban environments have the potential to significantly improve and enrich the daily lives of its users. This value can be maximised through intelligent design and careful consideration.

WHAT ARE CITIES AND WHY ARE THEY IMPORTANT?

A city can best be explained as a large and permanent, densely populated, built-up area of human settlement. For the past 3 000 years, cities have been the central places of activity whereby the majority of people, money and goods converge. Cities are the physical manifestation of bigger forces at play, whether those forces are economic, social or environmental. Cities such as London, Shanghai, New York and Hong Kong have become the epicentres of our modern global society and the places where the majority of mankind's greatest achievements have taken place. They are an expression of our collective will: our ambitions, dreams and desires. Cities can be considered as both our greatest invention and our greatest experiment.

Cities too have evolved and expanded over centuries. The majority of cities we know today are very different to those of the past. Cities remained relatively small and insignificant for many centuries, and it was only until a few hundred years ago that they started growing in importance and influence. In the early 19th century, shortly after the Industrial Revolution commenced, only around 3% of the world's populations lived in cities. But industrialisation led to massive urbanisation through the influx of people to cities and urban areas from rural farmlands. The booming factory businesses that were located in cities created many more jobs, and soon enough a significant portion of the population began to flock to these urban areas. As this process has continued over the last few hundred years, we now have a situation where the majority of mankind lives in urban areas. As of 2008, over half of the human population lived in cities, and this has increased substantially since. As a result, the value and importance of cities and urban areas in society has increased.

City growth shows no sign of slowing down in the foreseeable future, with three out of every four humans predicted to live in cities by 2050. This rapid rise in urbanisation has led to the emergence of megacities — large metropolitan areas with populations

"CITIES ARE NEVER RANDOM. NO MATTER HOW CHAOTIC THEY MIGHT SEEM, EVERYTHING ABOUT THEM GROWS OUT OF A NEED TO SOLVE A PROBLEM. IN FACT, A CITY IS NOTHING MORE THAN A SOLUTION TO A PROBLEM, THAT IN TURN CREATES MORE PROBLEMS THAT NEED MORE SOLUTIONS."
-NEAL SHUSTERMAN

of over 10-million people. Today, there are roughly 25 megacities worldwide, with around 80% of them located in developing nations. Megacities are increasing in number and size, and with this comes a great deal of influence too. It is estimated that by 2025, China will have experienced one of the fastest urban expansions in history, as planners intend to merge nine cities together to create an urban area that is roughly 26 times larger than Greater London.

If cities do not adapt to the demands of this rapid process of urbanisation, the added pressure on city systems and infrastructure could lead to inefficiency, redundancy, failed service delivery, urban sprawl and increasing inequality between rich and poor. This would likely lead to the spread of slums on the periphery of the city. It is estimated that around one-billion people already live in slums worldwide, and by 2050 the slum population could reach as much as three-billion. Forecasts suggest that the slum population in Mumbai alone may be greater than the populations of London and New York City combined.

The trend of dramatic city growth looks likely to continue well into the foreseeable future, with city populations expected to increase dramatically year after year. With this in mind, our focus should be on finding the most sustainable and effective ways to meet the demand. The situation at hand carries with it both incredible opportunity and risk, as cities have a profound influence on the relationship between mankind and the environment.

As the trend of urbanisation accelerates so too will issues of urban sustainability. Ironically though, the solutions to the challenges facing the city will more than likely stem from within the city itself. That is because cities exist as hotspots for innovation and collaboration to take place. They provide the opportunity for people of incredibly diverse backgrounds and cultures to work together to solve today's problems, effectively turning cities into engines of art, commerce, science and progress.

More than 75% of the world's natural resources are consumed within urban areas, and the built environment accounts for roughly 40% of all carbon emission. As a result, small changes in the city's approach to resource consumption can have significant impacts across the globe.

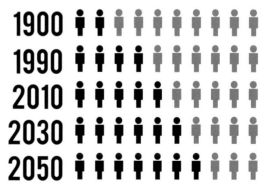

RATIO OF WORLD POPULATION LIVING IN URBAN AREAS

WHAT IS A BUILDING LIFE CYCLE?

The 'life cycle' of a building is a term used to describe all the activities that surround the creation and use of a building throughout its existence. These activities range from the extraction and manufacturing of the materials used in the construction, to the final demolition or dismantling of the building's components and what becomes of them. A life cycle analysis considers all the various processes that take place in the creation of a building. These include the design, manufacturing, resource management, waste treatment and demolition processes. It is important to realise that a buildings' impact reaches far beyond the finished structure, and their materials have the opportunity to carry value long after the buildings themselves are gone.

Unfortunately, when it comes to the environmental impact and sustainable aspects of a building, it is often only the final product that receives attention and critique. Often, many people fail to understand and appreciate the many activities and processes that take place long before construction commences and continue long after the building is complete.

If we are to create and manage buildings in a sustainable way that reduces their environmental impact on the Earth, then we need to adopt a 'cradle-to-cradle' approach to their design as opposed to a 'cradle-to-grave' approach. Under a cradle-to-grave model, building materials and components are designed with a single use in mind; once that use is exhausted, the materials are unusable. In a cradle-to-cradle model, building materials can be used over and over again for other purposes. If we can discover and implement methods that allow us to extend the lifespan of a building's materials beyond their initial use, then we will be able to reach a level of sustainability that truly matters.

MATERIAL EXTRACTION & MANUFACTURING

Every single wall, ceiling, door and beam within a building, despite having already gone through a manufacturing process, has originated from natural resources and raw materials from the earth. Whether it be the steel railing, masonry bricks, timber decking, aluminium window frames, concrete columns, or even the plaster and paint, every single material used in a building originates from resources that only the natural environment can provide. They are extracted from the earth from one location, transported to another for manufacturing and development, and later transported to the site for final construction. All of these processes, from extraction to manufacturing to construction, generally take place great distances from one another. The transportation of these goods increases the demand and cost of fuel, which contribute severely to carbon emissions and the overall carbon footprint of the building project.

The sheer amount of energy that is needed for the extraction, manufacturing and transportation process is enormous. Creating usable building materials from the raw materials found in nature requires a signifi-cant amount of human labour, heat energy, water and machinery.

The environmental impact of each material needs to be considered. Both the material itself, the manner in which it is manufactured, and the location from where it was sourced all have an influence on the overall environmental footprint of the building. Steelwork, for example, consumes vast amounts of energy in its manufacturing, yet it has great recycling potential. Timber can be an incredibly sustainable building material, yet this depends entirely on the type of timber used, the location from where it is sourced and the manner in which it is forested.

A building's location has a significant influence on the sustainable nature of each material. If more locally-sourced materials and resources, especially from the area surrounding the building site itself, can be utilised, then the environmental impact and overall building costs can be reduced significantly in the early stages of the project. By adopting a more local approach to the building's design and construction, social benefits can be achieved as well by providing labour and income to the local community.

CONCRETE
IS THE WORLD'S MOST COMMON BUILDING MATERIAL, AND THE SECOND – MOST CONSUMED SUBSTANCE AFTER WATER.

CONSTRUCTION

During the construction phase of the building life cycle, all the materials and labour for building come together and are ultimately assembled. The workforce, comprising of construction workers, specialists and managers, refer to the designs of the architects and engineers and use them to create the actual structure. This process is extremely labour intensive, as many skilled workers, specialists and machinery is needed to effectively construct and assemble the building as envisioned. Large amounts of energy, water and fuel are required in this process of construction and assembly. Additionally, the transportation of materials and machinery, as well as the altering of the land require these resources. The construction and assembly of a building can range from just a few months to many years, and relies on a number of factors for completion, such as the size and nature of the project, distance of the materials and resources to the site, and the type of weather experienced during construction. Rainstorms, for instance, can hinder the completion time of a project and cause significant setbacks and challenges.

As the construction phase is highly expensive, energy-intensive and often at the mercy of weather conditions, the concept and practice of pre-fabrication has grown in popularity. Under this approach, components of the building are created off-site in controlled factory environments. The components are designed for quick assembly when they get to the site. By using pre-fabricated components, a building project can significantly reduce the time taken to complete construction on-site. Pre-fabrication has shown to be more environmentally friendly as it is often less energy-intensive, produces less waste, and provides the opportunity for greater accuracy and efficiency when assembly and construction takes place. As pre-fabricated materials are manufactured in controlled environments they are less susceptible to the effects of weather, material wastage and pollution that often occur on a building site.

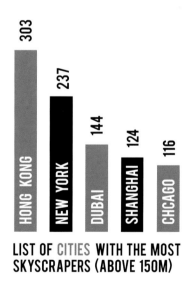

LIST OF CITIES WITH THE MOST SKYSCRAPERS (ABOVE 150M)

MAINTAINANCE & USE

After the building has been constructed and becomes operational and usable, it is able to fulfil the purpose for which it was ultimately created. Buildings should not only be designed to function in a particular way, but also cater for many other uses. The spaces created, materials used and the technologies installed, all allow the building to provide for the various needs and activities of its users, whether that be for educational, social, commercial or industrial purposes.

Over a buildings' lifetime, which spans well into decades, maintenance within the building needs to take place regularly to allow the building to remain robust, usable and safe. This is due to the fact that the materials and technologies of a building often become outdated, inefficient or overused. Some of these materials and technologies can even become an obstruction for the changing and shifting needs of the buildings' users. Without regular and ongoing maintenance, the building will deteriorate and ultimately become inhabitable, reducing its lifespan and overall worth.

Water and electricity are resources that become everyday needs throughout a building's lifetime. Visitors, residents and workers require water for drinking, bathing, washing and cooking. Electricity is needed for heating, cooling and the powering of machines and utilities, such as computers, fridges, toasters and other appliances. Electricity also provides artificial lighting during the night or for those areas of the building that do not receive enough natural sunlight during the day. In order to prevent the wastage and mismanagement of such resources it becomes important to identify and adopt ways of reducing the need for electricity and water altogether.

Through the use and integration of energy- and water-efficient technologies, as well as smart design strategies and responsible building management, these resources can be properly conserved, thereby reducing the environmental footprint of the building and its users. The resulting savings are both economically and environmentally beneficial.

DID YOU KNOW?

Approximately 30% of energy used in a building is used inefficiently or unnecessarily.

"IN THE BIG PICTURE, ARCHITECTURE IS THE ART AND SCIENCE OF MAKING SURE THAT OUR CITIES AND BUILDINGS FIT IN WITH THE WAY WE WANT TO LIVE OUR LIVES."
-RENZO PIANO

DID YOU KNOW?

All steel created as long ago as 150 years can be recycled & used in new products & applications.

DEMOLITION & RECYCLING

At some point, it may become necessary for the existing building to be demolished or disassembled. When this situation arises, it is important that the materials and systems used in the building are designed for easy disassembly and reuse. If the future of these building materials and systems have been planned for, then the opportunity exists for them to be reused and recycled for other building projects or, at the very least, be safely retuned to the natural environment without causing damage or pollution. Through these considerate and intelligent practices, we effectively engage in a form of sustainability. The sheer amount of resources, energy and materials which are needed for a building's planning and construction can be significantly reduced, or in some cases not required at all, when such materials have been sourced from a previous building project.

Using recycled materials such as steel, timber, brickwork and glass, holds great opportunities for the building industry, as it lowers costs and the environmental footprint of a building project. Reusing and recycling building materials lowers energy requirements and resource consumption of building projects by up to 90%. Studies show that roughly 30% of global waste generated comes from the building industry. Considering the sheer amount of materials and resources wasted in the construction and demolition of buildings, it becomes imperative that we find ways of extending the lifespan of these materials once their primary use has expired. It is clear that the decisions we make now will impact long into the future, as every stage of the building's life cycle has an impact on the other.

"REUSING OLD BUILDINGS IS THE TRUE GREEN ARCHITECTURE. BUILDINGS DESIGNED FOR DECADES MUST GIVE WAY TO BUILDINGS DESIGNED FOR CENTURIES."
-RENZO PIANO

"THOSE AREAS OF ASIA, AFRICA AND PARTS OF SOUTH AMERICA THAT WILL SEE URBAN TERRITORY GROW MOST RAPIDLY TEND TO OVERLAP WITH BIODIVERSITY HOTSPOTS AND CONCENTRATIONS OF EXOTIC PLANTS AND ANIMALS."
–BRIAN WALSH

WHAT EFFECT DO BUILDINGS AND CITIES HAVE ON THE ENVIRONMENT?

At the turn of the 21st century, cities occupied a mere 3% of Earth's land surface, yet their environmental impact extended greatly across the globe. Considering the vast amount of resources and energy consumed within cities, their drastic altering of natural landscapes, and the waste and pollution they often produce, every city on Earth carries an environmental impact. For much of the 20th century, the majority of society stood ignorant of the effect cities were having on both human health and the environment. It has now become clear to many that cities do indeed have a profound impact on the natural world, and their influence extends well beyond their immediate borders.

A city's infrastructure, urban layout, geographic location, and the type of activities that take place within them all contribute to extent of their influence over the surrounding landscape and environment. Port cities such as Cape Town or Sydney may have more influence over our oceans than inland cities such as Paris or Moscow. Densely populated cities such as New York or Hong Kong may have different levels of fuel and energy consumption per person than more sprawled out cities such as Beijing or Los Angeles. Regardless of the many differences between cities, their environmental impacts can be organised into three categories: ecological invasion and disruption, resource consumption, as well as waste and pollution.

ECOLOGICAL DAMAGE & DISRUPTION

The construction and development of buildings and other forms of human infrastructure often causes a significant disturbance to the surrounding natural environment. The issue of urban sprawl, whereby human populations move away from the dense urban fabric of the city centre into low-density areas, generally accelerates and expands this process of ecological damage. Forests, wetlands, lakes and grassland areas are chopped down, dammed up, cleared away and destroyed in order to make way for expanding human settlements and infrastructure.

City expansion is being experienced throughout the globe at unprecedented levels. As cities and urban areas expand, they cause major disturbances to the surrounding landscape. When a population moves into an area with a thriving and balanced ecosystem, such as a river or coastline, the urbanisation process often alters the existing landscape dramatically in a very short space of time. When land is cleared to make way for buildings, roads, ports and other infrastructure, the existing ecosystem experiences drastic and significant transformation. The disturbance created as a result of the urbanisation process, and the associated noise pollution, air pollution and ecological destruction that comes with it, sends the existing ecosystem into a state of shock, from which it may never fully recover. People can effectively obstruct and deplete the flow of resources within an ecosystem, such as the flow of water, food and shelter, by building infrastructure that prohibits certain natural processes. For example, underground sewage systems built with concrete can block the natural pathways of underground water supplies.

Healthy ecosystems can be wiped out when we build and expand our cities. An example of this includes the Middle Eastern city of Dubai, where massive developments, such as the 'World Island' and the 'Palm Islands', have caused permanent damage to previously pristine marine ecosystems. The construction of the islands off the coast of Dubai has resulted in damage to the existing coral reef, as well as accelerated coastal erosion and natural wave patterns.

Opportunities do exist to reduce the ecological invasion and disruption of cities. Cities officials can plan carefully and strategically when their expansion poses a threat to sensitive ecosystems. By doing so, the ecological invasion of cities can be reduced considerably, in order to allow both the natural and built environments to coexist and thrive.

However, the unfortunate reality is the large scale process of urbanisation currently being experienced in developing countries is oftentimes uncontrolled, as city developers fail to meet the growing and rapid demand for well-planned and environmentally considerate housing and infrastructure for their growing populations. The ecological invasion and disruption is nothing short of disastrous, with entire ecosystems being wiped out for expanding informal urban settlements, in the form of townships, favelas and slums. These environments often prove to be hostile to the health of both the people living within them and the surrounding ecosystems within reach.

RESOURCE CONSUMPTION

Cities are the epicentre of human production and consumption. Electricity, fuel, food, water, building materials, consumer goods and many other valuable resources are produced and consumed in massive amounts within cities. These can be categorised into two stages: the building of the city, and the maintaining of the city. The first activity considers the construction and development of the city's infrastructure. Excessive amounts of natural resources, such as steel, water, concrete, brickwork and timber are needed for construction. Each and every single building in a city requires a variety of materials for construction, most of which are transported from across the globe and have undergone energy-intensive manufacturing processes.

China provides a good example of the excessive resource consumption of cities. Over the next decade, China plans to spend $6.5 trillion – the financial equivalent of nearly three years of Britain's total output – on building ten new cities to accommodate for over 400-million people. Studies have shown that if China continues to use conventional building methods to construct these cities, they will completely run out of all their topsoil and coal reserves. These cities will a total population of over 400-million people, yet they will have no means of producing energy or food. Based on this shocking revelation, it is clear that the drastic consumption of resources in the building industry is of alarming concern.

The second activity considers the ongoing maintenance and consumption within the city. Large amounts of resources such as food, water and electricity are needed in massive and endless supplies to sustain a city's population. These resources also allow the activities and operations within the city to function correctly without grounding to a halt or suffering deterioration. Consider the sheer amount of food and water needed to feed the citizens of a city such as London or New York on a daily basis.

For example, New York City's daily water consumption averaged over four-billion litres in the year 2012. New York has a population of around nine-million people: now imagine the amount of food and water needed on a daily basis to sustain the residents of a city like Tokyo, which has an urban population of over 37-million people. The sheer amount of fuel that is needed to transport all the goods and services to and from such a city in order to meet the demands of its residents is beyond our imagination. The transport systems alone that are used to move people and goods around a city, such as underground trains, busses, trams and cars require significant amounts of oil to operate. Add to this the sheer amount of electricity needed to power every household, streetlamp and office blocks. The resources demanded in these extensive urban environments are nothing short of excessive.

POLLUTION & WASTE

The large amounts of resources needed by city dwellers on a daily basis, as well as the amount of energy and materials used in the construction of new buildings and urban infrastructure, directly results in the production of large amounts of waste and pollution. Waste from cities generally exists in the form of hazardous substances, garbage and sewage, while pollution includes harmful gases such as carbon dioxide, ozone and sulphur dioxide. This is both a result of unsustainable methods of industrial production and consumption, as well as the many inefficient and wasteful systems set in place within our city environments.

Waste and pollution is released into the atmosphere, seeps into lakes and oceans, or is transported to landfill sites that are outside city limits. The Yamuna River that flows through New Delhi is widely considered one of the most polluted rivers in the world, with over 1.8-billion litres of untreated sewage entering the river every day. New York City produces around 12-million kg's of residential waste daily, most of which is sent to landfill sites in other states. It is estimated that 76% of the New York's residential trash is sent to landfills, whilst only 14% is recycled and 10% is converted to energy. Many cities throughout the world produce so much waste that they are running out of landfill sites. One of Dubai's only two landfill sites, for example, is already full to capacity whilst the other is expected to reach capacity around 2020. These examples illustrate the sheer amounts of waste produced by cities.

Air pollution in cities, mostly caused from pollutants emitted by factories, transport systems (especially vehicles), power-plants and the incineration plants, not only deplete the atmosphere via the release of greenhouse gases, but also poses excessive threats to human health. The World Heath Organisation (WHO) reported in 2012 that around seven-million people died as a result of exposure to air pollution around the world. Ozone, nitrogen oxide and sulphur dioxide are the leading causes of these heath problems. By reducing air pollution levels, cities can reduce the risk of stroke, heart disease, lung cancer and asthma amongst its citizens. In heavily polluted cities such as Beijing, the air is so polluted with smog that people wear masks to prevent the inhalation of toxic pollutants. The quality of Beijing's air is 12 times above the minimum safety level for human health set out by WHO. The city of Delhi in India, with a metropolitan population of over 16-million people, is considered the most air polluted city in the world. With the sheer amount of people exposed to such harmful environments, WHO has confirmed that air pollution within cities is now the world's largest environmental health risk. Reducing air pollution levels in cities could indeed save millions of lives.

"THE PROCESS OF URBANISATION WILL ONLY INCREASE IN THE DECADES TO COME, WITH AN ENORMOUS IMPACT ON BIODIVERSITY AND POTENTIALLY ON CLIMATE CHANGE."
–BRIAN WALSH

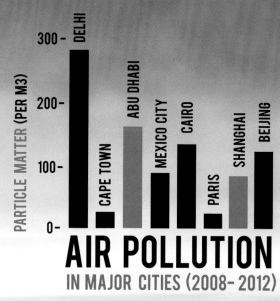

PARTICLE MATTER (PER M3)

300 –
200 –
100 –
0 –

DELHI
CAPE TOWN
ABU DHABI
MEXICO CITY
CAIRO
PARIS
SHANGHAI
BEIJING

AIR POLLUTION
IN MAJOR CITIES (2008– 2012)

WHAT ARE THE PROBLEMS WITH OUR CITIES TODAY?

As cities and urban environments continue to grow in size, number and significance, it becomes alarmingly clear that the major problems of our building and planning methods needs to be addressed. Modern planning has increasingly expanded the physical divide between communities and the benefits of the city. Instead of dense urban areas that foster a sense of community, we increasingly subdivide and sprawl out our urban areas, expanding the distances and connection between them. This situation has contributed to greater resource consumption and waste. It has simultaneously resulted in an absent consideration for the cultural and social values of city inhabitants. In many cases, urban environments become characterised by rapid deterioration, discomfort and hostility, as opposed to inspiration, progress and wellbeing. These factors impact negatively on both city inhabitants and the surrounding natural environment. Conventional but flawed building and planning methods, slums and informal settlements, and the lack of consideration for the environmental, economical and cultural character of a place as a result of globalisation, are amongst the most pressing issues facing our cities today.

DID YOU KNOW?

The large scale adoption of the motor vehicle in the 2nd half of the 20th century has completely transformed modern city planning. Instead of narrow alleyways & pedestrian friendly streets, highways & roads have become the dominant form of movement around the city.

"IN THE TRADITIONAL MODERNIST PLANNING THAT CREATED THE SUBURBS, YOU PUT RESIDENTIAL BUILDINGS IN SUBUR- BAN NEIGHBORHOODS, OFFICE SPACES INTO BRAIN PARKS AND RETAIL IN SHOPPING MALLS. BUT YOU FAIL TO EXPLOIT THE POSSIBILITY OF SYMBIOSIS OR SYNTHESIS THAT WAY."

-BJARKE INGELS

CONVENTIONAL BUILDING METHODS

In a rapidly urbanising world, the speed of construction and cost of materials often takes preference over the long-term durability, quality and sustainability of a building or urban environment. In place of buildings that are durable, adjustable and multifunctional, many conventional buildings today are absent of these qualities. Studies show that modern urban environments decay far quicker than those inherited from the past. As users and needs change, buildings are rather destroyed than adapted. This recurring condition can be attributed to both our ongoing culture of consumerism, and inferior building techniques and materials. In Great Britain, a new public housing unit lasts around 40 years. In New York, the average lifespan of a skyscraper is only 35 years. In our modern society buildings are often treated like disposable consumer products, as opposed to enduring investments.

The careless planning and design methods we have adopted over the 20th century have resulted in a host of problems for our urban areas, often driving them into a state of social, economical and environmental decay. In most parts of the world, people flee decaying suburbs and parts of the city as opposed to re-investing in them. The increased and widespread dependence on motorised transport as a result of urban sprawl and car-dominated city planning has had a profound effect on both the environment and the life of urban residents. Not only does the widespread dependence on an individually owned car increase the consumption of fuel and the manufacturing of more vehicles (both of which increase carbon emissions) but it also destroys the very benefits of a city – the heightened connectivity of people to resources. This increases the social and economic divide between rich and poor, by segregating communities and increasing consumption rates. It also creates a difficult life for those who cannot afford their own transport. Instead of building upwards and closer together, urban infrastructure is spread outward across rural land, disconnecting the workplace from the marketplace, and public spaces from private ones. The condition of urban sprawl and car dominated city planning can be observed in cities such as Johannesburg in South Africa, Los Angeles and Detroit in the US, and Beijing in China.

"WE'VE BEEN BUILDING CITIES AS IF THE MOST IMPORTANT ELEMENT IS THE CAR. WE SHOULD BE BUILDING LIKE THE MOST IMPORTANT ELEMENT IS THE PEOPLE."
–BRENT TODERIAN

SLUMS & INFORMAL SETTLEMENTS

Due to the largely uncontrolled, rapid and ongoing influx of rural populations to cities, especially in developing countries, a host of problems have emerged. As a result of the failure to provide for the urgent demand for housing and services for the growing urban population, poor communities have settled on the fringes of the city, in an attempt to be as close as possible to the benefits and opportunities they provides. Informal housing areas, in the form of slums, have sprung up and expanded. Much in the same way rural communities in Europe and America flooded to urban environments during the early days of the Industrial Revolution, the populations of emerging economies in parts of Africa, South America and Asia are doing the same today, but on a scale unlike anything seen before. Currently, over one-billion people across the planet live in slums, and that number continues to grow. Due to the lack of professional planning, services and construction, these informal settlements are subject to poor living conditions commonly plagued by crime, pollution, sickness, overcrowding and lack of fresh water, sanitation, transport and electricity. Statistics show that in many of these areas one in every six children die before the age of five and the life expectancy of people living in these environments is less than half of those living in the world's healthiest cities.

The favelas of Rio De Janeiro, the townships of Johannesburg, Cape Town and Lagos, and the slums of Mumbai, Jakarta and Delhi are prime examples of these urban conditions, and reveal the failure of local governments to provide adequate housing and services to its poorest communities. The growth of these informal settlements shows no sign of slowing down, and will most likely continue to spread as more and more people in developing nations relocate to the city seeking opportunities and a better life.

The pollution and waste produced by these informal settlements, left uncontrolled, seeps into groundwater systems and nearby rivers and lakes, increasing the threat of water contamination and creating health problems for both the community and surrounding ecosystems. The situation will not improve until governments and city officials take greater responsibility for the wellbeing of its poorest residents. There is, however, significant change happening in many local governments, as they are now beginning to acknowledge informal settlements and collaborate with these communities to provide for their necessary health, housing and transport needs.

33%

THE TOTAL URBAN POPULATION LIVING IN SLUMS IN THE DEVELOPING WORLD

GLOBALISATION

With each day, the communication and trade barriers that once separated people across the world are being broken down due to the ongoing process of globalisation. The building industry itself has benefited immensely as a result, as technologies, ideas and resources are more easily shared and transported across great distances. At the same time though, a host of issues have come along with it. In a world where modern technologies, design methods and planning models are easily copied from one part of the world and pasted in another, a great disregard for location has resulted. In the past, buildings and cities were designed with a careful consideration of the unique conditions of their location. Absent of the convenience of air conditioning, mechanical heating and artificial lighting, buildings and cities were carefully designed to withstand the harsh outdoor weather conditions by making considerate use of the resources that were locally available.

Globalisation and industrialisation have changed this dramatically. The modernist movement that began in the early stages of the 20th century sought to take advantage of the opportunities that globalism provided by creating an autonomous, universal approach to architecture and urban planning. Detached from their unique geographic, climatic and cultural conditions, buildings adopted a uniform approach to design and construction, abandoning the values of traditional building methods. Instead of creating urban environments that are unique and respond to their cultural, social and geographic surroundings, building methods today increasingly embrace a culture of mass production, whereby a one-size-fits-all approach is adopted. Such places fail to address the problems and opportunities of their location and as a result, become increasingly expensive to maintain, consume vast amounts of resources and energy, contribute little social value and lack an overall sense of rootedness and identity.

A prime example of this condition can be found in the desert cities of Abu Dhabi and Dubai, where the poor planning and building methods have created a heat island effect. Along with extensive landscaping of non-indigenous plant life that requires large amounts of water to flourish, the energy and water demands of the city are excessively high in order to deal with the harsh desert climate. Having embraced outdated 20th century building models, completely unsuited to the desert climate, these cities have become increasingly unsustainable. Thankfully, some large-scale projects, such as Masdar City in Abu Dhabi, seek to successfully respond to the conditions of the desert heat by creating buildings that facilitate comfortable living environments without the need for air conditioning, heating or artificial lighting. By embracing century-old traditional building methods, combined with modern technology, Masdar City shows how the benefits of globalisation can be used in line with location.

"AS LONG AS YOU USE PARTICULAR TECHNIQUES THAT AROSE WHEN HUMAN BEINGS IN THE EARLY INDUSTRIAL AGE WERE DRUNK ON CONSUMING ENERGY, YOU CANNOT JUST FIX THOSE BUILDINGS BY STICKING SOMETHING ON TOP. YOU COULD ADD A FEW PERCENTAGE POINTS THAT MAKE IT BETTER, BUT IT'S THE WHOLE APPROACH TO THE DESIGN THAT HAS TO CHANGE."

-NIKOS SALINGAROS

HOW CAN WE MAKE BUILDINGS SUSTAINABLE?

An environmentally sustainable building is a term that is relatively new to the construction industry, yet it has long been one of the founding principles of architectural design. At a basic level, a sustainable building is simply a structure that is able to sustain itself and its occupants without a heavy dependence on resources. They also carry a lower environmental impact throughout their life cycle as a result of smart design strategies, choice of materials during construction, and the management of waste. They are seen to add tremendous value not only to the surrounding natural environment, but to those that occupy the building on a daily basis.

If a building is to add true value in an environmental, social and economic manner, it should steer away from conventional building designs by offering unique opportunities that can enhance the value of the building whilst still reducing its environmental impact. Buildings that carry value well into the future will be able to adapt to various conditions, reduce environmental impact throughout their life cycle, and enhance the wellbeing and quality of life of its users.

The basic approach to creating any sustainable building should be to reduce the overall need for energy and other resources such as water, heat, lighting and cooling through passive design strategies. The second should be to harness technologies and strategies that increase the performance and efficiency of the resources used. Then, when energy and resources are needed, we should harness and retrieve these resources in ways that are socially, economically and environmentally sustainable.

There are many different approaches to making a building sustainable, all of which should be integrated into the overall design and management of the building. They can effectively be broken down into three categories: construction and materials, passive design strategies, and active design strategies. Each approach to sustainability should be carefully considered in accordance with each other, and should simultaneously account for the buildings surroundings and environmental footprint.

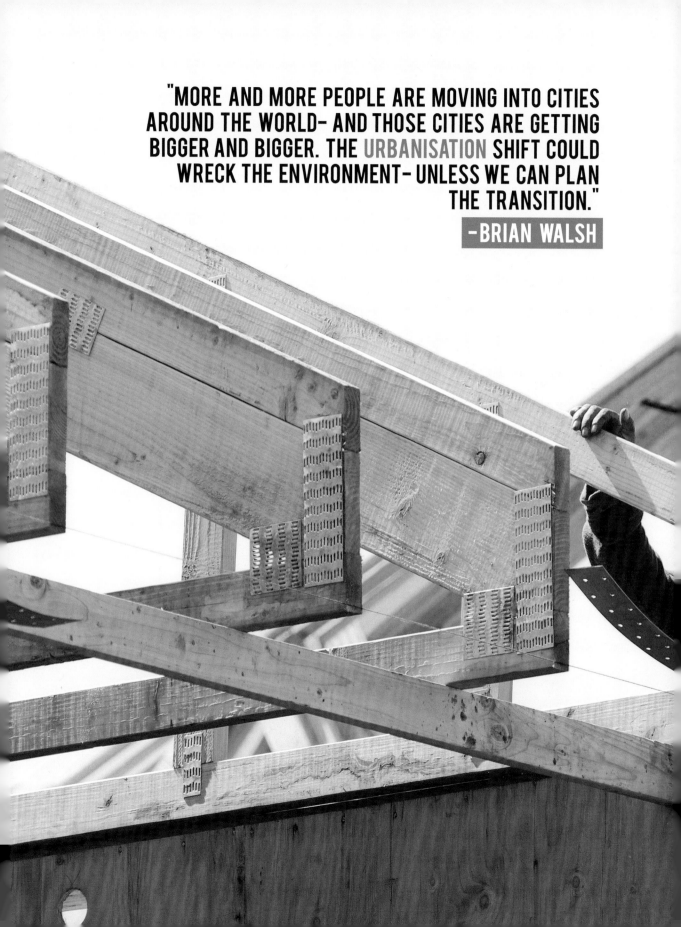

"MORE AND MORE PEOPLE ARE MOVING INTO CITIES AROUND THE WORLD- AND THOSE CITIES ARE GETTING BIGGER AND BIGGER. THE URBANISATION SHIFT COULD WRECK THE ENVIRONMENT- UNLESS WE CAN PLAN THE TRANSITION."
-BRIAN WALSH

CONSTRUCTION & MATERIALS

By preserving indigenous trees, natural water networks and other resources of value to the surrounding environment, the ecological footprint of the building can be reduced, thus making the building more environmentally sustainable.

During the development of a building, many resources and materials are needed. Due to the convenience and availability of globally sourced products, it is often easy to import them from elsewhere, without any consideration for the use of materials and resources found near the actual site. If someone is building a house in a forest, why create a building out of steel and brickwork when timber from the surrounding trees can be used instead? In our globalised world, design and planning is often detached from the building process, thus the foundational principle of making the most of locally available resources is lost. Even in the process of repairs and maintenance, increasing the use of locally-sourced materials provides the opportunity for more sustainable construction. Buildings should be designed to reduce the need for energy, materials and fuel throughout their construction process.

Utilising the resources of the site that would otherwise be overlooked or even discarded in the construction process goes a long way in reaching a higher level of sustainability, effectively rooting and connecting the building with its surrounding environment. Buildings should be designed in a manner that reduces the need for energy, materials and fuel throughout the construction process. Materials better suited to the local climate and weather conditions should take top priority.

On-site waste management is another important part of sustainable construction. The building industry produces incredible amounts of waste that goes to landfill sites, and many of the chemicals and materials used on-site can damage the surrounding environment if not properly handled and controlled. It is important that a site waste management plan is put in place and enforced throughout the construction process. With the correct management, storage, disposal and recycling of building materials, the environmental footprint of a building project can be substantially reduced.

"DESIGNS ARE INCREASINGLY WINNING COMPETITIONS BECAUSE THEY ARE LITERALLY GREEN, AND BECAUSE SOMEWHERE THEY FEATURE A SMALL WINDMILL."
-REM KOOLHAUS

PASSIVE DESIGN

Before the invention of air-conditioning or the lightbulb, architects and builders had to make use of the natural elements and smart design practices to make buildings liveable and hospitable. They would build thick walls with good insulating properties to regulate the internal temperatures, keeping out the harsh heat or freezing cold. They would create overhangs and shading devices to block out the direct sunlight, and they would design and build strategically placed windows and openings to let in the natural daylight and outdoor breeze.

Over the course of the 20th century, as technology progressed and global building methods and materials grew in popularity and availability, many sustainable design strategies were left behind. Artificial lighting, air conditioning and mechanical ventilation have replaced traditional design practices that were once essential principles of building design. Passive design is an age-old approach and a practical and sustainable form of design. When buildings are designed to respond to the geography, climate and weather patterns of their location, they are able to regulate indoor temperatures, maximise daylight and provide natural ventilation with little need for additional resources and energy.

Passive design strategies are able to provide cooling, heating, lighting and ventilation within a building in a way that is sustainable, optimising the use of naturally occurring phenomena. The need to generate or produce artificial forms of heating, cooling, lighting and ventilation is reduced significantly. Passive design strategies use their built and physical form to provide for such needs. By intentionally designing buildings to function with a reduced reliance on resources such as water or electricity, passive design strategies harness the power of nature. Such examples include solar radiation, natural airflow, shading, insulating materials, building orientation and positioning, light wells and openings, rainfall capture and even indigenous plants and biodiversity. Once a passively designed building has been constructed, it is inherently sustainable.

Passive design uses simple design solutions to create an enjoyable and productive internal environment. Passively designed buildings place a great deal of importance on the symbiosis between the building and the natural environment, whether it be through natural daylighting, shading or ventilation. By reducing the need for mechanical methods of cooling, heating, lighting and ventilation, the costs of energy and water are reduced significantly and the building ultimately carries a lower environmental footprint.

DID YOU KNOW?

Due to the extreme heat island effect within Abu Dhabi, the city is 5°C hotter than the surrounding desert.

DID YOU KNOW?

The building sector is one of the main contributors to carbon emissions, consuming approximately 40% of global energy. The building industry consumes 12% of all freshwater & generated 40% of the total volume of waste.

ACTIVE DESIGN

At a basic level, active design deals with two basic factors: the methods in which the resources within a building are used and managed, and the ways in which such resources are produced. Active design strategies reduce the amount of energy and water needed via resource-efficient technologies. By adopting such systems, the consumption of resources and the overall efficiency of a building is improved. Not only do active systems reduce the amount of energy and water needed within a building, they also allow buildings to generate their own electricity through on-site renewable energy technologies, harvest rainwater to provide for the water needs of the occupants, and recycle the waste produced by its users.

There are many ways in which design can reduce the need for electricity in buildings. Efficient technologies, such as energy-saving light bulbs or solar geysers, demand fewer units of electricity to perform the same functions as older technologies. Behavioural technology can reduce energy requirements for lighting and heating by detecting the movements and presence of its users, and effectively reduce the amount of lighting or heating required in unused parts of the building. Such technologies reduce electricity wastage by effectively limiting resources to only those areas of the building being used at any given time. Many buildings with active strategies also generate their own electricity. Renewable energy technologies are often installed on building rooftops to generate power, as opposed to being dependent on the city grid. Most city grids generate power through coal-powered plants to meet the city's needs. By generating significant amounts of energy on-site, through clean renewable energy sources, buildings can effectively become more sustainable.

Water is another key resource that is consumed in large amounts by building occupants, and significant and unnecessary waste can often occur due to poor systems and technologies. Water-saving technologies, such as low-flow shower heads or dual-flush toilets, can go a long way to saving this precious resource and reducing overall water consumption in buildings and cities as a whole. By harnessing a naturally occurring water supply, such as a nearby river or lake, buildings are able to use what is closely available to provide for the occupants' needs. By capturing rainfall on the building's roof or other areas of the site and storing it in rainwater tanks, buildings can use an available natural resource and reduce the need to rely on costly external sources such as a municipal water grid. While rainwater can sometimes be used as drinkable water, it can always be used for flushing toilets and irrigating gardens. Many older buildings have unfortunately been designed to use clean, drinkable water in every part of the building, whether they are toilets, showers, sinks, or irrigation systems. They then send the waste water to a sewerage system. By recycling the water within the building, and using the greywater from showers, baths, washing machines and bathroom sinks for toilets and irrigation systems, the building can alleviate the need for clean water.

WHAT SHOULD CITIES OF THE FUTURE LOOK LIKE?

It is important that both new and existing city developments avoid the mistakes of the past by adopting new ideas and strategies that can help solve today's challenges. This can only be achieved if we are bold enough to implement strategies that go against the status quo, and look to investments that will prove valuable and beneficial for our future. It is important that our actions in the design, management and transformation of the city takes a long-term approach and cast a vision that will meet the needs of society in the future. Fortunately, urban planners throughout the globe are exploring a host of creative ideas that can reduce the consumption of resources in buildings and improve the well-being of city residents. Such technologies and practices can effectively reduce energy consumption, water use, waste and carbon emissions. Smart city planning can create more efficient methods of transport around the city, and reduce our need for personal car ownership altogether. Cities of the future need embrace whatever means necessary to dramatically reduce their environmental impact.

We know the importance of cities will continue to increase well into the future, as more and more of the world's population moves from countryside to the city. Every city today has an influence over, to a large extent, the amount of energy and resourc-

"WHEN TALKING ABOUT THE FUTURE CITY, IT'S ALL TOO EASY TO SPEAK ONLY OF CHINA AND INDIA. THERE IS GOOD REASON FOR THAT: BRITAIN AND THE WEST ARE IN DANGER OF GETTING LEFT BEHIND."
—NORMAN FOSTER

es consumed by its inhabitants. In light of this, dense urban environments have been found to consume far less resources than those that are sprawled out. In mega cities, like New York and Los Angeles in the US, the carbon footprint per person has been shown to decrease as the population density increases. For example, the average carbon footprint of a person in New York City - a highly densified urban environment - is roughly seven metric tonnes of carbon dioxide per year. On the other hand, the average carbon footprint of a person in Los Angeles - an extremely sprawled out city - is estimated to be over 18 metric tonnes of carbon dioxide per year. Densifying the city will therefore play a fundamental part in reducing a city's environmental impact.

Dense areas reduce travel distances, and in turn reduce our dependence on transport and fuel. In Los Angeles, for example, the biggest contributor of greenhouse gas emissions is transport. In New York City, on the other hand, the biggest contributor is the food industry. This is related to the differences in density between the two cities. Population density also constrains family size, limits the consumption of all kinds of goods, reduces ownership of wasteful appliances, decreases the generation of solid waste. Adding to this, it encourages residents to live in some of the world's most inherently energy-efficient residential structures: apartment buildings. The difference between the carbon footprints of people in New York and Los Angeles is testament to the massive opportunity urban density can play in overcoming our challenges.

The term 'future cities' is often misinterpreted in the sense that many people understand it to relate to cities that are yet to be built. But the term has broader implications. Cities of the future also include those that already exist and must undergo transformation. In order to see a sustainable future for mankind we will need to improve the existing built environment wherever we can by replacing outdated, inefficient, environmentally damaging building and planning methods with newer and more suitable ones. Since over half of the buildings already existing today are expected to still be in use around 2050, adapting and transforming them will be key to achieving authentic sustainability within cities. After all, it is far more sustainable to upgrade an existing building than to build a new one from scratch.

Future cities should focus largely on their systems. Buildings of the future should harvest and recycle water through water catchment systems, and generate their own electricity by installing renewable energy technologies on their rooftops. Cities should reduce the consumption of resourc-

DID YOU KNOW?

In 2050 there will be almost as many people in Nigeria as in the United States, & the population of many African countries will have doubled.

KARACHI, PAKISTAN
SHENZHEN, CHINA
LAGOS, NIGERIA

THE WORLDS FASTEST
GROWING MEGACITIES
(BY POPULATION)

es by increasing their own capacity to generate and produce them. Urban farming, rainwater harvesting, black and grey water recycling and waste-to-energy processes are great examples of this.

The preservation and creation of green spaces within cities, such as large parks and botanical gardens, will also have a vital role to play in the sustainable future of cities. Green spaces absorb rainwater, resulting in an improvement of the city's drainage systems. This significantly reduces the risk of flooding within cities. The trees also absorb pollutants such as carbon dioxide, thereby reducing the overall carbon footprint of the city and its inhabitants. They also reduce the urban heat island effect within cities by absorbing the heat and providing shading. Green spaces are a good indicator of a city's overall ecological health. In many studies, urban environments have been excluded from the list of effective 'carbon sinks', as the amount of forests and parks within cities are significantly smaller than rural and wilderness areas. However, a recent study undertaken by the British Council on the city of Leicester found that carbon dioxide absorption in the city's parks, industrial land, gardens, golf courses, natural areas and river banks was over 10 times what they expected. As such, future cities should place great emphasis and priority on not only the abundant provision of indigenous green spaces within the city environment, but the quality of them too.

A building must be extremely adaptable to change if it is to provide value for years and even generations to come. The most sustainable buildings will be the ones that are clearly able to adapt to varying circumstances. We cannot determine what role or purpose a building will have in 50 years time, or the needs of its users. It therefore becomes important to design and construct buildings that are flexible and adaptable to the changing needs of society.

Our future objective should be to create cities that work in harmony with nature rather than against it. The future city needs to become an ecosystem that allows both humans and nature to partner equally in reducing the negative effects of rapid urbanisation. By doing so, both the natural environment and human health can be improved. In Copenhagen, for example, many years of investments in the city's sewage system has revitalised and completely transformed the quality of water in the harbour. At one stage, the water was so heavily polluted with sewage, algae, industrial waste and oil from its harbour activities that it posed severe health threats to both humans and marine species. The revitalisation was mainly due to a remarkable reduction in wastewater discharge, brought about by improvements in the city's infrastructure. The cleaning up of the harbour has resulted in a water quality so high that people can now swim in it. At the same time, marine populations are once again able to thrive within the area.

93%

THE PERCENTAGE OF TOTAL URBAN GROWTH PREDICTED TO OCCUR IN DEVELOPING COUNTRIES IN THE NEAR FUTURE.

THE WORLD'S MOST SUSTAINABLE CITIES:
FRANKFURT, GERMANY
LONDON, ENGLAND
COPENHANGEN, DENMARK

DO CITIES HOLD THE KEY TO SUSTAINABILITY?

It has been estimated that 75% of all natural resources are consumed within cities. If local governments and city citizens across the world are able to reduce their environmental impact by becoming more sustainable, the positive effects will be felt across the globe.

The perception of cities has changed dramatically over the centuries. Since the early days of the Industrial Era, the city was for a long time considered to be a necessary evil. It was seen as a place of both opportunity and despair, whereby both human health and the natural environment was neglected for the sake of human ambition and economic progress. Even prominent thinkers such as Thomas Jefferson and Gerald Ford tended to view the city as a place of poverty, crime, pollution, congestion and overall poor health. The mass retreat of people from city centres to the outlying suburbs during the 1960s and 1970s showed evidence of this commonly held belief.

In complete contrast to this, the popular view of our day is that cities may actually hold the greatest opportunity for sustainable human living. Many experts have come to realise that people are better off when they reside in a city. Many of the fastest growing cities in the world, especially those of developing countries found in Asia, South America and Africa, have many urban problems and are places of great human suffering. However, even a city slum or informal settlement has advantages and benefits that one cannot find in the rural countryside.

With time, the city has come to look less like the source of our problems, and more like places of opportunity to improve human wellbeing and mankind's overall environmental footprint. Large investments in education and sanitation, as well as clean water and electricity infrastructure, have transformed cities from places of decay, pollution and sickness into places of improved health and wellbeing. This is true even in some of the poorest cities in developing countries.

Cities have remarkable potential to facilitate and amplify human creativity, communication and innovation. It is within a diverse and dynamic urban framework that the greatest human innovations and breakthroughs have occurred. It was within the creative hub of the Renaissance city of Florence where the ideas and masterpieces of Leonardo Da Vinci and Michelangelo came to life. It was within the densely populated city of London that saw the discovery and invention of some of the finest systems and machines that steered Europe through the Industrial Era. And today, it is within the technologically savvy cities of Silicon Valley, such as San Francisco and Palo Alto, where cutting edge companies such as Google, Apple, Facebook and Tesla thrive.

It is imperative that cities continue to become centres of excellence in the face of our current and future challenges. If cities are designed to maximise the exchange of ideas, information and resources, they can be an extremely powerful too in helping us find solutions to our problems.

The main ingredient to the ingenuity and innovation of successful cities comes down to one unifying element: people. By fostering a close connection between a diverse and talented community of people of different ages, cultures and experiences, cities become incubators and facilitators for the exchange of information and resource. It is only through the collective intelligence of a diverse range of engineers, designers, economists, ecologists, policymakers and the general public,

that our challenges can be overcome and sustainable solutions can be found.

The greatest opportunity cities provide is the ability to combine our collective intelligence to solve the problems of our day. While the new era we find ourselves in - the 'Information Age' - can facilitate this collaborative process through digital technology, the face-to-face contact that is made possible by the close proximity afforded by cities cannot be underestimated.

The city is never complete: it has a beginning but no end; it is a work in progress. Because the modern city today encompasses a host of challenges that will extend well into the future, it becomes vital to transform the city into a more sustainable environment. The on-going challenge facing urban growth is whether or not human creativity is able to innovate fast enough to sustain an ever-growing urban population. At the same time, cities must decrease the consumption of resources and overall environmental impact of each and every one of its citizens. When the size of a city doubles, its material infrastructure surprisingly does not. Compared with suburban or rural areas, cities have shown to do considerably more with less. The bigger cities get the more productive and efficient they tend to become. It is clear that well designed cities will play the key role in achieving longterm sustainability.

"CITIES ARE MUCH MORE EFFICIENT IN THE CONSUMPTION OF RESOURCES AND LAND BECAUSE OF THEIR HIGHER DENSITIES."
-STEVEN CHERRY

"SUSTAINABILITY CAN'T BE LIKE SOME SORT OF MORAL SACRIFICE, POLITICAL DILEMMA OR PHILANTHROPICAL CAUSE. IT HAS TO BE A DESIGN CHALLENGE."
—BJARKE INGELS

THE TIPPING POINT

AFTERWORD

Throughout the pages of this book we have sought to provide a clear and definitive understanding of the most crucial environmental challenges present in our world today. We face these challenges not only as individuals, communities and nations, but as the entire human race. These issues are very real and take place across the globe. Every decision we make in the present will have an effect on the future.

Today, we use the equivalent of 1.5 planets in order provide for the vast amounts of resources we demand as a society. It has been estimated that if our populations continue and consumption behaviours do not change, we will need the equivalent of two Earth's to support us by the year 2030. This fact clearly reveals the sheer unsustainable nature of our current existence. With no back-up planet – at least not within our reach – that is capable of supporting life, we must confront the reality that nothing in our solar system can help us. We have no choice but to overcome the host of environmental challenges if we are to leave behind a healthy planet for future generations to come.

Without doubt, the toughest challenge we face in the transition to a sustainable existence is that of rapid population growth. It took 250 000 years for civilisation to reach a population of one-billion. Today, we add around 250 000 people to the planet every single day. Several studies have shown that at our current rate of consumption, Earth's resources are enough to sustain only around only two-billion people. The current global population of over seven-billion is thus already between two to three times higher than the level Earth can sustain. With the changing consumption and waste disposal behaviours that will accompany this growth in population, it quickly becomes clear that we are entering a critical period in human history characterised with difficulties, uncertainties and, most importantly, dramatic change.

To add to the pressing challenges of rapid population growth, the industries that exist to provide for our way of life operate on a very linear system of production, consumption and disposal. Although highly effective for generating economic growth under an industrial society model, it is no longer relevant to the challenges of the world we now live in. The most important industries known to man are in desperate need of transformation if we are to secure a sustainable place on Earth. The world is currently undergoing a drastic shift from the Industrial Age to what we are now calling the 'Information Age', whereby digital technology, and the knowledge and ideas spread within it, is becoming the currency of the day. We must harness and adapt to these new opportunities if we are to create a more sustainable world.

Although a daunting thought, the reality is if we do not become sustainable, we will not necessarily destroy Earth, but instead destroy ourselves. Despite what horrid condition we may leave the planet, it will remain. The decision to change will not necessarily be for the future of the planet, but for the future of humanity.

"THE PAST IS A SAFE REFUGE. THE PAST IS A CONSTANT TEMPTATION. AND YET THE FUTURE IS THE ONLY PLACE WE HAVE TO GO, IF WE REALLY HAVE SOMEWHERE TO GO."

– RENZO PIANO

THE TIPPING POINT

A tipping point is described as a critical moment in a situation, process or system beyond which a significant and often unstoppable effect or change takes place. Our quest to achieve sustainability has been slow in light of the transformation we so urgently need. The point at which we reach this defining moment will take place only once a series of small changes become significant enough to trigger a larger transformation across the world – a tipping point.

Think of this example: if you are standing in a room with over 100 people, and two people run out of the room screaming, how would you react? Many of us would stand there silently, wondering why two crazy people ran out the room. Now, consider 80 people ran out of the room screaming. Surely you would let survival instincts take over, and follow the crowd? If just the right amount of people went running out the room, we would assume it was for a very good reason. This analogy can be used for our current situation: when will we reach that specific point where everybody becomes involved and willing to change?

To what depths must the environment be degraded before our survival instincts kick in? Will it only be when our homes are flooded from sea level rise, brought about from the melting of the ice caps due to global warming? Will it be when the price of commodities and resources such as food and water become scarce and so expensive that is shatters our economies?

Or will it be when the pollution of cities and the contamination of our water supplies starts to affect our health so much so that we can no longer bear it? In truth, the utter destruction we have witness to the environment in the last 200 years should be enough to send us into a state of high alert.

We certainly do not want to reach a point whereby our actions become irreversible and cause permanent damage to both the planet and our very lives. If we are to reach this critical point of transformation before it is too late, we need to plan ahead and take the necessary actions to diminish the turbulent future we face. In essence, planning is about bringing the issues of the future into our present situation so that we can do something about it before the problem overwhelms us. If we can successfully plan ahead then we can identify the risks, prioritise them and then respond in a way that will lead us onto a sustainable path. If we do not plan accordingly, we will be unprepared as how to deal with these problems when they eventually boil over into our everyday lives. We have to be proactive about our future.

If we are to reach the all-important tipping point, then sustainability can no longer be a mere side project of company initiatives, government policy or education systems overshadowed by other short-term priorities. Rather, becoming sustainable and setting sustainability strategies needs to become integrated into every decision we make.

GETTING THERE

Change is generally never easy. It is said that it takes a person 30 days of conscious effort to break a habit. After living in a world marked by overconsumption and environmental neglect, getting real change to occur across the entire human race is by no means an easy task. Governments and policy makers will play a huge role in setting the boundaries, limitations and incentives to steer society in the right direction and facilitate the change needed.

By setting the right legal framework, financial incentives and economic investments, we can expect to see real, tangible and effective transformation take place. With appropriate structures in place and clear strategies to move forth with, our cities, institutions, companies and communities can be steered on the right path toward a sustainable way of living and doing business. Sustainability as a matter of free choice has proven ineffective in bringing the transformation we need, at the rate we need it.

National governments, policy makers and city officials have a fundamental role to play in bringing about this necessary transformation. By providing innovative long-term strategies and practical steps to follow them through, sustainability and environmental protection across sectors and industries can be achieved rapidly and effectively.

Innovation and creativity will be the key drivers that will allow us to prosper in a resource-constrained world. Unfortunately, we cannot continue to sustain a growing global population without radical improvements in technology, as the majority of our current practices, as we have seen, are both unsustainable and environmentally harmful.

But to fully understand the role of technology in achieving sustainability, we must first acknowledge the role that it has had in steering us off track in the first place. It was the unintended consequences of innovation in capitalist societies that

"SOME PEOPLE DON'T LIKE CHANGE, BUT YOU NEED TO EMBRACE CHANGE IF THE ALTERNATIVE IS DISASTER."
-ELON MUSK

"NEVER DOUBT THAT A SMALL GROUP OF THOUGHTFUL, COMMITTED CITIZENS CAN CHANGE THE WORLD. INDEED, IT IS THE ONLY THING THAT EVER HAS."
– MARGARET MEAD

"INNOVATION DISTINGUISHES BETWEEN A LEADER AND A FOLLOWER."
– STEVE JOBS

ultimately brought rise to the environmental issues we face today. So while technology is often seen as the means to solve the challenges we face, we need to ensure these advancements are contributing positively to the cause, not against it. We cannot make the same mistake again by adopting methods and behaviours that destroy the planet's ecosystems and exploit its resources. We have been smart enough to invent a great deal of extremely powerful things, yet shortsighted in terms of considering their long-term effects. We need to learn from the past in this regard. Fortunately, as you have seen throughout the pages of this book, many of the innovations and technologies of our day are beginning to steer towards more environmentally sustainable solutions.

We have to continue to work tirelessly to facilitate a culture that breeds innovation and creativity, thereby allowing us to progress in such a way that we correct the mistakes of the past and solve the problems of our future. In schools, universities and in the workplace, creative problem solving must be both encouraged and nurtured to allow us to create a world different from the one we have inherited. We cannot improve if we continue doing things the old way, and we cannot do things differently if we are not taught how. If education is unable to evolve and adapt to the relevant issues of our day, then we will undoubtedly be ill-equipped to conquer the challenges so prevalent in our world. As we have discussed throughout the pages of this book, the environmental challenges before us are some of, if not the greatest challenges of our era. Without the necessary structures in place to solve them, they will overwhelm us.

"THE SCIENTIFIC MAN DOES NOT AIM AT AN IMMEDIATE RESULT. HE DOES NOT EXPECT THAT HIS ADVANCED IDEAS WILL BE READILY TAKEN UP. HIS WORK IS LIKE THAT OF THE PLANTER–FOR THE FUTURE. HIS DUTY IS TO LAY THE FOUNDATION FOR THOSE WHO ARE TO COME, AND POINT THE WAY."
–NIKOLA TESLA

Often people suggest that they are not prepared to live sustainably as individuals until there is a collective movement with those around them doing the same. When this is the case, there is a feeling of self-sacrifice whilst those around them continue to live with relative ease. Unfortunately, these shortsighted ways of thinking are all too prevalent in today's societies, and is significantly hindering our transition to a sustainable future.

The commonly held misconception that sustainability is considered to be a 'sacrifice' or 'inconvenience'. With the existing systems we have in place in our world, this is often true. Although our unsustainable and over-consuming lifestyles seem mostly convenient to us, we are beginning to see their slow degradation. The cost of food, medicine, fuel and conventionally-sourced electricity is ramping up and revealing to us that the age of easily accessible resources has reached its peak. The existing concept of sustainability as an inconvenience or moral sacrifice is rather ingrained in us, and remains perhaps the biggest obstacle that we will need to overcome in our quest for long-term prosperity in our world.

As resources wear thin, and knowledge of our environmental impact increase, the growth of the sustainability movement will continue to gain traction, but will it be enough to bring the real change that is needed, and in the right space of time we need it to take place? Many films, books and other works of fiction today paint a bleak picture of the future we may face if we continue the trajectory we have maintained over the past century. The motive that will drive our much needed change could well be steered by such an outlook – a fear of an impending environmental apocalypse, where resources we once took for granted become the most valued of commodities.

On the other hand, the motive that will bring about our much needed change could be steered by something else entirely – opportunity. The concept of 'hedonistic sustainability', advocated by Danish architect Bjarke Ingels, brings forth the idea that sustainability in business and in life does not need to be an inconvenience or a sacrifice. Environmental protection, conservation and stewardship can indeed go hand-in-hand with economic and social prosperity. Traditionally, sustainabil-

"HEDONISTIC SUSTAINABILITY IS THE IDEA THAT YOU CAN ACTUALLY BE SUSTAINABLE BUT IN-CREASE THE QUALITY OF LIFE WHILE DOING SO."
–BJARKE ENGLELS

ity has been viewed as a side project of governments, institutions and industries as a way of demonstrating goodwill and moral obligation. This attitude has to change in order to secure our sustainable future. The approach of 'hedonistic sustainability' allows us to advance and progress in such a way that we are able to enrich human lives whilst caring for the planet at the very same time.

The New York High Line is a great example of this concept. An old railway elevated above the busy streets of Manhattan was scheduled for demolition in 2009, as it had been inoperable for some time and considered an eye-sore to many. But with a dramatic change of plans, first brought forward by the inhabitants of the city, it was decided that the railway would not be removed. Instead, it was converted into a 2km long public park, with benches, gardens and walkways for the public to use. Today, the New York High Line is one of the city's grandest attractions for both locals and international visitors, and hosts some of the most spectacular views in the entire city.

The High Line provides the city with biodiversity, greenery and much-needed public space for citizens to enjoy. An average of five-million people make use of the public park every year. It allows the city inhabitants to walk along lush, beautiful vegetation whilst being suspended 20m above the busy streets. What was to be destroyed has now become an incredibly popular attraction that has significantly improved the lives of millions of people while at the same time bringing the environment into consideration. The city realised that the

energy, labour and materials that were used to construct the railway line were still locked up in it; they weren't prepared to lose the opportunity of reusing such resources. The city of New York has thus 'upcycled' the High Line by giving the structure and its materials new purpose, new meaning and new life for all to enjoy.

If we are to understand our role in all that has been discussed in this book, it is important to come to terms with the importance of legacy and its meaning. Legacy is a fundamental part of what it means to be human. If youthful ambition speaks of the difference one can make in their lifetime, legacy speaks to what impact we leave behind for generations to come. It is the inheritance we leave to others; the sum total of all we have achieved, and what we have left to offer those who remain when our time here is done. It is commonly believed that the act of 'living in the present, in light of eternity' should be one of life's great virtues and pursuits. The way in which we choose to deal with the issues of today whilst planning for an uncertain future will define the legacy of both ourselves and our generation.

Yet sustainability itself is essentially about solving the difficult challenges of the present whilst simultaneously accounting for an unknown future. In essence, the very word 'sustainability' is defined as the endurance of systems and processes. If we, as humanity, can correctly create a sustainable place for ourselves in this world, then we can indeed achieve a prosperous way of living that preserves planet Earth for future generations.

"NO ONE IS ASKING YOU TO SAVE THE PLANET. JUST DREAM UP AND WORK ON A COUPLE GOOD IDEAS. NO ONE EXPECTS YOU TO FIND A SOLUTION TO EVERYTHING. JUST MAKE A DIFFERENCE WHERE YOU CAN."

-RICHARD BRANSON

GLOSSARY

Active Design

Innovative technologies that reduce both the need for and amount of energy used within a building.

Agriculture

The science or practice of farming, including cultivation of the soil for the growing of crops and the rearing of animals to provide food

Architecture

The art or practice of designing and constructing buildings or the complex or carefully designed structure of something.

Assembly Line

A series of workers and machines in a factory by which a succession of identical items is progressively assembled.

Atmosphere

The envelope of gases surrounding the earth.

Biodiversity

The variety of life in the world or in a particular habitat or ecosystem.

Biodegradability

Chemical dissolution of materials by bacteria, fungi, or other biological means.

Biofuels

A fuel that is derived directly from living matter.

Carbon Dioxide

A colourless, odourless gas produced by burning carbon and organic compounds. It is the primary cause of global warming.

Climate Change

A change in global or regional climate patterns, in particular a change apparent from the mid to late 20th century onwards and attributed largely to the increased levels of atmospheric carbon dioxide produced by the use of fossil fuels.

Consumption

The using up of a resource.

Conventional Energy Sources

Includes the fossil fuels oil, gas and coal. Their use leads to increased greenhouse gas emissions and other environmental damage.

Cultivation

To prepare and use land for crops or livestock.

Deforestation

The permanent destruction of forests in order to make the land available for other uses.

Degrade

Break down or deteriorate chemically.

Densification

The increased use of space both horizontally and vertically within existing areas and new developments accompanied by an increased number of units and/or population thresholds.

Discharge

Allow a liquid, gas, or other substance to flow out from where it has been confined.

Dispose

To get rid of something by throwing it away.

Ecosystem

A biological community of interacting organisms and their physical environment.

Efficiency

Achieving maximum productivity with minimum wasted effort or expense.

Electricity

A form of energy that is carried through wires and is used to operate machines, lights, etc.

Energy

The power derived from the utilisation of physical or chemical resources, especially to provide light and heat or to work machines.

Energy-Efficient

Something that delivers more services for the same energy input, or the same services for less energy input.

Engineering

Designing or creating structures, products or systems throguh the use of scientific methods.

Environment

The natural world, as a whole or in a particular geographical area, especially as affected by human activity.

Exploit

Make full use of and derive benefit from a resource.

Exponential

An increase — becoming more and more rapid.

Extract

Remove or take out, especially by effort or force.

Fossil fuel

A natural fuel such as coal, oil or gas that was formed in the geological past from the remains of living organisms.

Genetically Modified Foods

Foods produced from organisms that have had specific changes introduced into their DNA using the methods of genetic engineering.

Geologist

A scientist who studies the solid and liquid matter that constitutes the Earth as well as the processes and history that have shaped it.

Global Warming

A gradual increase in the overall temperature of the earth's atmosphere generally attributed to the greenhouse effect caused by increased levels of carbon dioxide or other pollutants.

Globalisation

A process of interaction and integration among the people, companies, and governments of different nations. It is driven by international trade and investment and aided by information technology.

Greenhouse Gas

A gas, such as carbon dioxide and methane, that contributes to the greenhouse effect by absorbing infrared radiation.

Hydrocarbons

A compound of hydrogen and carbon, such as oil, coal and natural gas.

Hydropower

Renewable source of energy which uses the force or energy of moving water to generate power.

Hydroponic

A method of growing plants using mineral nutrient solutions in water, without soil.

Incineration

Process of burning materials at temperatures high enough to destroy contaminants. Conducted in an "incinerator," which is a type of furnace designed for burning materials in a combustion chamber.

Industry

Economic activity concerned with the processing of raw materials and manufacture of goods in factories.

Industrial Agriculture

Otherwise known as intensive farming or intensive agriculture It is characterised by higher use of inputs such as capital and labour per unit land area.

Industrialisation

The process in which a society or country transforms itself from a primarily agricultural society into one based on the manufacturing of goods and services

Industrial Revolution

The transition to new manufacturing processes in the period from about 1760 to sometime between 1820 and 1840.

Innovation

A new idea, more effective device or process. Can be viewed as the application of better solutions that meet new requirements.

Legislation

Laws, considered collectively.

Life Cycle

A series of stages through which something passes during its lifetime.

Livestock

Farm animals such as cows, goats and sheep that are regarded as an asset.

Material

The matter from which a thing is or can be made from.

Manufacture

Process of making something on a large scale using machinery.

Methane

A colourless, odourless flammable gas that is the main constituent of natural gas. Is 21 times more potent than carbon dioxide

Modernisation

Transformation from a traditional, rural society to an urban, industrial society.

Natural Resources

Materials or substances such as minerals, forests, water and fertile land that occur in nature and can be used for economic gain.

Natural Service

Any positive benefit that ecosystems provides to people, either directly or indirectly.

Non-renewable

Any natural resource from the earth that exists in limited supply and cannot be replaced if consumer. Also, it cannot be replenished by natural means at the same rates that it is consumed.

Nuclear Energy

The energy released during nuclear fission or fusion, especially when used to generate electricity.

Passive Design

Design that takes advantage of the climate to maintain a comfortable temperature range in a building.

Performance

The accomplishment of something measured against preset known standards of accuracy, cost and speed.

Policy

A course of action adopted or proposed by a government, party, business, or individual.

Pollution

The presence in or introduction into the environment of a substance or thing that has harmful or poisonous effects.

Precision Agriculture

A modern farming practices that make production more efficient. With precision agriculture, farmers and soils work better, not harder.

Production

The action of making or manufacturing from components or raw materials.

Recycle

The process of converting waste into reusable materials.

Renewable Energy

Energy from a source that is not depleted when used, such as wind or solar power.

Replenish

Restore (a stock or supply of something) to the former level or condition.

Resource

A source or supply from which benefit is produced. Typically resources are materials, energy, services, knowledge, or other assets that are transformed to produce benefit and in the process may be consumed or made unavailable.

Soil Erosion

The wearing away of topsoil by the natural physical forces of water and wind, or through forces associated with farming activities such as soil overuse or deforestation.

Solar Energy

Radiant energy emitted by the sun.

Steward

Responsibly manage or look after.

Subsistence Farming

Self-sufficiency farming in which the farmers focus on growing enough food to feed themselves and their families.

Sustainability

Based on a simple principle that everything that we need for our survival and well-being depends, either directly or indirectly, on our natural environment.

Sustainable Development

Economic development that is conducted without depletion of natural resources.

Technology

Machinery and equipment developed from the application of scientific knowledge.

Transportation

The action of transporting someone or something.

Upcycling

The reuse of discarded objects or material in such a way as to create a product of a higher quality or value than the original.

Urban Sprawl

The uncontrolled expansion of urban areas, generally resulting in city borders expanding.

Urban Planning

Improve the welfare of people and their communities by creating more convenient, efficient and attractive urban places for present and future generations.

Urbanisation

The process in which the number of people living in cities increases compared with the number of people living in rural areas. A country is considered to be urbanised when over 50% of its population lives in urban places.

Waste

Material that is not wanted: the unusable remains or byproducts of something.

Waste-to-energy

Process of generating energy in the form of electricity or heat from the incineration of waste.

REFERENCES

Preface

Blumstein, D. & Saylan, C. 2011. The Failure of Environmental Education (And How We Can Fix It). University of California Press: Los Angeles.

Quotes

Page 13. goodreads.com. n,d. Ken Robinson Quotes. Available at: http://www.go-odreads.com/quotes/1110428-what-you-do-for-your-self-dies-with-you-when-you [April, 2015].

Page 15. CNN. 2012. Interview with Architect Bjarke Ingels. Available at: http://edition.cnn.com/TRAN-SCRIPTS/1204/22/nl.01.html [June, 2015].

Page 17. United Nations. n,d. Education for All: Quotations. Available at: http://www.un.org/en/globalis-sues/briefingpapers/efa/quotes.shtml [June, 2015].

The World As We Knew It

Our Planet Earth

Bryner, M. 2012. How Did Earth Get its Name? Available at: http://www.live-science.com/32274-how-did-earth-get-its-name.html [April, 2015].

Space Facts, n.d. Earth Facts. Available at: http://space-facts.com/earth/ [April, 2015].

Gore, A. 2013. The Future. Random House: New York.

What is the environment?

Fact Monster Science, n.d. What is the Environment? Available at: http://www.factmonster.com/ip-ka/A0775267.html [April, 2015].

Encyclopaedia of Life. n,d. What is Biodiversity? Available at: http://labs.eol.org/info/464 [September, 2105].

Giller, G. 2014. Are We Any Closer to Knowing How Many Species There are on Earth? Available at: http://www.sci-entificamerican.com/article/are-we-any-clos-er-to-knowing-how-many-species-there-are-on-earth/ [September, 2015].

Louv, R. 2014. Ten Reasons Why We Need More Contact With Nature. Available at: https://www.theguard-ian.com/commentisfree/2014/feb/13/10-rea-sons-why-need-more-contact-with-nature [September, 2015]

Natural resources

United States Environmental Protection Agency, n.d. Natural Resources. Available at: http://www.epa.gov-/wastes/educa-tion/quest/pdfs/unit1/chap1/u1_natresources.pdf [April, 2015].

Ecosystems

National Geographic, n.d. Ecosystems. Available at: http://education.nationalgeographic.com/encyclope-dia/ecosystem/ [April, 2015].

Nature Works, n.d. Ecosystems. Available at: http://ww-w.nhptv.org/natureworks/nwepecosystems.htm [April, 2015].

The Industrial Revolution

Griffin, E. 2010. A Short History of the British Industrial Revolution. Palsgrave Macmillan: New York.

history.com, n.d. The Industrial Revolution. Available at: http://www.history.com/topics/industrial-revolution [April, 2015].

Montagna, J. 2006. The Industrial Revolution. Available at: http://www.yale.edu/ynhti/curricu-lum/units/1981/2/81.02.06.x.html [April, 2015].

Hackett, L. 1992. Industrial Revolution. Available at: http://history-world.org/Industrial%20Intro.htm [April, 2015].

Population growth & increased demand

Brimlow, J. & Snider, S. 2013. An Introduction to Population Growth. Available at: http://www.na-ture.com/scitable/knowledge/library/an-introduc-tion-to-population-growth-84225544 [April, 2015].

Gates, B. 2014. Have You Hugged a Concrete Pillar Today? Available at: http://www.gatesnotes.com/Books/-Making-the-Modern-World [May, 2015].

Gore, A. 2013. The Future. Random House: New York.

Population Reference Bureau, n.d. Human Population: Population Growth. Available at: http://www.prb.org/Publi-cations/Lesson-Plans/HumanPopulation/-PopulationGrowth.aspx {april, 2015}.

World Health Organisation, n.d. Urban Population Growth. Available at: http://www.who.int/gho/urban_health/situa-tion_trends/urban_population_growth/en/ [May, 2015].

What is global warming and climate change?

David Suzuki Foundation, n.d. What is Climate Change? Available at: http://www.davidsuzuki.org/issues/cli-mate-change/science/cli-mate-change-basics/climate-change-101-1/ [April, 2015].

Dow, K. 2006. The Atlas of Climate Change: Mapping the worlds greatest challenge. University of California PressL Berkeley.

Gore, A. 2009. Our Choice: A plan to solve the climate crisis. Penguin Books: New York

Jarman, M. 2007. Climate Change. Palgrave Macmillan: London.

Moran, A. 2015. Climate Change: The Facts. Stockade Books: New Hampshire.

Philander, G. 2012. Encyclopaedia of Global Warming and Climate Change. Sage Publications: Thousand Oaks,

Stern, H. 2007. The Economics of Climate Change: The Stern Review. Cambridge University Press: Cambridge.

United States Environmental Protection Agency, n.d. Climate Change: Basic Information. Available at: http://www.epa.gov/climatechange/basics/ [April, 2015].

The state of the planet

Food and Agriculture Organisation of the United Nations. 2014. State of the World's Forests: Enhancing the socioeconomic benefits from forests. Available at: http://www.fao.org/3/a-i3710e.pdf [May, 2015].

Gore, A. 2013. The Future. Random House: New York.

Gore, A. 2009. Our Choice: A plan to solve the climate crisis. Penguin Books: New York

grida.no, n.d. What is the State of the Planet? Available at: http://www.grida.no/publications/et/ep1/page/2509.aspx [April, 2015].

NASA Global Climate Change, n.d. The Relentless Rise of Carbon Dioxide. Available at: http://climate.nasa.gov/climate_resources/24/ [May, 2015].

NASA Global Climate Change, n.d. Vital Signs of the Planet. Available at: http://climate.nasa.gov/vital-signs/carbon-dioxide/ [May, 2015].

World Wildlife Foundation (WWF), n.d. Soil Erosion and Degradation: An overview. Available at: http://www.worldwildlife.org/threats/soil-erosion-and-degradation [June, 2015].

U.S. Geological Survey, n.d. How much water is there on, in, and above the Earth? Available at: http://water.usgs.gov/edu/earthhowmuch.html [May, 2015].

What is sustainability?

de Vries, B. 2013. Sustainability Science. Cambridge University Press: New York.

Farrington, J. & Kuhlman, T. 2010. What is Sustainability? Sustainability: Vol 2: pages 3436-3448.

Swilling, M. & Annecke, E. 2012. Just transitions: Explorations of Sustainability in an Unfair World. UCT Press: South Africa.

World Bank, n.d. What is Sustainable Development? Available at: http://www.worldbank.org/depweb/english/sd.html [May, 2015].

Graphs & Stats

Page 30. Discovery Education, n.d. The Immense Ocean. Available at: http://school.discoveryeducation.com/-schooladventures/planetocean/ocean.html [May, 2015].

Page 41. Countries in the World (Ranked by 2014 Population). Available at: http://www.worldometers.info/world-population/population-by-country/ [April, 2015].

Page 49. GISS Surface Temperature Analysis (GISSTEMP). Available at: http://data.giss.nasa.gov/gistemp/ [April, 2015].

Page 56. Renewable Energy Policy Network (REN) 21. 2014. Renewables 2014: Global Status Report. Available at: http://www.ren21.net/portals/0/documents/resources/gsr/2014/gsr2014_full%20report_low%20re s.pdf [April, 2015].

Did You Knows

Page 23. National Oceanic and Atmospheric Administration, n.d. Ocean. Available at: http://www.noaa.gov/-ocean.html [April, 2015].

Page 25. Environment and Ecology, n.d. What is Ecology? Available at: http://environment-ecology.com/what-is-ecology/205-what-is-ecology.html [March, 2015].

Page 27. Biodiversity Information System for Europe, n.d. Ecosystem Services. Available at: http://biodiversity.europa.eu/topics/ecosystem-services [April, 2015].

Page 29. Food and Agriculture Organisation of the United Nations. 2014. State of the World's Forests: Enhancing the socioeconomic benefits from forests. Available at: http://www.fao.org/3/a-i3710e.pdf [May, 2015].

Page 31. World Wildlife Foundation (WWF). n,d. How Many Species Are We Loosing? Available at: http://wwf.panda.org/about_our_earth/biodiversity/biodiversity/ [September, 2015].

Page 32. history.com, n.d. The Industrial Revolution. Available at: http://www.history.com/topics/industrial-revolution [April, 2015].

Page 35. history.com, n.d. The Industrial Revolution. Available at: http://www.history.com/topics/industrial-revolution [April, 2015].

Page 37. normschriever.com, 2013. 25 Amazing Facts About World Population. Available at: http://www.normschriever.com/blog/25-amazing-facts-about-world-population [March, 2015].

Page 38. compassion.com, n.d. Population Facts. Available at: http://www.compassion.com/poverty/population.htm [April, 2015].

Page 39. Population Reference Bureau. 2012. Fact Sheet: World Population Trends 2012. Available at: http://www.prb.org/Publications/Datasheets/2012/world-population-data-sheet/fact-sheet-world-population.aspx [April, 2015].

Page 40. normschriever.com, 2013. 25 Amazing Facts About World Population. Available at: http://www.normschriever.com/blog/25-amazing-facts-about-world-population [March, 2015].

Page 43. The World Counts, n.d. Tons of Ice Melted This Year. Available at: http://www.theworld-counts.com/counters/why_is_climate_change_important/melting_ice_caps_facts [April, 2015].

Page 45. National Centres for Environmental Information, 2014. Global Analysis - December 2014. Available at: http://www.ncdc.noaa.gov/sotc/global/201412 [April, 2015].

Page 49. Publius, G. 2014. How Climate Change Could Cause an Ice Age in Europe. Available at: http://america-blog.com/2014/03/climate-change-gulf-stream-could-cause-ice-age-europe.html [April, 2015].

Page 50. Organisation for Economic Cooperation & Development (OECD). 2011. OECD Environmental Outlook to 2015: Climate Change Chapter. Available at: http://www.oecd.org/env/cc/49082173.pdf [May, 2015].

Page 55. The World Counts, n.d. Tons of Ice Melted This Year. Available at: http://www.theworld-counts.com/counters/why_is_climate_change_important/melting_ice_caps_facts [April, 2015].

Quotes

Page 22. brainyquote.com, n.d. Dmitar Sasselov Quotes. Available at: http://www.brainy-quote.com/quotes/quotes/d/dimitarsas643196.html [March, 2015].

Page 24. brainyquote.com, n.d. Albert Einstein Quotes. Available at: http://www.brainy-quote.com/quotes/quotes/a/alberteins165189.html [March, 2015].

Page 28. Weld, W., n.d. What Government Does Well/What Government Does Badly. Available at: http://www.go-thamgazette.com/lessons/weld.shtml [March, 2015].

Page 30. brainyquote.com, n.d. Jim Fowler Quotes. Available at: http://www.brainyquote.com/quotes/quotes/j/-jimfowler254362.html [April, 2015].

Page 43. World Preservation Foundation, n.d. The 11th Hour. Available at: http://www.worldpreservationfounda-tion.org/ecotrailers.php?id=13#.VeQn4mAxFTY [April, 2015].

Page 46. brainyquote.com, n.d. Peter Garrett Quotes. Available at: http://www.brainyquote.com/quotes/quotes/p/-petergarre249008.html [March, 2015].

Page 47. sustainablebabysteps.com, n,d. Green Living, Simple Living, and Environmental Quotes. Available at: http://www.sustainablebabysteps.com/environ-ment-quotes.html [March, 2015].

Page 48. brainyquote.com. n.d. Earl Nightingale Quotes. Available at: http://www.brainy-quote.com/quotes/quotes/e/earlnighti386795.html [March, 2015].

Page 51. Gore, A. 2013. The Future. Random House: New York.

Page 53. usnews.com, 2015. Obama: Climate Change a Growing National Security Threat. Available at: http://www.usnews.com/news/articles/2015/02/06/obama-cli-mate-change-urgent-and-growing-threat-to-national-security [March, 2015].

Page 57. World Preservation Foundation, n.d. The 11th Hour. Available at: http://www.worldpreservationfounda-tion.org/ecotrailers.php?id=13#.VeQn4mAxFTY [April, 2015].

Page 58. brainyquote.com, n.d. Richard Rogers Quotes. Available at: http://www.brainy-quote.com/quotes/quotes/r/richardrog228217.html [March, 2015].

Page 59. Helman, C. 2014. All-Of-The-Above (But No Coal or Nukes): Decoding Obama's SOTY Energy Comments. Available at: http://www.forbes.com/sites/christopherhel-man/2014/01/28/what-obama-said-and-didnt-say-about-ene rgy/ [April, 2015].

Energy

What is electricity and how do we make it?

About.com, n.d. Understanding Electricity. Available at: http://inventors.about.com/library/inventors/blelectric1.htm. [April, 2015].

originenergy.com, 2015.What is Electricity? Available at: http://www.originenergy.com.au/blog/about-ener-gy/what-is-electricity.html [April, 2015].

Patrick, D. & Fardo, S. 2008. Electricity and electronics fundamentals. Fairmont Press: Lilburn

What are fossil fuels?

Epstein, E. 2014. The Moral Case For Fossil Fuels. Penguin Books: New York.

Gore, A. 2009. Our Choice: A plan to solve the climate crisis. Penguin Books: New York

Jaccard, M. 2005. Sustainable Fossil Fuels: The unusual suspect in the quest for clean and enduring energy. Cambridge University Press: Cambridge

U.S. Department of Energy. 2013. How Fossil Fuels Were Formed. Available at: http://www.fe.doe.gov/education/en-ergylessons/coal/gen_howformed.html [May, 2015].

Coal

Jurling, J., n.d. What is coal? - Facts, types, formations & uses. Available at: http://study.com/academy/les-son/what-is-coal-facts-types-formation-uses.html [May, 2015].

Energy Information Administration (EIA). 2012. International Energy Statistics. Available at: http://www.eia.gov/c-fapps/ipdbproject/IEDIndex3.cfm?tid=2&pid=2&aid=7# [March, 2015].

International Energy Association (IEA). 2010. Coal Information 2010. Available at: http://wds.iea.org/wds/pd-f/documentation_Coal_prelim2010.pdf [March, 2015].

World Coal Association, n.d. What is coal? Available at:

http://www.worldcoal.org/coal/what-is-coal/ [May 2015].

Oil

Gore, A. 2009. Our Choice: A plan to solve the climate crisis. Penguin Books: New York

livescience.com, 2005. The Mysterious Origin and Supply of Oil. Available at: http://www.livescience.com/9404-mysterious-origin-supply-oil.html [March, 2015].

Maugeri, L. 2012. Oil: The Next Revolution. Available at: http://belfercenter.ksg.harvard.edu/files/Oil-%20The%20Next%20Revolution.pdf [March, 2015]

San Joaquin Valley Geology, n.d. What is Oil? Available at: http://www.sjvgeology.org/oil/oil.html [June, 2015].

Natural gas

Energy Information Administration (EIA). 2015. How much oil is consumed in the United States? Available at: http://www.eia.gov/tools/faqs/faq.cfm?id=33&t=6 [March, 2015].

Gore, A. 2009. Our Choice: A plan to solve the climate crisis. Penguin Books: New York

Holloway, M. & Rudd, M. 2013. Fracking: The operations and environmental consequences of hydraulic fracturing. Scrivener Publishing: Hoboken.

Zuckerman, G. 2013. The Frackers: The outrageous inside story of the new billionaire wildcatters. Penguin Group: New York.

What are the problems with conventional energy sources?

Conserve Energy Future, n.d. What are fossil fuels? Available at: http://www.conserve-energy-future.com/Disadvantages_FossilFuels.php [June, 2015].

Gore, A. 2009. Our Choice: A plan to solve the climate crisis. Penguin Books: New York

Joan Pye Project, n.d. Problems With Fossil Fuels. Available at: http://joanpyeproject.org/news/problems-with-fossil-fuels/ [March, 2015].

United Nations Educational, Scientific and Cultural Organisation (Unesco), n.d. Problems With Fossil Fuels. Available at: http://www.unesco.org/education/educprog/ste/pdf_files/sourcebook/module4.pdf [March, 2015].

Union of Concerned Scientists, n.d. The Hidden Costs of Fossil Fuels. Available at: http://www.ucsusa.org/clean_energy/our-energy-choices/coal-and-other-fossil-fuels/the-hidden-cost-of-fossil.html#.VeAZxWAxFTZ [March, 2015].

When will fossil fuels run out?

Epstein, E. 2014. The Moral Case For Fossil Fuels. Penguin Books: New York.

Gore, A. 2009. Our Choice: A plan to solve the climate crisis. Penguin Books: New York.

Senior, K. 2015. When Will Fossil Fuels Run Out? Available at: http://www.carboncounted.co.uk/when-will-fossil-fuels-run-out.html [March, 2015].

Is greater efficiency with fossil fuels enough?

Gore, A. 2009. Our Choice: A plan to solve the climate crisis. Penguin Books: New York

Hordeski, M. 2011. Megatrends for Energy Efficiency and Renewable Energy. Fairmont Press: Lilburn.

Kreith, F. & Goswami, Y. 2007. Handbook of Energy Efficiency and Renewable Energy. CRC Press: Boca Ranton.

International Energy Association (EIA). 2014. Capturing the Multiple Benefits of Energy Efficiency, Executive Summary. Available at: https://www.iea.org/Textbase/npsum/MultipleBenefits2014SUM.pdf [March, 2015].

Do we have alternative energy sources?

altenergy.org, n.d. Alternative Energy. Available at: http://www.altenergy.org [March, 2015].

Gore, A. 2009. Our Choice: A plan to solve the climate crisis. Penguin Books: New York

What is renewable energy?

Boyle, G. 2004. Renewable Energy: Power for a sustainable future . Oxford University Press: Oxford.

Scheer, H. 2007. Energy Autonomy: The economic, social and technological case for renewable energy. Earthscan: London.

Seifred, D. 2010. Renewable Energy: The Facts. CRC Press: Boca Raton.

U.S. Department of Energy, 2001. Renewable Energy: An overview. Available at: http://www.nrel.gov/docs/fy01osti/27955.pdf [March, 2015].

Solar energy

Leveque, F. 2006. Competitive Electricity Markets and Sustainability. Edward Elgar Publishing: Cerna

Gomez, T. & Licetti, M. 2011. The Power of Renewable Energy: Fostering Investment and Competition to Generate Electricity. Investment Climate in Practice. Vol. 18: Pages 1-7

Wind energy

U.S. Department of Energy. 2013. Wind Power: Today and tomorrow. Available at: http://www.nrel.gov/docs/fy04osti/34915.pdf [March, 2015].

Hydropower

Altenergy.org, n.d. Hydroelectric Power. Available at: http://www.altenergy.org/renewables/hydroelectric.html [March, 2015].

Waste-to-energy

covanta.com, n,d. Understand How Energy-from-Waste Works. Available at: http://www.covanta.com/sustainable-solutions/energy-from-waste.aspx [April, 2015].

sweden.se, n.d. The Swedish Recycling Revolution: Towards zero waste. Available at: https://sweden.se/nature/the-swedish-recycling-revolution/ [April, 2015].

United States Environmental Protection Agency, n.d. Energy Recovery From Waste. Available at: http://epa.gov/wastes/nonhaz/municipal/wte/ [April, 2015].

Are there any problems with renewable energy?

Bryce, R. 2010. The Real Problems With Renewables. Available at: http://www.forbes.com/2010/05/11/renewables-energy-oil-economy-opinions-contributors-robert-bryce.html [May, 2015].

Smith, L. 2012. Limitations of Renewable Energy. Available at: http://www.templar.co.uk/downloads/Renewable%20Energy%20Limitations.pdf [March, 2015].

What about nuclear energy?

Cravens, G. 2007. Power to Save The World: The truth about nuclear energy. Vintage Books: New York.

Hore-Lacy, I. 2006. Nuclear Energy in the 21st Century: The World Nuclear University Primer. Elsevier: London.

Nuclear Energy Agency (NEA) * Organisation for Economic Co-operation and Development (OECD). 2012. The Role of Nuclear Energy in a Low-Carbon Future. Available at: https://www.oecd-nea.org/nsd/reports/2012/nea6887-role-nuclear-low-carbon.pdf [March, 2015].

Graphs / Stats

Page 65. Breakdown of Electricity Generation by Energy Source, 2012. Available at: http://www.tsp-data-portal.org/Breakdown-of-Electricity-Generation-by-Energy-Source#tspQvChart [May 2015].

Page 69. Energy Information Administration (EIA). 2015. How much carbon dioxide is produced when different furls are burned? Available at: http://www.eia.gov/tools/faqs/faq.cfm?id=73&t=11 [June, 2015].

Page 79. co2now.org, 2015. Available at: http://co2now.org [June, 2015].

Page 108. World Nuclear Association. 2015. Nuclear Power in the World Today. Available at: http://www.world-nuclear.org/info/Current-and-Future-Generation/Nuclear-Power-in-the-World-Today/ [April, 2015].

Page 109. World Nuclear Association. 2015. Nuclear Power in the World Today. Available at: http://www.world-nuclear.org/info/Current-and-Future-Generation/Nuclear-Power-in-the-World-Today/ [April, 2015].

Did You Knows

Page 62. Woodford, C. 2015. Electricity. Available at: http://www.explainthatstuff.com/electricity.html [April, 2015].

Page 64. Global Edison Corporation, n.d. Available at: http://www.globaledison.com/History_FirstPowerPlant.html [May, 2015].

Page 72. Energy Information Administration (EIA). 2015.

How much oil is consumed in the United States. Available at: http://www.eia.gov/tools/faqs/faq.cfm?id=33&t=6 [March, 2015].

Page 72. one.org. 2014. What's Driving Africa's Strongest Economies? Available at: http://www.one.org/international/blog/whats-driving-africas-strongest-economies/ [April, 2015].

Page 78. Gore, A. 2009. Our Choice: A plan to solve the climate crisis. Penguin Books: New York.

Page 80. Our Finite World. 2012. World Energy Consumption since 1820 in Charts. Available at: http://ourfiniteworld.com/2012/03/12/world-energy-consumption-since-1820-in-charts/ [May, 2015].

Page 84. serve.gov, n.d. Energy Efficiency: The facts. Available at: http://www.serve.gov/?q=site-page/toolkits/audit-home/index [March, 2015].

Page 92. Wisconsin Valley Improvement Company, n.d. Facts About Hydropower. Available at: http://www.wvic.com/Content/Facts_About_Hydropower.cfm [March, 2015].

Page 96. American Wind Energy Association, n.d. Wind Power Myths vs. Facts. Available at: http://www.pawindenergynow.org/wind/MythsvsFacts-FactSheet.pdf [June, 2015].

Page 99. Wisconsin Valley Improvement Company, n.d. Facts About Hydropower. Available at: http://www.wvic.com/Content/Facts_About_Hydropower.cfm [March, 2015].

Page 100. Energy Recovery Council, n.d. Waste To Energy Reduces Greenhouse Gas Emissions. Available at: http://www.energyrecoverycouncil.org/waste-energy-reduces-greenhouse-gas-emissions-a2966 [July, 2015].

Page 101. Energy Recovery Council. 2010. An Overview of Waste-to-Energy in the US Today. Available at: http://www.ct.gov/deep/lib/deep/waste_management_and_disposal/solid_waste/transforming_matls_mgmt/gov_recycling_work_group/energy_recovery_council_presentation_091112.pdf [July, 2015].

Page 104. Bryce, R. 2010. The Real Problems With Renewables. Available at: http://www.forbes.com/2010/05/11/renewables-energy-oil-economy-opinions-contributors-robert-bryce.html [May, 2015].

Page 109. World Nuclear Association. 2014. Outline History of Nuclear Energy. Available at: http://www.world-nuclear.org/info/Current-and-Future-Generation/Outline-History-of-Nuclear-Energy/ [April, 2015].

Quotes

Page 63. braintquote.com, n.d. Bill Bryson Quotes. Available at: http://www.brainyquote.com/quotes/quotes/g/georgecarl145996.html [March, 2015].

Page 65. goodreads.com, n.d. George Carlin Quotes. Available at: http://www.goodreads.com/quotes/19061-electricity-is-really-just-organized-lightning [March, 2015].

Page 67. Conserve Energy Future, n.d. 151 Inspiring Environmental Quotes. Available at: http://www.conserve-energy-future.com/inspiring-environmental-quotes.php [May, 2015].

Page 68. Lovins, A. 2012. A 40-year Plan for Energy. Available at: https://www.ted.com/talks/amory_lovins_a_50_year_plan_for_energy/transcript?language=en [March, 2015].

Page 71. Greene, 2014. Bill Nye of Sandy, Climate Change and the 2012 Election. Available at: http://www.huffingtonpost.com/richard-greene/bill-nye-on-sandy_b_2068609.html [March, 2015].

Page 75. Gold, R. 2014. The Boom: How fracking ignited the American energy revolution and changed the world. Simon & Schuster: New York.

Page 77. brainyquote.com, n.d. Dennis Weaver Quotes. Available at: http://www.brainyquote.com/quotes/quotes/d/dennisweav345562.html [March, 2015].

Page 82. Bryce, R. 2010. The Real Problems With Renewables. Available at: http://www.forbes.com/2010/05/11/renewables-energy-oil-economy-opinions-contributors-robert-bryce.html [May, 2015].

Page 84. brainyquote.com, n.d. Mac Thornberry Quotes. Available at: http://www.brainyquote.com/quotes/quotes/m/macthornbe262476.html [March, 2015].

Page 85. Branson, R. 2010. Business Stripped Bear: Adventures of a global entrepreneur. Penguin Group: New York.

Page 87. brainyquote.com, n.d. Martin Rees Quotes. Available at: http://www.brainyquote.com/quotes/quotes/m/martinrees643565.html [March, 2015].

Page 89. goodread.com, n.d. Nikola Tesla Quotes. Available at: http://www.goodreads.com/author/quotes/278.Nikola_Tesla?page=2 [March, 2015].

Page 90. Vista Solar, n.d. Solar Energy: The future power source. Available at:http://www.vista-solar.com/solar-energy-future-power-source/ [March, 2015].

Page 95. Naughton, J. 2015. Power to the People: Bring on the super battery. Available at: http://www.theguardian.com/commentisfree/2015/apr/11/super-battery-elon-musk-tesla-renewable-energy [April, 2015].

Page 97. U.S. Department of Energy. 2013. Wind Power: Today and tomorrow. Available at: http://www.nrel.gov/docs/fy04osti/34915.pdf [March, 2015].

Page 106. brainyquote.com, n.d. Ronald Reagan Quotes. Available at: http://www.brainyquote.com/quotes/quotes/r/ronaldreag102041.html [March, 2015].

Food and Agriculture

What is the history of modern agriculture?

Advanced BioTech. n,d. The History of Agriculture. Available at: http://www.adbio.com/science/agri-history.htm [July, 2015].

Crop Life. n,d. About Modern Agriculture. Available at: http://www.croplifeamerica.org/crop-protection/modern-agriculture [July, 2015].

New World Encyclopaedia. n,d. History of Agriculture. Available at: http://www.newworldencyclopedia.org/entry/History_of_agriculture [August, 2015].

Stephen, G. 2001. Agriculture, Modern. Available at: http://www.encyclopedia.com/doc/1G2-3408000013.html [August, 2015].

Wikipedia, n.d. History of Agriculture. Available at: https://en.wikipedia.org/wiki/History_of_agriculture [July, 2015].

What effect is population growth having on the food industry?

Smith, R. 2010. Population growth demands improved farm efficiency. Available at: http://southwestfarmpress.com/management/population-growth-demands-improved-farm-efficiency

Wikipedia, n.d. History of Agriculture. Available at: https://en.wikipedia.org/wiki/History_of_agriculture [July, 2015].

WorldWatch Institute. n,d. World Population, Agriculture, and Malnutrition. Available at: http://www.worldwatch.org/node/554 [August, 2015].

How does industrial farming affect the environment?

Morris, J. & Burgess, P. 2012. Environmental Impacts of Modern Agriculture. RSC Publishing: UK.

Hamuda, H. & Patko, I. 2010. Relationship between Environmental Impacts and Modern Agriculture. Óbuda University e-Bulletin. Vol. 1(1): pg 87-98.

Deforestation

Food and Agriculture Organisation of the United Nations. n,d. Livestock's role in deforestation. Available at: http://www.fao.org/agriculture/lead/themes0/deforestation/en/ [July, 2015].

Howden, D. 2007. Deforestation: The hidden cause of global warming. Available at: http://www.independent.co.uk/environment/climate-change/deforestation-the-hidden-cause-of-global-warming-6262622.html [August, 2015].

Morris, J. & Burgess, P. 2012. Environmental Impacts of Modern Agriculture. RSC Publishing: UK.

NASA Earth Observatory. n,d. Causes of Deforestation. Available at: http://earthobservatory.nasa.gov/Features/Deforestation/deforestation_update3.php [August, 2015].

Soil Erosion

Morris, J. & Burgess, P. 2012. Environmental Impacts of Modern Agriculture. RSC Publishing: UK.

Grace Communications Foundation. n,d. Environment. Available at: http://www.sustainabletable.org/265/environment [August, 2015].

Grace Communications Foundation. n,d. Soil Quality. Available at: http://www.sustainabletable.org/207/soil-quality [August, 2015].

World Wildlife Foundation (WWF). n,d. Soil Erosion and Degradation. Available at: http://www.worldwildlife.org/threats/soil-erosion-and-degradation [July, 2015].

World Wildlife Foundation (WWF). n,d. Farming: Soil erosion and degradation. Available at: http://wwf.panda.org/what_we_do/footprint/agriculture/impacts/soil_erosion/ [July, 2015].

Livestock-related problems

Food and Agriculture Organisation of the United Nations. n,d. The Role of Livestock in Climate Change. Available at: http://www.fao.org/agriculture/lead/themes0/climate/en/ [August, 2015].

Goodland, R. & Anhang, J. 2009. Livestock and Climate Change. Available at: http://www.worldwatch.org/files/pdf/Livestock%20and%20Climate%20Change.pdf [July, 2015].

Gore, A. 2009. Our Choice: A plan to solve the climate crisis. Penguin Books: New York.

TedX. 2013. Community health impacts of factory farms: Steve Wing at TEDx Manhattan 2013. Available at: https://www.youtube.com/watch?v=7ZW8-LQftnY [August, 2015].

Farming techniques

Pan North America. n,d. Environmental Impacts. Available at: http://www.panna.org/issues/persistent-poisons/environmental-impacts [July, 2015].

study.com. n,d. Use of Pesticides: Benefits and Problems Associated with Pesticides. Available at: http://study.com/academy/lesson/use-of-pesticides-benefits-and-problems-associated-with-pesticides.html [July, 2015].

United States Environmental Protection Agency. n,d. Pesticides: Environmental Effects. Available at: http://www.epa.gov/pesticides/ecosystem/ [July, 2015].

Water wastage and contamination

lenntech.com. n,d. Use of Water in Food and Agriculture. Available at: http://www.lenntech.com/water-food-agriculture.htm [July, 2015].

Grace Communications Foundation. n,d. Water Quality. Available at: http://www.sustainabletable.org/267/water-quality [August, 2015].

Trautmann, N., Porter, K. & Wagnet, R. n,d. Modern Agriculture: Its effects on the environment. http://psep.cce.cornell.edu/facts-slides-self/facts/mod-ag-grw85.aspx [August, 2015].

World Wildlife Foundation (WWF). n,d. Farming: Wasteful water use. Available at: http://wwf.panda.org/what_we_do/footprint/agriculture/impacts/water_use/ [August, 2015].

What impact are we having on marine life?

TedX. 2010. Jeremy Jackson: How we wrecked the ocean. Available at: https://www.youtube.com/watch?v=u0VHC1-DO_8 [August, 2015].

TedX. 2013. Overfished Ocean Strategy: Nadya Zhexembayeva at TEDx Klagenfurt. Available at: https://www.youtube.com/watch?v=FTNI_ToDISc [August, 2015].

Overfishing

TedX. 2010. Jeremy Jackson: How we wrecked the ocean. Available at: https://www.youtube.com/watch?v=u0VHC1-DO_8 [August, 2015].

tedx.com. 2013. Overfished Ocean Strategy: Nadya Zhexembayeva at TEDx Klagenfurt. Available at: https://www.youtube.com/watch?v=FTNI_ToDISc [August, 2015].

Environmental Defence Fund. n,d. Overfishing: Worse than you might think. https://www.edf.org/oceans/overfishing-worse-you-might-think [July, 2015].

Greenpeace International,. n,d. Overfishing. Available at: http://www.greenpeace.org/international/en/campaigns/oceans/fit-for-the-future/overfishing/ [August, 2015].

National Geographic. n,d. Pristine Seas: Overfishing. Available at: http://ocean.nationalgeographic.com/ocean/explore/pristine-seas/critical-issues-overfishing/ [August, 2015].

un.org. n,d. Overfishing: A threat to marine biodiversity. Available at: http://www.un.org/events/tenstories/06/story.asp?storyID=800 [August, 2015].

Pollution

marinebio.org. n,d. Ocean Pollution. Available at: http://marinebio.org/oceans/ocean-dumping/ [July, 2015].

National Geographic. n,d. Pristine Seas: Marine pollution. Available at: http://ocean.nationalgeographic.com/ocean/explore/pristine-seas/critical-issues-marine-pollution/ [July, 2015].

TedX. 2010. Jeremy Jackson: How we wrecked the ocean. Available at: https://www.youtube.com/watch?v=u0VHC1-DO_8 [August, 2015].

TedX. 2013. Overfished Ocean Strategy: Nadya Zhexembayeva at TEDx Klagenfurt. Available at: https://www.youtube.com/watch?v=FTNI_ToDISc [August, 2015].

World Wildlife Foundation (WWF). n,d. Marine Problems: Pollution. Available at: http://wwf.panda.org/about_our_earth/blue_planet/problems/pollution/ [August, 2015].

How will climate change affect food production?

United States Environmental Protection Agency. n,d. Agriculture and Food Supply. Available at: http://www.epa.gov/climatechange/impacts-adaptation/agriculture.html [July, 2015].

World Future Council. n,d. How Does Climate Change Affect Agriculture? Available at: http://www.worldfuturecouncil.org/2324.html [July, 2015].

Agriculture

Climate Institute. n,d. Agriculture. Available at: http://www.-climate.org/topics/agriculture.html [July, 2015].

European Commission. n,d. Agriculture and Climate Change. Available at: http://ec.europa.eu/agriculture/climate-change/index_en.htm [July, 2015].

Gore, A. 2009. Our Choice: A plan to solve the climate crisis. Penguin Books: New York.

National Climate Assessment. n,d. Agriculture. Available at: http://nca2014.globalchange.gov/report/sectors/agriculture [August, 2015].

United States Environmental Protection Agency. n,d. Agriculture and Food Supply. Available at: http://www.epa.gov/climatechange/impacts-adaptation/agriculture.html [July, 2015].

World Future Council. n,d. How Does Climate Change Affect Agriculture? Available at: http://www.worldfuturecouncil.org/2324.html [July, 2015].

Marine life

Fujita, R. 2013. 5 Ways Climate Change is Affecting our Oceans. Available at: https://www.edf.org/blog/2013/11/14/five-ways-climate-change-affecting-our-oceans [July, 2015].

TedX. 2010. Jeremy Jackson: How we wrecked the ocean. Available at: https://www.youtube.com/watch?v=u0VHC1-DO_8 [August, 2015].

TedX. 2013. Overfished Ocean Strategy: Nadya Zhexembayeva at TEDx Klagenfurt. Available at: https://www.youtube.com/watch?v=FTNI_ToDISc [August, 2015].

New England Aquarium. n,d. Climate Change and the Oceans. Available at: http://www.neaq.org/conservation_and_research/climate_change/-climate_change_and_the_oceans.php [July, 2015].

New England Aquarium. n,d. Climate Change Effects on Ocean Animals. Available at: http://www.neaq.org/conservation_and_research/climate_change/effects_on_ocean_animals.php [August, 2015].

United States Environmental Protection Agency. n,d. Climate Change Indicators in the United States. Available at: http://www.epa.gov/climatechange/science/indicators/-oceans/ [July, 2015].

Wikipedia. n,d. Effects of Global Warming on Oceans. Available at: https://en.wikipedia.org/wiki/Effects_of_-global_warming_on_oceans [August, 2015].

Are we consuming more than the planet can provide?

Global Footprint Network. 2015. Earth Overshoot Day. Available at: http://www.footprintnetwork.org/en/index-.php/GFN/page/earth_overshoot_day/ [July, 2015].

TristamStuart.co.uk, n,d. Food Waste Facts. Available at: http://www.tristramstuart.co.uk/foodwastefacts/ [August, 2015].

United Nations Environmental Programme (UNEP). n,d. Seven Billion Dreams. One Planet. Consume with Care. Available at: http://www.unep.org/wed/theme/sustainable-consumpion.asp [August, 2015].

What methods can we adopt to solve these issues?

Guerrini, F. 2015. The Future of Agriculture: Smart farming. Available at: http://www.forbes.com/sites/federicoguerrini/2015/02/18/the-future-of-agriculture-smart-farming/ [August, 2015].

Hydroponic agriculture

Agriculture and Agri-Food Canada. n,d. What is Hydroponics. Available at: http://www.agr.gc.ca/eng/science-and-innovation/science-publications-and-resources/resources/what-is-hydroponics-/?id=1238524974996 [July, 2015].

The Environmental Benefits of Hydroponics. Available at: https://ecopostblog.wordpress.com/2014/07/14/the-environmental-benefits-of-hydroponics/ [July, 2015].

Jensen, M. n,d. What is Hydroponics? Available at: http://ag.arizona.edu/ceac/what-hydroponics [July, 2015].

NASA. 2004. Farming For the Future. Available at: http://www.nasa.gov/missions/science/biofarming.html [July, 2105].

Turner, B. n,d. How Hydroponics Works. Available at: http://home.howstuffworks.com/lawn-garden/professional-landscaping/alternative-methods/hydroponics.htm [August, 2015].

Genetic modification

Food Standards Australia & New Zealand. n,d. Genetically Modified Foods. Available at: http://www.foodstandards.gov.au/consumer/gmfood/gmoverview/Pages/default.aspx [AUgust, 2015].

Paturel, A. & Yamakawa, R. 2015. GMOs: What you need to know. Available at: http://www.webmd.com/food-recipes/truth-about-gmos [July, 2015].

World Health Organization. n,d. Food, Genetically Modified. Available at: http://www.who.int/topics/food_genetically_-modified/en/ [August, 2015].

Precision farming

CEMA. n,d. Precision Farming: Producing more with less. Available at: http://www.cema-agri.org/page/precision-farming-0 [August, 2015].

DeJoia, A. & Duncan, M. 2015. What is Precision Agriculture and Why is it Important? Available at: https://soilsmatter.wordpress.com/2015/02/27/what-is-precision-agriculture-and-why-is-it-important/ [August, 2015].

Guerrini, F. 2015. The Future of Agriculture: Smart farming. Available at: http://www.forbes.com/sites/federicoguerrini/2015/02/18/the-future-of-agriculture-smart-farming/ [August, 2015].

Pfister, B. n,d. What is Precision Agriculture. Available at:

http://www.directionsmag.com/entry/what-is-precision-agriculture/124210 [July, 2015].

Organic farming

agriinfo.com n,d. Organic Farming and Its Importance. Available at: http://www.agriinfo.in/?page=topic&superid=1&topicid=685 [August, 2015].

Food and Agriculture Organisation of the United Nations. n,d. What are the environmental benefits of organic agriculture? Available at: http://www.fao.org/organicag/oa-faq/oa-faq6/en/ [July, 2015].

gardenforever.com. n,d. Age Defying Gardening! The Importance of Organic Farming! Available at: http://www.gardenforever.com/pages/age-defying-gardening.html [July, 2015].

Grace Communications Foundation. n,d. Sustainable Livestock Husbandry. Available at: http://www.sustainabletable.org/248/sustainable-livestock-husbandry [July, 2015].

Health and Lifestyle. n,d. Advantages of Free Range Farming. Available at: http://www.streetdirectory.com/etoday/advantages-free-range-farming-lcpf.html [August, 2015].

TedX. 2013. Community health impacts of factory farms: Steve Wing at TEDx Manhattan 2013. Available at: https://www.youtube.com/watch?v=7ZW8-LQftnY [August, 2015].

How can we consume more sustainably?

TedX. 2013. Overfished Ocean Strategy: Nadya Zhexembayeva at TEDx Klagenfurt. Available at: https://www.youtube.com/watch?v=FTNI_ToDISc [August, 2015].

Wikipedia. n,d. Deforestation in Brazil. Available at: https://en.wikipedia.org/wiki/Deforestation_in_Brazil [August, 2015].

Graphs / Stats

Page 118. geohive.com. n,d. Population of the entire world, yearly, 1950 - 2100. Available at: http://www.geohive.com/earth/his_history3.aspx [August, 2015].

Page 122. United Nations Food and Agriculture Organisation. 2012. State of the World's Forests. Available at: http://www.fao.org/docrep/016/i3010e/i3010e.pdf [July, 2015].

Page 132. United Nations Food and Agriculture Organisation. n,d. General Situation of World's Fish Stocks. Available at: http://www.fao.org/newsroom/common/ecg/1000505/en/stocks.pdf [August, 2015].

Page 141. McDonnell, T. 2015. There's a Horrifying Amount of Plastic in the Ocean. This Chart Shows Who's to Blame. Available at: http://www.motherjones.com/environment/2015/02/ocean-plastic-waste-china [July, 2015].

Page 155. Ecopost. 2014. The Environmental Benefits of Hydroponics. Available at: https://ecopostblog.wordpress.com/2014/07/14/the-environmental-benefits-of-hydroponics/ [July, 2015].

Page 165. lenntech.com. n,d. Use of Water in Food and Agriculture. Available at: http://www.lenntech.com/water-food-agriculture.htm [July, 2015].

Did You Knows

Page 116. United Nations Food and Agriculture Organisation.n,d. 2050: A third more mouths to feed. Available at: http://www.fao.org/news/story/en/item/35571/icode/ [August, 2015].

Page 125. botany.uwc.ac.za. n,d. Soil Erosion. Available at: http://www.botany.uwc.ac.za/envfacts/facts/erosion.htm [August, 2015].

Page 133. TedX. 2010. Jeremy Jackson: How we wrecked the ocean. Available at: https://www.youtube.com/watch?v=u0VHC1-DO_8 [August, 2015].

Page 134. Vince, G. 2012. How the World's Ocean Could be Running Out of Fish. Available at: http://www.bbc.com/future/story/20120920-are-we-running-out-of-fish [August, 2015].

Page 136. United Nations Food and Agriculture Organisation. n,d. General Situation of World's Fish Stocks. Available at: http://www.fao.org/newsroom/common/ecg/1000505/en/stocks.pdf [August, 2015].

Page 137. The World Counts. n,d. Tons of Discarded Fish. Available at: http://www.theworldcounts.com/counters/ocean_ecosystem_facts/how_to_stop_overfishing [August, 2015].

Page 140. The World Counts. n,d. Tons of Plastic Waste Dumped in Oceans. Available at: http://www.theworldcounts.com/counters/ocean_ecosystem_facts/plastic_in_the_ocean_facts [August, 2015].

Page 141. McDonnell, T. 2015. There's a Horrifying Amount of Plastic in the Ocean. This Chart Shows Who's to Blame. Available at: http://www.motherjones.com/environment/2015/02/ocean-plastic-waste-china [July, 2015].

Page 145. Climate Institute. n,d. Agriculture. Available at: http://www.climate.org/topics/agriculture.html [July, 2015].

Page 146. Vince, G. 2012. How the World's Ocean Could be Running Out of Fish. Available at: http://www.bbc.com/future/story/20120920-are-we-running-out-of-fish [August, 2015].

Page 160. Ecological Footprint Tips. n,d. Food. Available at: http://www.epa.vic.gov.au/ecologicalfootprint/calculators/personal/docs/EF-tips-food.pdf [July, 2015].

Page 162. Vince, G. 2012. How the World's Ocean Could be Running Out of Fish. Available at: http://www.bbc.com/future/story/20120920-are-we-running-out-of-fish [August, 2015].

Page 165. Webber, M. 2011. More Efficient Foods, Less Waste. Available at: http://www.scientificamerican.com/article/webber-more-efficient-foods-less-waste/ [August, 2015].

Page 166. Borrell, B. n,d. Sustainable Salads: Which fruits, vegetables, and other crops have the smallest environmental footprints? Available at: http://www.slate.com/articles/health_and_science/the_green_lantern/2009/11/sustainable_salads.html [August, 2015].

Quotes

Page 121. quoteunited.com, n,d. Allan Savory Quotes. Available at: http://www.quoteunited.com/273416 [August, 2015]

Page 122. TristamStuart.co.uk. n.d. Food Waste Facts. Available at: http://www.tristramstuart.co.uk/foodwastefacts/ [August, 2015].

Page 127. TristamStuart.co.uk. n.d. Food Waste Facts. Available at: http://www.tristramstuart.co.uk/foodwastefacts/ [August, 2015].

Page 132. Branson, R. 2010. Business Stripped Bear: Adventures of a global entrepreneur. Penguin Group: New York.

Page 136. TedX. 2013. A recipe for cutting food waste: Peter Lehner at TEDx Manhattan. Available at: https://www.youtube.com/watch?v=UwOHpWTRsbE [July, 2015].

Page 137. TristamStuart.co.uk, n.d. Food Waste Facts. Available at: http://www.tristramstuart.co.uk/foodwastefacts/ [August, 2015].

Page 139. TedX. 2013. Overfished Ocean Strategy: Nadya Zhexembayeva at TEDx Klagenfurt. Available at: https://www.youtube.com/watch?v=FTNI_ToDISc [August, 2015].

Page 142. Howden, D. 2007. Deforestation: The hidden cause of global warming. Available at: http://www.independent.co.uk/environment/climate-change/deforestation-the-hidden-cause-of-global-warming-6262622.html [August, 2015].

Page 149. goodreads.com. n,d. Peter Singer Quotes. Available at: http://www.goodreads.com/quotes/820548-it-takes-twenty-one-pounds-of-protein-fed-to-a-calf [July, 2015].

Page 150. TedX. 2013. A War on Food Waste: Dr. Patrizia La Trecchia at TEDx USF. Available at: https://www.youtube.com/watch?v=enblsQloxvE [July, 2015].

Page 153. TristamStuart.co.uk, n.d. Food Waste Facts. Available at: http://www.tristramstuart.co.uk/foodwastefacts/ [August, 2015].

Page 163. goodreads.com. n,d. Edward O. Wilson Quotes. Available at: http://www.goodreads.com/quotes/549052-the-great-challenge-of-the-twenty-first-century-is-to-raise [August, 2015].

Page 164. TedX. 2013. A recipe for cutting food waste: Peter Lehner at TEDx Manhattan. Available at: https://www.youtube.com/watch?v=UwOHpWTRsbE [July, 2015].

Page 166. TedX. 2013. A recipe for cutting food waste: Peter Lehner at TEDx Manhattan. Available at: https://www.youtube.com/watch?v=UwOHpWTRsbE [July, 2015].

Transport

How does modern transport differ to that of the past?

bitlanders.com, 2015. The Difference Between Old Transport Systems and Modern Transport Systems and its Advantages. Available at: http://www.bitlanders.com/blogs/the-difference-between-old-transport-system-and-modren-transport-system-and-its-advantages/102704 [April, 2015].

International Transport Forum. 2010. The Global Transport System of the Future. Available at: http://www.internationaltransportforum.org/2010/pdf/GlobalTrSum.pdf [May, 2015].

wikipedia.com, n.d. History of Transport. Available at: https://en.wikipedia.org/wiki/History_of_transport [April, 2015].

World Highways. 2013. A Global Perspective on Sustainable Transportation Systems. Available at: http://www.worldhighways.com/sections/environment/features/a-global-perspective-on-sustainable-transportation-systems/ [May, 2015].

What is the relationship between globalisation and transport?

Corbett, J. & Winebrake, J. 2008. The Impacts of Globalisation on International Maritime Transport Activity: Past trends and future perspectives. Available at: http://www.oecd.org/greengrowth/greening-transport/41380820.pdf [May, 2015].

International Transport Forum, n.d. Transport for a Global Economy: Challenges and opportunities in the downturn. Available at: http://www.internationaltransportforum.org/2009/forum2009.html

Janelle, D. & Beuthe, M. 1997. Globalisation and Research Issues in Transportation. Journal of Transport Geography. Vol. 5(3): pages199-206.

Organisation for Economic Cooperation and Development (OECD), n.d. Globalisation, Transport and the Environment. Available at: http://www.oecd.org/greengrowth/greening-transport/45095528.pdf [May, 2015].

Rodrigue, JP. n,d. Transportation, Globalisation and International Trade. Available at: https://people.hofstra.edu/geotrans/eng/ch5en/conc5en/ch5c2en.html [May, 2015].

What opportunities does modern transport provide?

Rodrigue, JP. n,d. Transportation, Globalisation and International Trade. Available at: https://people.hofstra.edu/geotrans/eng/ch5en/conc5en/ch5c2en.html [May, 2015].

Kumar, P. n.d. Transportation Issues in Disaster Management. Available at: http://nidm.gov.in/idmc2/PDF/Presentations/Urban_Risk/Pres5.pdf [June, 2015].

Wikipedia, n.d. Humanitarian Response to the 2004 Indian Ocean Earthquake. Available at: https://en.wikipedia.org/wiki/Humanitarian_response_to_the_2004_Indian_Ocean_earthquake [June, 2015].

What are the problems with modern day transport?

Herron, D. 2014. Modern Transport Causes Grave Problems for Society. Available at: http://longtailpipe.com/2014/03/31/modern-transportation-causes-grave/ [June, 2015].

ramboll.com, n.d. Transport is Key for Prosperity. Available at: http://www.ramboll.com/megatrend/feature-arti-cles/transport-is-key-for-prosperity [June, 2015].

Perrels, A., Himanen, V. & Lee-Gosselin, M. 2008. Building Blocks for Sustainable Transport: Obstacles, trends, solutions. Emerald Group Publishing Limited: Bingley.

Pollution and global warming

Arup Foresight. 2014. Future of Rain 2015. Available at: http://www.driversofchange.com/projects/fu-ture-of-rail-2050/ [March, 2015].

Centre for Biological Diversity, n.d. Transportation and Global Warming. Available at: http://www.biologicaldiversi-ty.org/programs/climate_law_insti-tute/transportation_and_global_warming/ [June, 2015].

Union of Concerned Scientists, n.d. Car Emissions and Global Warming. Available at: http://www.ucsusa.org/-clean-vehicles/car-emissions-and-glob-al-warming#.VeRihWAxGYU [June, 2015].

Vehicle Manufacturing

Statistic Brain Research Institute. 2015. Total Cars Produced in the World. Available at: http://www.statistic-brain.com/cars-produced-in-the-world/ [August, 2015].

Worldometers.info, b.d. Cars Produced This Year. Available at: http://www.worldometers.info/cars/ [June, 2015].

Dependence on oil

Lefton, R. & Weiss, D. 2010. Oil Dependence is a dangerous habit. Available at: https://www.americanprog-ress.org/issues/green/re-port/2010/01/13/7200/oil-dependence-is-a/dangerous-habit [June, 2015]

Macrotrends.net. nd.Crude Oil price History Chart. Available at: http//www.macro-trends.net/1369/crude-oil-price-history-chart [June, 2015]

Urban sprawl

Grabkowski, L. n,d. Negative Effects of Urban Sprawl. Available at: http://homeguides.sfgate.com/negative-ef-fects-urban-sprawl-1716.html [July, 2015].

Mitchell, J. n,d. Urban Sprawl. Available at: http://environ-ment.nationalgeographic.com/environment/habi-tats/urban-sprawl/# [June, 2015].

Are there more eco-friendly ways to travel?

Arup Foresight. 2014. Future of Rain 2015. Available at: http://www.driversofchange.com/projects/fu-ture-of-rail-2050/ [March, 2015].

Evans, M. 2011. Sustainable Transport. Available at: http://www.earthtimes.org/encyclopaedia/environmental-is-sues/sustainable-transport/ [June, 2015].

Mooney, G. 2010. Making Transport More Sustainable. Available at: http://www.environmentallead-er.com/2010/11/10/making-transpor-tation-more-sustainable/ [July, 2015].

Tagliabue, J. 2013. The Dutch Prize Their Pedal Power, but a Sea of Bikes Swamps Their Capital. Available at: http://www.nytimes.com/2013/06/21/world/eu-rope/a-sea-of-bikes-swamps-amsterdam-a-city-fond-of-ped aling.html?_r=0 [July, 2015].

What alternative fuel sources are available?

Gore, A. 2013. The Future. Random House: New York.

Meyers, G. 2012. Top Eight Alternative Fuels. Available at: http://cleantechnica.com/2012/03/08/top-eight-alterna-tive-fuels/ [July, 2015].

Gore, A. 2009. Our Choice: A plan to solve the climate crisis. Penguin Books: New York

Biodiesel

Scientific American. 2013. Waste Energy: Converting discarded food into biofuels promises global energy boon. Available at: http://www.scientificamerican.com/article/-food-waste-to-energy/ [September, 2015].

International Energy Agency. 2011. Technology Roadmap: Biofuels for transport. Available at: http://www.iea.org/publi-cations/freepublications/publica-tion/technology-roadmap-biofuels-for-transport.html [July, 2015].

Transport and Environment, n.d. Biofuels. Available at: http://www.transportenvironment.org/what-we-do/biofuels [June, 2015].

Meyers, G. 2012. Top Eight Alternative Fuels. Available at: http://cleantechnica.com/2012/03/08/top-eight-alterna-tive-fuels/ [July, 2015].

Worldwatch Institute. 2006. Biofuels for Transportation: Global potential and implications for sustainable agriculture and energy in the 21st century. Available at: http://ww-w.worldwatch.org/system/files/EBF008_1.pdf [July, 2015].

Hybrid fuels

Conservative Energy Future, n.d. What is a Hybrid Car? Available at: http://www.conserve-energy-future.com/ad-vantages-and-disadvantages-of-hybrid-cars.php [July, 2015].

Oliver, R. 2007. All About: Hybrid Transportation. Available at: http://edition.cnn.com/2007/BUSINESS/09/14/al-labout.hybrid/ [June, 2015].

United Nations Environmental Programme (UNEP). 2009. Hybrid Electric Vehicles: An overview of current technology and its application in developing and transitional countries. Available at: http://www.unep.org/transport/pcfv/pdf/hev_re-port.pdf [July, 2015].

Electric power

Crothers, B. 2015. Faraday's Electric Vehicle Future: A Factory And Tesla Talent. Available at: http://www.-forbes.com/sites/brookecrothers/2015/07/23/fara-days-electric-vehicle-future-a-factory-and-tesla-talent/ [August, 2015].

Schaal, E. 2015. 7 Reasons Electric Cars are the Future in America. Available at: http://www.cheatsheet.com/automo-biles/7-reasons-electric-vehicle-adoption-is-inevitable-in-america.html/?a=viewall [July, 2015].

White, S. 2015. Electric Cars: Their past, present and future. Available at: http://www.cio.com/article/2955025/-consumer-technology/elec-tric-cars-their-past-present-and-future.html [August, 2015].

Can transport become more sustainable?

Mooney, G. 2010. Making Transport More Sustainable. Available at: http://www.environmentalleader.com/2010/11/10/making-transpor-tation-more-sustainable/ [July, 2015].

Kielgast, L. n,d. The Cities of the Future are People-Friendly Cities. Available at: http://den-mark.dk/en/green-living/bicycle-culture/the-cit-ies-of-the-future-are-people-friendly-cities/ [June, 2015].

Public transport

Arup Foresight. 2014. Future of Rain 2015. Available at: http://www.driversofchange.com/projects/fu-ture-of-rail-2050/ [March, 2015].

Gore, A. 2013. The Future. Random House: New York.

Fuel-efficient technologies

virgin.com, n.d. World-first low carbon aviation fuel to be developed for Virgin Atlantic. Available at: http://www.vir-gin.com/travel/world-first-low-carbon-avia-tion-fuel-be-developed-virgin-atlantic [July, 2015].

Gore, A. 2009. Our Choice: A plan to solve the climate crisis. Penguin Books: New York

Urban design and densification

Arup Foresight. 2013. Its Alive: Can you imagine the urban building of the future? Available at: http://www.arup.com/~/-media/Files/PDF/Publications/Re-search_and_whitepapers/Arup_Foresight_Future_Urban_Buildings%20FINAL.ashx [April, 2015].

BBC News. 2013. Why is cycling so popular in the Netherlands? Available at: https://web.ar-chive.org/web/20140307050642/http://ww-w.bbc.com/news/magazine-23587916 [July, 2015].

Lewis, E. 2013. Fietsstad 2014: which is the Netherlands' best bicycle city? Available at: http://www.iamex-pat.nl/read-and-discuss/life-style/news/dutch-cities-compete-fietsstad [July, 2015].

Tagliabue, J. 2013. The Dutch Prize Their Pedal Power, but a Sea of Bikes Swamps Their Capital. Available at: http://www.nytimes.com/2013/06/21/world/eu-rope/a-sea-of-bikes-swamps-amsterdam-a-city-fond-of-ped aling.html?_r=0 [July, 2015].

Consuming in locality

DeWeerdt, S. n,d. Is Local Food Better? Available at: http://www.worldwatch.org/node/6064 [July, 2015].

Murphy, T. 2013. The dilemma of eating locally and hurting others globally. Available at: http://www.humano-sphere.org/environment/2013/03/chang-

ing-how-food-is-produced-in-the-us-an-international-perspe ctive/ [June, 2015].

Behavioural change

BBC News. 2013. Why is cycling so popular in the Netherlands? Available at: https://web.ar-chive.org/web/20140307050642/http://ww-w.bbc.com/news/magazine-23587916 [July, 2015].

Kielgast, L. n,d. The Cities of the Future are People-Friend-ly Cities. Available at: http://denmark.dk/en/green-living/bi-cycle-culture/the-cit-ies-of-the-future-are-people-friendly-cities/ [June, 2015].

Graphs / Stats

Page 176. Wikipedia, n.d. List of World's Busiest Container Ports. Available at: https://en.wikipe-dia.org/wiki/List_of_world%27s_busiest_container_ports [May, 2015].

Page 181. Wikipedia, n.d. List of the World's Busiest Airports by International Passenger Traffic. Available at: https://en.wikipedia.org/wiki/List_of_the_world%27s_busi-est_airports_by_international_passenger_traffic [June, 2015].

Page 186. Statistic Brain Research Institute. 2015. Total Cars Produced in the World. Available at: http://www.statis-ticbrain.com/cars-produced-in-the-world/ [August, 2015].

Page 215. BBC News. 2013. Why is cycling so popular in the Netherlands? Available at: https://web.ar-chive.org/web/20140307050642/http://ww-w.bbc.com/news/magazine-23587916 [July, 2015].

Did You Knows

Page 170. idea finder.com, n.d. The Assembly Line. Available at: http://www.ideafinder.com/history/inven-tions/assbline.htm [May, 2015].

Page 173. Mathews, J. 2015. The Tesla Battery Heralds the Beginning of the End for Fossil Fuels. Available at: http://www.iflscience.com/technology/tesla-battery-her-alds-beginning-end-fossil-fuels [May, 2015].

Page 179. Schuyler, M. 2015. CSCL Globe Calls at Port of Hamburg. Available at: http://maritimenewstoday.com/?-cat=137 [June, 2015].

Page 184. whatsyourimpact.com, n.d. What are the main sources of carbon dioxide emissions? Available at: http://whatsyourimpact.org/greenhouse-gases/carbon-diox-ide-sources [June, 2015].

Page 192. howmany.org, n.d. Best Population Size: The big picture. Available at: http://www.howmany.org/big_pic-ture.php [June, 2015].

Page 193. Kielgast, L. n,d. The Cities of the Future are People-Friendly Cities. Available at: http://den-mark.dk/en/green-living/bicycle-culture/the-cit-ies-of-the-future-are-people-friendly-cities/ [June, 2015].

Page 194. Greener Journeys, n.d. Reducing Congestion & CO2. Available at: http://www.greenerjourneys.com/bene-fits/environment/ [June, 2015].

Page 198. Branson, R. 2010. Business Stripped Bear: Adventures of a global entrepreneur. Penguin Group: New York.

Page 202. Bullis, K. 2015. Why We Don't Have Battery Breakthroughs. Available at: http://www.technologyreview.com/review/534866/why-we-dont-have-battery-breakthroughs/ [July, 2015].

Quotes

Page 172. brainyquote.com, n.d. James Buchan Quotes. Available at: http://www.brainyquote.com/quotes/quotes/j/jamesbucha444684.html [May, 2015].

Page 185. brainyquote.com, n.d. John Boyd Orr Quotes. Available at: http://www.brainyquote.com/quotes/quotes/j/johnboydor322874.html [May, 2015].

Page 177. Moskowitz, C. 2012. Private Rocket Launch Vindicates Commercial Spaceflight Model. Available at: http://www.space.com/15809-spacex-private-capsule-launch-commercial-spaceflight.html [June, 2015].

Page 183. brainyquote.com, n.d. Elon Musk Quotes, Available at: http://www.brainyquote.com/quotes/quotes/e/elonmusk567198.html [June, 2015].

Page 188. brainyquote.com, n.d. James Woolsey Quotes. Available at: http://www.brainyquote.com/quotes/authors/j/james_woolsey.html [June, 2015].

Page 195. Carey, A. & Dowling, J. 2013. The Road to a Standstill. Available at: http://www.drive.com.au/it-pro/the-road-to-a-standstill-20130414-2hter [July, 2015].

Page 196. Branson, R. 2010. Business Stripped Bear: Adventures of a global entrepreneur. Penguin Group: New York.

Page 200. Branson, R. 2010. Business Stripped Bear: Adventures of a global entrepreneur. Penguin Group: New York.

Page 205. Robillard, K. 2014. Foxx Takes a Futurist Turn at DOT. Available at: http://www.politico.com/story/2014/09/anthony-foxx-department-of-transportation-110656 [July, 2015].

Page 213. quoteaddicts.com, n.d. Tyler Florence Quotes. Available at: http://quoteaddicts.com/124935 [June, 2015].

Consumer Goods

What are consumer goods?

Encyclopaedia Britannica. n,d. Economics: Consumer Good. Available at: http://www.britannica.com/topic/consumer-good [June, 2015].

How are consumer goods produced?

McDonough, W. & Braungart, M. 2013. The Upcycle: Beyond sustainability - Designing for abundance. North Point Press: New York.

Wikipedia. n,d. Final Good. Available at: https://en.wikipedia.org/wiki/Final_good [July, 2015].

Raw material extraction

cordaid.org. 2012. The Impact of Extracting Raw Materials. Available at: https://www.cordaid.org/en/projects/the-impact-of-extracting-raw-materials/107771/ [June, 2015].

Electronics TakeBack Coalition. n,d. Where's The Harm – From Materials Extraction? Available at: http://www.electronicstakeback.com/toxics-in-electronics/wheres-the-harm-extraction/ [June, 2015].

Land Learn. n,d. What is a Production Chain? Available at: http://www.landlearnnsw.org.au/production-chains/what-is [June, 2015].

Materials processing

Encyclopaedia Britannica. n,d. Materials Processing. Available at: http://www.britannica.com/technology/materials-processing [June, 2015].

Wikipedia. n,d. Materials Processing. Available at: https://www.google.com/search?client=safari&rls=en&q=materials+processing&ie=UTF-8&oe=UTF-8 [June, 2015].

Assembly

financesonline.com n,d. How iPhone Is Made: The Global Assembly Line. Available at: http://financesonline.com/hello-world-the-economics-of-iphone/ [July, 2015].

Wikipedia. n,d. Assembly Line. Available at: https://en.wikipedia.org/wiki/Assembly_line [June, 2015].

Where does all our waste go?

amsweb.com. 2009. Landfills And The Environmental Effects. Available at: http://livelifegreen.com/landfills-and-th-environmental-effects/ [July, 2015].

David Suzuki Foundation. 2013. Incinerating Trash is a Waste of Resources. Available at: http://www.davidsuzuki.org/blogs/science-matters/2013/09/incinerating-trash-is-a-waste-of-resources/ [June, 2015].

Mathiesen, K. 2014. Rubbish futures: can technology help us reach zero waste? Available at: http://www.theguardian.com/lifeandstyle/2014/jun/12/rubbish-futures-can-technology-help-us-reach-zero-waste [June, 2015].

Waste Management Resources. n,d. Incineration. Available at: http://www.wrfound.org.uk/articles/incineration.html [June, 2015].

West, K. 2015. Waste Not, Want Not: how the rubbish industry learned to look beyond landfill. Available at: http://www.theguardian.com/environment/2015/feb/27/waste-rubbish-industry-landfill-recycling-dumps-incineration [June, 2015].

What are the environmental effects of all our waste?

European Environment Agency. 2014. Waste: A problem or a resource? Available at: http://www.eea.europa.eu/signals/signals-2014/articles/waste-a-problem-or-a-resource

[June, 2015].

Fullcycle.co.za. n,d. What is Waste and Why is it a Problem? Available at: http://www.fullcycle.co.za/index-.php/what-is-waste-and-why-is-it-a-problem.html [June, 2015].

Toxics Action Center. n,d. The Problems With Waste. Available at: http://www.toxicsaction.org/problems-and-solutions/waste [June, 2015].

World Wildlife Foundation (WWF). Waste Disposal. Available at: http://wwf.panda.org/about_our_earth/teacher_resources/webfieldtrips/waste_disposal/ [July, 2015].

Hard trash

Cruice-Barnett, M. 2012. Littering and its Effect on the Environment. Available at: https://www.scienceleadership.org/blog/Littering_and_its_Effect_on_the_Environment [July, 2015].

environment.about.com n,d. Litter Trashes the Environment. Available at: http://environment.about.com/od/pollution/a/litter.htm [June, 2015].

Marine Conservation Society. n,d. What's the Big Deal? Available at: http://www.mcsuk.org/what_we_do/Clean+seas+and+beaches/Pollution+and+litter+problems/Pollution+and+litter+problems [July, 2015].

Hazardous waste

Environment Canada. n,d. Hazardous Waste and Recyclable Material. Available at: https://www.ec.gc.-ca/gdd-mw/default.asp?lang=En&n=39D0D04A-1 [June, 2015].

National Geographic. n,d. Toxic Waste: Man's poisonous byproducts. Available at: http://environment.nationalgeographic.com/environment/global-warming/toxic-waste-overview/ [July, 2015].

Wikipedia. n,d. List of Waste Disposal Incidents. Available at: https://en.wikipedia.org/wiki/List_of_waste_disposal_incidents [July, 2105].

Air pollution

Atmos News. 2014. Trash Burning Worldwide Significantly Worsens Air Pollution. Available at: https://www2.ucar.edu/atmosnews/news/12239/trash-burning-worldwide-significantly-worsens-air-pollution [June, 2015].

Conserve Energy Future. n,d. Industrial Pollution. Available at: http://www.conserve-energy-future.com/causes-effects-of-industrial-pollution.php [July, 2015].

Sutton, S. 2011. Landfill air pollution may be as unhealthy as it is unpleasant, study finds. Available at: http://hpdp.unc.edu/2011/07/07/landfill-air-pollution-may-be-as-unhealthy-as-it-is-unpleasant-study-finds/ [June, 2105].

How does the recycling process work?

Natural Resources Defence Council. n,d. To Good to Throw Away: Recycling's proven record. Available at:

http://www.nrdc.org/cities/recycling/recyc/chap1.asp [July, 2015].

Metals

Copper Development Association Inc. n,d. Recycling of Copper. Available at: http://www.copper.org/environment/lifecycle/ukrecyc.html [June, 2015].

Lallanilla, M. n,d. Aluminum Recycling: Yes You Can. Available at: http://greenliving.about.com/od/recycling-waste/a/Aluminum-Recycling-Can-Recycling.htm [June, 2015].

LeBlanc, R. n,d. Steel Recycling Facts and Figures. Available at: http://recycling.about.com/od/Recycling/a/Steel-Recycling-Facts-And-Figures.htm [June, 2015].

Plastics

Benefits of Recycling. n,d. Recycling Plastic Bottles. Available at: http://www.benefits-of-recycling.com/recyclingplasticbottles/ [June, 2015].

Chemical Engineers in Action. n,d. Recycle and Reuse: Turning waste into gold. Available at: http://www.chemicalengineering.org/enviro/recycle.html [June, 2015].

nikiso.com. n,d. Development of Chemical Recycling Processes for Plastic Waste. Available at: http://www.nikkiso.com/rd/main/011.html [July, 2015].

pollutionissues.com. n,d. Plastics. Available at: http://www.pollutionissues.com/Pl-Re/Plastic.html [June, 2015].

Priebe, M. n,d. How to Recycle LDPE (Plastic #4). Available at: http://www.ecolife.com/recycling/plastic/how-to-recycle-ldpe-plastic-4.html [June, 2015].

Chemicals

David Suzuki Foundation. n,d. How to Dispose of Household Hazardous Waste. Available at: http://www.davidsuzuki.org/what-you-can-do/queen-of-green/-faqs/cleaning/how-to-dispose-of-household-hazardous-waste/ [June, 2015].

Solid Waste Agency of Lake County. n,d. Household Chemical Waste (HCW) Recycling. Available at: http://www.swalco.org/Collections/HCW/Pages/default.aspx [June, 2015].

United States Environmental Protection Agency. n,d. Household Hazardous Waste. Available at: http://www.epa.gov/wastes/conserve/materials/hhw.htm [June, 2015].

Waste Management. n,d. Household Hazardous Waste Disposal. Available at: http://www.wm.com/enterprise/municipalities/residential-solutions/household-hazardous-waste.jsp [June, 2015].

Organics

Environment Victoria. n,d. Organic Waste. Available at: http://environmentvictoria.org.au/content/organic-waste [June, 2015].

Organic Disposal LLC. n,d. What is Organic Waste? Available at: http://www.organicdisposal.net/Pages/organicwaste.aspx [June, 2015].

United States Environmental Protection Agency. n,d. Anaerobic Digestion 101. Available at: http://www.epa.gov/outreach/agstar/anaerobic/ad101/index.html [July, 2015].

Waste Management. n,d. Organic Waste Recycling. Available at: http://www.wm.com/enterprise/food-and-retail/Restaurant-Solutions/organics-recycling.jsp [June, 2015].

Paper and Timber

biophysics.ac.at n,d. Paper Recycling. Available at: http://biophysics.sbg.ac.at/waste/paper.htm [June, 2015].

Wood Solutions. n,d. Recycling and Wood Waste. Available at: https://www.woodsolutions.com.au/Articles/Why-Wood/recycling-energy-wood-waste [June, 2015].

Glass

West, L. n,d. Benefits of Glass Recycling: Why Recycle Glass? Available at: http://environment.about.com/od/recycling/a/benefits_of_glass_recycling.htm [June, 2015].

Woodford, C. 2014. Glass. Available at: http://www.explainthatstuff.com/glass.html [June, 2015].

Rubber

Benefits of Recycling. n,d. Recycling Tires. Available at: http://www.benefits-of-recycling.com/recyclingtires/ [June, 2015].

Leather, T. 2010. Seas of Rubber: The Truth About Tire Recycling. Available at: http://recyclenation.com/2010/06/sea-rubber-truth-tire-recycling [July, 2015].

Rubber Manufacturers Association. n,d. Rubber FAQ's. Available at: http://www.rma.org/about-rma/rubber-faqs/ [July, 2015].

seekingalpha.com. 2010. A Look at the Global Tire Industry. Available at: http://seekingalpha.com/article/220104-a-look-at-the-global-tire-industry [June, 2015].

Woodford, C. 2015. Rubber. Available at: http://www.explainthatstuff.com/rubber.html [June, 2015].

What is the future of the recycling industry?

Natural Resource Defence Council. n,d. The Past, Present and Future of Recycling. Available at: http://www.nrdc.org/cities/recycling/fover.asp [June, 2015].

McDonough, W. & Braungart, M. 2013. The Upcycle: Beyond sustainability - Designing for abundance. North Point Press: New York.

Ted X. 2013. The Future of Recycling: Rajan Ahluwalia at TEDx Edmonton. Available at: https://www.youtube.com/watch?v=qImzHrJpzuo [June, 2015].

Tex X. 2012. Waste as Resource: Kevin Scoble at TEDx Fort McMurray. Available at: https://www.youtube.com/watch?v=Bqf3xTTCiu8 [June, 2015].

Ted X. 2009. Changing the paradigm of recyclin: Mário Silva at TEDx Edges. Available at: https://www.youtube.com/watch?v=PTWbvfrS_ig [June, 2015].

Mathiesen, K. 2014. Rubbish futures: Can technology help us reach zero waste? Available at: http://www.theguardian.com/lifeandstyle/2014/jun/12/rubbish-futures-can-technology-help-us-reach-zero-waste [June, 2015].

Are we designing products better than we did in the past?

Di Fiore, A. 2013. Even Cement Can Be Special. Available at: https://hbr.org/2013/06/even-cement-can-be-special [June, 2015].

Euro News. 2003. Building for the Future with Self-Repairing Concrete. Available at: http://www.euronews.com/2015/03/30/building-for-the-future-with-self-repairing-concrete/ [June, 2014].

Gates, B. 2014. Have You Hugged a Concrete Pillar Today? Available at: http://www.gatesnotes.com/Books/Making-the-Modern-World [March, 2015].

McDonough, W. & Braungart, M. 2013. The Upcycle: Beyond sustainability - Designing for abundance. North Point Press: New York.

Are there better ways to design, manufacture and use products?

futurenergie.org. n,d. Biodegradable plastics: are they better for the environment? Available at: http://www.futurenergia.org/ww/en/pub/futurenergia/chats/bio_plastics.htm [June, 2015].

Gates, B. 2014. Have You Hugged a Concrete Pillar Today? Available at: http://www.gatesnotes.com/Books/Making-the-Modern-World [March, 2015].

McDonough, W. & Braungart, M. 2013. The Upcycle: Beyond sustainability - Designing for abundance. North Point Press: New York.

Graphs / Stats

Page 226. World Steel Association. 2014. World Steel in Figures 2014. Available at: https://www.worldsteel.org/dms/internetDocumentList/bookshop/World-Steel-in-Figures-2014/document/World%20Steel%20in%20Figures%202014%20Final.pdf [Jul;y, 2015].

Page 237. The World Bank. 2015. 'What a Waste' Report Shows Alarming Rise in Amount, Costs of Garbage. Available at: http://www.worldbank.org/en/news/feature/2012/06/06/report-shows-alarming-rise-in-amount-costs-of-garbage [June, 2015].

Page 240. theworldcounts.com. n,d. Hazardous Waste Statistics. Available at: http://www.theworldcounts.com/counters/waste_pollution_facts/hazardous_waste_statistics [July, 2015].

Page 243. Electronics TakeBack Coalition. n,d. Facts and Figures on E-Waste and Recycling. available at: http://www.electronicstakeback.com/wp-content/uploads/

Facts_and_Figures_on_EWaste_and_Recycling.pdf [June, 2015].

Page 259. Advantage Environment. n,d. Revolutionising the Rubber Tire Recycling Industry. Available at: http://advantage-environment.com/transporter/revolutionizing-the-rubber-tire-recycling-industry/ [August, 2015].

Page 265. gdrc.org. n,d. Waste Management: Fact Sheet. Available at: http://www.gdrc.org/uem/waste/waste-fact-sheet.html [June, 2015].

Did You Knows

Page 230. gdrc.org. n,d. Waste Management: Fact Sheet. Available at: http://www.gdrc.org/uem/waste/waste-fact-sheet.html [June, 2015].

Page 232. gdrc.org. n,d. Waste Management: Fact Sheet. Available at: http://www.gdrc.org/uem/waste/waste-fact-sheet.html [June, 2015].

Page 247. World Steel Association. n,d. Steel Facts. Available at: http://www.worldsteel.org/Steel-facts.html [June, 2015].

Page 248. Lallanilla, M. n,d. Aluminum Recycling: Yes You Can. Available at: http://greenliving.about.com/od/recycling-waste/a/Aluminum-Recycling-Can-Recycling.htm [June, 2015].

Page 253. theworldcounts.com. n,d. World Food Waste Statistics. Available at: http://www.theworldcounts.com/counters/world_food_consumption_statistics/world_food_waste_statistics [September, 2015].

Page 259. Rubber Manufacturers Association. n,d. Rubber FAQ's. Available at: http://www.rma.org/about-rma/rubber-faqs/ [July, 2015].

Page 266. Gates, B. 2014. Have You Hugged a Concrete Pillar Today? Available at: http://www.gatesnotes.com/Books/Making-the-Modern-World [March, 2015].

Page 272. Goldstein, J. 2011. Consumer Pulse: Part Two. Available at: http://blogs.waggeneredstrom.com/under-the-influence/2011/02/09/consumer-pulse-part-two/ [June, 2015].

Page 275. The Independent. 2011. Global resource consumption to triple by 2050: UN. Available at: http://www.independent.co.uk/environment/global-resource-consumption-to-triple-by-2050-un-2284007.html [July, 2015].

Quotes

Page 218. azquotes.com. n,d. Tim Cook Quotes. Available at: http://www.azquotes.com/quote/677919 [June, 2015].

Page 221. azquotes.com. n,d. Robert Rodrigues Quotes. Available at: http://www.azquotes.com/quote/677929 [June, 2015].

Page 224. quoteaddicts.com. n,d. Chris Kilham Quotes. Available at: http://quoteaddicts.com/166604 [June, 2015].

Page 225. brainyquote.com. n,d. Stewart Udall Quotes. Available at: http://www.brainyquote.com/quotes/s/stewartuda112381.html [July, 2015].

Page 231. Ted X. 2013. Smart cities for 11 billion people: Mitchell Joachim at TEDx Berlin. Available at: https://www.youtube.com/watch?v=eWpgidvBqHw [June, 2015].

Page 234. TedX. 2013. A recipe for cutting food waste: Peter Lehner at TEDx Manhattan. Available at: https://www.youtube.com/watch?v=UwOHpWTRsbE [July, 2015].

Page 235. Tex X. 2012. Waste as Resource: Kevin Scoble at TEDx Fort McMurray. Available at: https://www.youtube.com/watch?v=Bqf3xTTCiu8 [June, 2015].

Page 239. The American Presidency Project. n,d. The Environment Message to the Congress. Available at: http://www.presidency.ucsb.edu/ws/?pid=7561 [July, 2015].

Page 243. Tex X. 2012. Waste as Resource: Kevin Scoble at TEDx Fort McMurray. Available at: https://www.youtube.com/watch?v=Bqf3xTTCiu8 [June, 2015].

Page 245. Morris, D. 1966. Recycling and the New York Times. Available at: http://ilsr.org/recycling-and-the-new-york-times-2/ [June, 2015].

Page 262. brainyquote.com. n,d. R. Buckminster Fuller Quotes. Available at: http://www.brainyquote.com/quotes/r/rbuckmins101926.html [July, 2015].

Page 263. brainyquote.com. n,d. Ted Danson Quotes. Available at: http://www.brainyquote.com/quotes/t/teddanson263560.html [June, 2015].

Page 267. Booth, W. 2000. Recycling: How Long Will a Can-Do Feeling Last? Available at: http://www.washingtonpost.com/wp-srv/WPcap/2000-01/05/039r-010500-idx.html [June, 2015].

Page 269. Veen, J. 2000. The Art and Science of Web Design. New Riders Press: San Fransisco.

Page 271. Price, D. 2013. The 13 most philosophical Jony Ive quotes. Available at: http://www.macworld.co.uk/news/apple/13-most-philosophical-jony-ive-quotes-3490442/ [June, 2015].

Page 272. Price, D. 2013. The 13 most philosophical Jony Ive quotes. Available at: http://www.macworld.co.uk/news/apple/13-most-philosophical-jony-ive-quotes-3490442/ [June, 2015].

Page 273. Branson, R. 2010. Business Stripped Bear: Adventures of a global entrepreneur. Penguin Group: New York.

Page 273. Branson, R. 2010. Business Stripped Bear: Adventures of a global entrepreneur. Penguin Group: New York.

Page 274. brainyquote.com. n,d. Albert Einstein Quotes. Available at: http://www.brainyquote.com/quotes/a/alberteins385842.html [June, 2105].

Buildings & Cities

Why do we build so much?

Klepeis, N., Nelson, W., Ott, W., Robinson, J., Tsand, A. & Swizer, P. n,d. The National Human Activity Pattern Survey (NHAPS) A Resource for Assessing Exposure to Environmental Pollutants. Available at: https://indoor.lbl.gov/sites/all/files/lbnl-47713.pdf [September, 2015].

What are cities and why are they important?

Florida, R. 2011. Why Cities Matter. Available at: http://www.citylab.com/design/2011/09/why-cities-matter/123/ [July, 2015].

Gore, A. 2009. Our Choice: A plan to solve the climate crisis. Penguin Books: New York

The Economist. 2012. The Importance of Cities: Joy of crowds. Available at: http://www.economist.com/node/21559585 [June, 2015].

Satell, G. 2013. Why Cities Are Our Most Important Innovation Platform. Available at: http://www.forbes.com/sites/gregsatell/2013/11/09/why-cities-are-our-most-important-innovation-platform/ [June, 2015].

Ted X. 2013. The Importance of Reconnecting Our Cities to Nature: Brian Heather at TEDx Seattle. Available at: https://www.youtube.com/watch?v=9HVdS9qLrfo [July, 2015].

Urbanised. 2011. Documentary. Directed by Gary Hustwit.

What is a building life cycle?

Wikipedia. n,d. Building Life Cycle. Available at: https://en.wikipedia.org/wiki/Building_life_cycle [June, 2015].

Construction

British Research Establishment (BRE). 2001. DTI Construction Industry Directorate Project Report : Current Practice and Potential Uses of Prefabrication. Available at: http://projects.bre.co.uk/prefabrication/prefabrication.pdf [September, 2015].

Burgess, J., Buckett, N. & Page, I. 2013. Study Report: Prefabrication impacts in the New Zealand construction industry. Available at: http://www.branz.co.nz/cms_show_download.php?id=2935644f1d998595f3a2d8f5e8167dd08a42a179 [September, 2015].

Demolition and recycling

Your Home. n,d. Waste Minimisation. Available at: http://www.yourhome.gov.au/materials/waste-minimisation [June, 2015].

What effect do buildings and cities have on the environment?

Brian Walsh. Walsh, B. 2012. Urban Planet: How Growing Cities Will Wreck the Environment Unless We Build Them Right. Available at: http://science.time.com/2012/09/18/urban-planet-how-growing-cities-will-wreck-the-environment-unless-we-build-them-right/ [April, 2015].

earthscienceeducation.com. n,d. Environmental Effects of Cities. Available at: http://www.earthscienceeducation.org/UofU-UrbEnviG/C-Content-ForSessions/A-Intro/y081201ENCY-GEOG-EnviImpctOfCities-Shortened.htm [July, 2015].

Newman, P. 2006. The Environmental Impact of Cities. Environment and Urbanisation. Vol. 18 (2): pages 275-295.

Seto Lab. n,d. Environmental Impacts of Urban Growth. Available at: http://urban.yale.edu/research/theme-4 [July, 2015].

Ecological damage and disruption

Newman, P. 2006. The Environmental Impact of Cities. Environment and Urbanisation. Vol. 18 (2): pages 275-295.

Seto Lab. n,d. Environmental Impacts of Urban Growth. Available at: http://urban.yale.edu/research/theme-4 [July, 2015].

Walsh, B. 2012. Urban Planet: How Growing Cities Will Wreck the Environment Unless We Build Them Right. Available at: http://science.time.com/2012/09/18/urban-planet-how-growing-cities-will-wreck-the-environment-unless-we-build-them-right/ [April, 2015].

Resource consumption

Bentham, J. n,d. Future Cities in a Resource Constrained World. Available at: http://www.leekuanyewworldcityprize.com.sg/features_cities.htm [July, 2015].

boundless.com. n,d. The Environmental Impact of Cities. Available at: https://www.boundless.com/u-s-history/textbooks/boundless-u-s-history-textbook/the-gilded-age-1870-1900-20/the-rise-of-the-city-145/the-environmental-impact-of-cities-769-8652/ [June, 2015].

Dodman, D. 2009. Blaming Cities for Climate Change? An analysis of urban greenhouse gas emissions inventories. Environment and Urbanisation. Vol. 21(1): pages 185-201.

Gore, A. 2009. Our Choice: A plan to solve the climate crisis. Penguin Books: New York

Oliver, R. 2007. All About: Cities and energy consumption. Available at: http://edition.cnn.com/2007/TECH/12/31/eco.cities/ [June, 2015].

Phillips, T. 2013. From sand to skyscrapers: Inside China's newest city as 400 million move to towns. Available at: http://www.telegraph.co.uk/news/worldnews/asia/china/10123620/From-sand-to-skyscrapers-Inside-Chinas-newest-city-as-400-million-move-to-towns.html [September, 2015].

ted.com. 2007. William McDonough: Cradle to cradle design. Available at: http://www.ted.com/talks/william_mcdonough_on_cradle_to_cradle_design/transcript?language=en [September, 2015].

Tyrnauer, M. 2008. Industrial Revolution, Take Two. Available at: http://www.vanityfair.com/culture/2008/05/mcdonough200805 [September, 2015].

Pollution and waste

Dodman, D. 2009. Blaming Cities for Climate Change? An analysis of urban greenhouse gas emissions inventories.

Environment and Urbanisation. Vol. 21(1): pages 185-201.

Fell, D. 2012. Why Waste is Still a Built Environment Concern for Sustainable Cities. Available at: http://www.-theguardian.com/sustainable-business/waste-built-environment-sustainable-cities [July, 2015].

Satterthwaite, D. 2015. How Urban Societies Can Adapt to Resource Shortage and Climate Change. Philosophical Transactions of the Royal Society. Vol. 1(369); pages 1762 - 1783.

Wilson, D. 2014. Cities and Waste: Current and emerging issues. Waste Management and Research. Vol. 32(9): pages 797 - 799.

Queen, S. 012. 11 Most Polluted Rivers in the World. Available at: http://www.takepart.com/photos/10-most-polluted-rivers-world/yamuna-river-new-delhi-india [September, 2015].

What are the problems with our building methods today?

McGuirk, J. 2011. Urbanised: a documentary about city design that comes in the nick of time. Available at: http://www.theguardian.com/artanddesign/2011/oct/25/urbanized-documentary-design-7-billion [June, 2015].

Mitchell, J. n,d. Urban Sprawl. Available at: http://environment.nationalgeographic.com/environment/habitats/urban-sprawl/ [June, 2015].

Renn, A. 2015. What's the Perfect Size for a City? Available at: http://www.theguardian.com/cities/2015/apr/23/sane-way-run-megalopolis-urban-governance [August, 2015].

Urbanised. 2011. Documentary. Directed by Gary Hustwit

Conventional building methods

Florida, R. 2011. Why Cities Matter. Available at: http://www.citylab.com/design/2011/09/why-cities-matter/123/ [July, 2015].

Slums and informal settlements

Da Silva, I. 2013. The Rise and Rise of Slums in the World. Available at: http://moonofthesouth.com/rise-rise-slums-africa/ [June, 2015].

Florida, R. 2011. Why Cities Matter. Available at: http://www.citylab.com/design/2011/09/why-cities-matter/123/ [July, 2015].

National Geographic. n,d. Urban Threats. Available at: http://environment.nationalgeographic.com/environment/habitats/urban-threats2/ [June, 2015].

Globalisation

Newman, P. & Thornlet, A. Globalisation, World Cities and Urban Planning: Developing a conceptual framework. Available at: http://www.kas.de/upload/dokumente/megacities/megacities1/allgemein/newman.pdf [June, 2015].

Wang, W. 2013. Culture: City: How Culture Leaves its Mark on Cities and Architecture Around the World. Lars Muller Publishers: Berlin.

Wikipedia. n,d. Masdar City. Available at: https://en.wikipedia.org/wiki/Masdar_City [June, 2015].

How can we make buildings sustainable?

United States Environmental Protection Agency. n,d. What is a Green Building; Fundamental principles of green building and sustainable site design. Available at: http://www.epa.gov/statelocalclimate/documents/pdf/12_8_what_is_green_GGGC.pdf [July, 2015].

Passive design

Autodesk Education Community. n,d. Passive Design Strategies. Available at: http://sustainabilityworkshop.autodesk.com/buildings/passive-design-strategies [June, 2015].

Dietrich, B. n,d. Vernacular Design: Architecture's Regional Voices. Available at: http://www.houzz.com/ideabooks/12164610/list/vernacular-design-architectures-regional-voices [July, 2015].

Foster and Partners. 2011. Performance' Norman Foster. RIBA talk, October 2010. Available at: https://www.youtube.com/watch?v=PEa6Cl2vfz8 [June, 2015].

Active design

Centre for Active Design. n,d. What is Active Design? Available at: http://centerforactivedesign.org/WhatIsActiveDesign/ [July, 2015].

Foster and Partners. 2011. Performance' Norman Foster. RIBA talk, October 2010. Available at: https://www.youtube.com/watch?v=PEa6Cl2vfz8 [June, 2015].

Yaghooti, J. 2013. Active Design: The intersection of architecture and public health. Available at: http://pagethink.com/media/uploads/news-docs/active_design_part_one.pdf [July, 2015].

What should cities of the future look like?

Chandran, N. 2015. World's Smartest Cities Will Look Like This. Available at: http://www.cnbc.com/2015/06/08/this-is-what-the-smart-cities-will-look-like.html [July, 2015].

Cherry, S. 2013. Want to Save the Environment? Build More Cities. Available at: http://spectrum.ieee.org/podcast/energy/environment/want-to-save-the-environment-build-more-cities [June, 2015].

CNN. 2012. Interview with Architect Bjarke Ingels. Available at: http://edition.cnn.com/TRANSCRIPTS/1204/22/nl.01.html [June, 2015].

Foster, N. 2011. The city of the future: It's a story of camels, penguins and cars you don't drive. Available at: http://www.dailymail.co.uk/home/moslive/article-1348558/Norman-Foster-City-future-camels-penguins-cars-dont-drive.html#ixzz3c2JqKvDd [June, 2015].

Fraioli, P. 2012. The Invention and Reinvention of the City: An Interview with Rem Koolhaas. Available at: http://jia.sipa.columbia.edu/online-articles/invention-and-reinvention-city-interview-rem-koolhaas/ [June, 2015].

Wakefield, J. 2013. How will our future cities look? Available at: http://www.bbc.com/news/technology-20770518 {April, 2015].

Adwell, M. 2011. Cities Absorb More Carbon Than Previously Thought. Available at: http://www.the9billion.com/2011/07/14/cities-absorb-more-carbon-than-previously-thought/ [September, 2015].

Biello, D. 2011. How Green Is My City. American Scientific. Vol. 305(3): pg 66-69.

Dac & Cities. n,d. Copenhagen: From sewer to harbour bath. Available at: http://www.dac.dk/en/dac-cities/sustainable-cities/all-cases/water/copenhagen-from-sewer-to-harbour-bath/ [September, 2015].

Dickerson, K. 2014. These Maps Show Which Areas Of The Country Have The Biggest Carbon Footprints. Available at: http://www.businessinsider.com/carbon-footprint-maps-2014-1 [September, 2015].

Glaeser, E. 2011. Engines of Innovation. American Scientific. Vol. 305(3): pg 50-55.

Owen, D. 2009. Greenest Place in the U.S.? It's Not Where You Think. Available at: http://e360.yale.edu/feature/greenest_place_in_the_us_its_not_where_you_think/2203/ [September, 2015].

Do cities hold the key to sustainability?

Berg, N. 2015. Book Review of Design for a Living Planet: Settlement, Science and the Human Future. Available at: http://www.architectmagazine.com/design/exhibits-books-etc/-book-review-of-design-for-a-living-planet-settlement-science-and-the-human-future_o [June, 2015].

Chandran, N. 2015. World's Smartest Cities Will Look Like This. Available at: http://www.cnbc.com/2015/06/08/this-is-what-the-smart-cities-will-look-like.html [July, 2015].

Chu, J. 2015. Bjarke Ingels On The Future Of Architecture. Available at: http://www.fastcodesign.com/3041276/slicker-city/bjarke-ingels-on-the-future-of-architecture [April, 2015].

Cherry, S. 2013. Want to Save the Environment? Build More Cities. Available at: http://spectrum.ieee.org/podcast/energy/environment/want-to-save-the-environment-build-more-cities [June, 2015].
Jensen, F. 2014. Cities Hold the Key to a Sustainable Future. Available at: http://cities-today.com/cities-hold-the-key-to-a-sustainable-future/ [July, 2015].

Glaeser, E. 2011. Engines of Innovation. American Scientific. Vol. 305(3): pg 50-55.

Graphs / Stats

Page 283. Arup Foresight. 2014. Future of Rain 2015. Available at: http://www.driversofchange.com/projects/future-of-rail-2050/ [March, 2015].

Page 286. Brownell, B. 2015. Two Natural Rebar Alternatives for Concrete. Available at: http://www.architectmagazine.com/technology/two-natural-rebar-alternatives-for-concrete_o [June, 2015].

Page 289. Wikipedia. n,d. List of Cities With the Most Skyscrapers. Available at: https://en.wikipedia.org/wiki/List_of_cities_with_the_most_skyscrapers [June, 2015].

Page 306. Wikipedia. n,d. Slum. Available at: https://en.wikipedia.org/wiki/Slum [June, 2015].

Page 321. Kotkin, J. & Cox, W. 2013. The World's Fastest-Growing Megacities. Available at: http://www.forbes.com/sites/joelkotkin/2013/04/08/the-worlds-fastest-growing-megacities/ [September, 2015].

Page 323. Wikipedia. n,d. Urbanisation. Available at: https://en.wikipedia.org/wiki/Urbanization [June, 2015].

Page 324. Mead, N. 2015. Frankfurt Beats London to Most Sustainable City Title. Available at: http://www.theguardian.com/cities/2015/feb/09/most-sustainable-city-frankfurt-london [July, 2015].

Did you knows

Page 290. Class Energy. n,d. 12 Energy Efficiency Fun Facts to Include in Your Next Communication. Available at: http://class5energy.com/blog/12-energy-efficiency-fun-facts-to-include-in-your-next-communication/ [June, 2015].

Page 292. Aim Steel International. 2015. 10 Facts About the Steel Industry. Available at: http://www.aimsteel.com/10-facts-about-the-steel-industry.html [June, 2015].

Page 315. Foster, N. 2011. The city of the future: It's a story of camels, penguins and cars you don't drive. Available at: http://www.dailymail.co.uk/home/moslive/article-1348558/Norman-Foster-City-future-camels-penguins-cars-dont-drive.html#ixzz3c2JqKvDd [June, 2015].

Page 316. United Nations Environment Programme (UNEP). n,d. Sustainable Buildings and Climate Initiative: Promoting policies and practices for the built environment. Available at: http://www.unep.org/sbci/pdfs/sbci_2pager_eversion_Feb2011.pdf [June, 2015].

Page 320. Pflanz, M. 2013. Africa's Population to Double to 2.4 billion by 2050. Available at: http://www.telegraph.co.uk/news/worldnews/africaandindianocean/10305000/Africas-population-to-double-to-2.4-billion-by-2050.html [July, 2015].

Quotes

Page 278. Jodidio, P. 2014. Piano: Complete Works 1966-2014. Taschen: Berlin.

Page 281. Segarra, M. 2015. Our favorite quotes about cities, and what they have to do with Pennsylvania. Available at: http://crossroads.newsworks.org/index.php/local/keystone-crossroads/85337-our-favorite-quotes-about-cities-and-what-they-have-to-do-with-pennsylvania [August, 2015].

Page 291. Jodidio, P. 2014. Piano: Complete Works

1966-2014. Taschen: Berlin.

Page 293. Jodidio, P. 2014. Piano: Complete Works 1966-2014. Taschen: Berlin.

Page 294. Walsh, B. 2012. Urban Planet: How Growing Cities Will Wreck the Environment Unless We Build Them Right. Available at: http://science.time.com/2012/09/18/urban-planet-how-growing-cities-will-wreck-the-environment-unless-we-build-them-right/ [April, 2015].

Page 301. Walsh, B. 2012. Urban Planet: How Growing Cities Will Wreck the Environment Unless We Build Them Right. Available at: http://science.time.com/2012/09/18/urban-planet-how-growing-cities-will-wreck-the-environment-unless-we-build-them-right/ [April, 2015].

Page 303. brainyquote.com. n,d. Bjarke Ingels Quotes. Available at: http://www.brainyquote.com/quotes/quotes/b/bjarkeinge547903.html [May, 2015].

Page 305. railbotforum.org. n,d. Useful Quotes on Public and Active Transport. Available at: http://railbotforum.org/mbs/index.php?topic=9787.20;wap2 [June, 2015].

Page 309. Berg, N. 2015. Book Review of Design for a Living Planet: Settlement, Science and the Human Future. Available at: http://www.architectmagazine.com/design/exhibits-books-etc/-book-review-of-design-for-a-living-planet-settlement-science-and-the-human-future_o [June, 2015].

Page 311. Walsh, B. 2012. Urban Planet: How Growing Cities Will Wreck the Environment Unless We Build Them Right. Available at: http://science.time.com/2012/09/18/urban-planet-how-growing-cities-will-wreck-the-environment-unless-we-build-them-right/ [April, 2015].

Page 313. Fraioli, P. 2012. The Invention and Reinvention of the City: An Interview with Rem Koolhaas. Available at: http://jia.sipa.columbia.edu/online-articles/invention-and-reinvention-city-interview-rem-koolhaas/ [June, 2015].

Page 319. Foster, N. 2011. The city of the future: It's a story of camels, penguins and cars you don't drive. Available at: http://www.dailymail.co.uk/home/moslive/article-1348558/Norman-Foster-City-future-camels-penguins-cars-dont-drive.html#ixzz3c2JqKvDd [June, 2015].

Page 326. Cherry, S. 2013. Want to Save the Environment? Build More Cities. Available at: http://spectrum.ieee.org/podcast/energy/environment/want-to-save-the-environment-build-more-cities [June, 2015].

Page 343. CNN. 2012. Interview with Architect Bjarke Ingels. Available at: http://edition.cnn.com/TRANSCRIPTS/1204/22/nl.01.html [June, 2015].

Afterword

Bergmann, K. 2012. Hedonistic Sustainability. Available at: http://arcadenw.org/article/hedonistic-sustainability [August, 2015].

Bosak, S. n,d. What is Legacy? Available at: http://legacyproject.org/guides/whatislegacy.html [August, 2015].

Branson, R. 2010. Business Stripped Bear: Adventures of a global entrepreneur. Penguin Group: New York.

Gladwell, M. 2000. The Tipping Point: How little things can make a big difference. Little Brown: Great Britain.

Green, J. 2011. The Architecture of Hedonism: Putting the pleasure into green living. Available at: http://grist.org/cities/2011-12-24-the-architecture-of-hedonism-putting-the-pleasure-into-green-liv/ [July, 2015].

Ted X. 2011. Bjarke Ingels: Hedonistic Sustainability. Available at: http://www.ted.com/talks/bjarke_ingels_hedonistic_sustainability [August, 2015].

Wikipedia. n,d. High Line (New York City). Available at: https://en.wikipedia.org/wiki/High_Line_(New_York_City) [August, 2015].

Quotes

Page 332. Jodidio, P. 2014. Piano: Complete Works 1966-2014. Taschen: Berlin.

Page 334. brainyquote.com. n,d. Elon Musk Quotes. Available at: http://www.brainyquote.com/quotes/authors/e/elon_musk.html [August, 2015].

Page 335. brainyquote.com. n,d. Margaret Mead Quotes. Available at: http://www.brainyquote.com/quotes/quotes/m/margaretme100502.html [August, 2015].

Page 336. brainyquote.com. n,d. Steve Jobs Quotes. Available at: http://www.brainyquote.com/quotes/quotes/s/stevejobs173474.html [June, 2015].

Page 337. goodreads.com. n,d. Nikola Tesla Quotes. Available at: http://www.goodreads.com/quotes/878223-the-scientific-man-does-not-aim-at-an-immediate-result [August, 2015].

Page 338. Chu, J 2015. Bjarke Ingels On The Future Of Architecture. Available at: http://www.fastcodesign.com/3041276/slicker-city/bjarke-ingels-on-the-future-of-architecture [August, 2015].

Page 341. Branson, R. 2010. Business Stripped Bear: Adventures of a global entrepreneur. Penguin Group: New York.

LIGHTNING
LAB

Writing: Devan Valenti & Simon Atlas
Design & Production: Devan Valenti & Simon Atlas
Editing: Pippa Tsilik & Tom Sizeland
Proof Reading: Tom Sizeland
Photographs: Shutterstock.com

ISBN: 978-0-620-66016-7

Published by The Lightning Lab (Pty) Ltd.

Gardens, Cape Town, South Africa
Email: info@thelightninglab.org

Printing: Creda Communications

The publisher apologises for any errors or omissions, and would be grateful if notified of any corrections that should be incorporated in future reprints or editions of this book.

Books are available in bulk to companies and organisations. For more information, please contact the publisher. We would love to hear from you!

The Lightning Lab places great value on the environment. The paper used in the production of this book is FSC certified, and the cover is PEFC certified. They have been supplied by mills that source their raw materials from sustainably managed forests.

www.greenisnotacolour.org

Special thanks to:

Heather Marwick, Romano Valenti and Ashley Valenti for their encouragement and support. Graham Marwick for his guidance and wisdom along the way. Derryn Campbell for all her help in turning this dream into a reality. Tadek Tomaszewski for all his support and for believing in this project from the very start. Marilize Worst, Andrea Barausse and Brian Howarth for their advice and sharing their knowledge. Dominique Litkie for her support and optimism. Dr. Ricky Tsui, Bruce Kerswill and Dr. Michael Braungart for taking time off from saving the planet to invest in our work. All those who contributed with kind words and appraisals. Christopher Nolan for making such great films (especially Interstellar). Elon Musk.

FSC